Nature of Science • Biological World • Chemical World • Physical World • Earth and Space

Catalyst

Junior Cycle Science

**Your companion for change
to the new course**

Patrick Dundon

David King

Maria Sheehan

educate.ie

PUBLISHED BY:
Educate.ie

Walsh Educational Books Ltd
Castleisland, Co. Kerry, Ireland
www.educate.ie

EDITOR:
Julie Steenson

DESIGN AND LAYOUT:
Liz White Designs

COVER DESIGN:
Kieran O'Donoghue

PROOFREADERS:
Ciara McNee and
Antoinette Walker

PRINTED AND BOUND BY:
Walsh Colour Print, Castleisland

PHOTOGRAPHS:
Front-cover photograph: Bigstock

ISBN: 978-1-910052-89-1

Contents

Introduction: Nature of Science

Biological World

Chemical World

Physical World

Earth and Space

About *Catalyst*

For the Student

Welcome to *Catalyst*, your textbook for Junior Cycle Science. Over the next three years, you will engage with the world of science across the following areas:

- Biological World
- Physical World
- Chemical World
- Earth and Space

Throughout the course, you will learn through investigation and inquiry. You will engage with the Nature of Science, developing the skills, knowledge and values that inform how scientists work. You will also develop an appreciation for the important contributions that science has made and continues to make to society. You will develop scientific skills to build on what you have learned in primary school and that will take you beyond Junior Cycle, should you wish to study science at Leaving Certificate.

Your textbook comes with:

- A **Portfolio** to document your investigations, assess your learning and reflect on the scientific understanding, skills and values you have developed.
- A **Key Words book** to reference important science terms easily.
- An **ebook** and **digital resources** to reinforce your classroom learning.

We hope you enjoy *Catalyst* as much as we have enjoyed creating it for you!

For the Teacher

Catalyst is a three-year textbook with a variety of support materials for the new Junior Cycle Science Specification, leading to the Junior Cycle Profile of Achievement (JCPA).

This complete package follows the new Junior Cycle Science Specification and makes teaching and learning active and fun. It ensures that your students learn through tasks and activities that challenge, support and promote scientific inquiry.

This book is flexible in its approach to the teaching of science, allowing you to move through topics by chapter or across the strands. The four contextual strands of the new specification are represented, and are informed by the unifying Nature of Science strand.

Features

- Topics are conveniently organised into double-page spreads.
- Learning intentions and key words are identified at the start of each topic.
- Tasks are clearly distinguished under recognisable icons and promote the development of literacy and numeracy skills, as well as prompting students to engage with scientific inquiry.
- Many opportunities are provided to activate the eight key skills of Junior Cycle throughout.
- Assessment is integrated within and at the end of every chapter.
- Students are given the opportunity to self-assess at the end of every chapter.
- Collaborative learning is promoted through various challenges and investigations involving pair work and group work.
- Peer assessment is encouraged throughout the various tasks and challenges.

Differentiation

Differentiation is important in mixed-ability class settings. As such, the material within this book has been carefully selected to suit a range of abilities. The language is clear and concise. The end-of-chapter assessments are differentiated using a 'thermometer' scale from blue (lower order) to red (higher order) questions.

We are proud to present you with our interpretation of the Junior Cycle Science Specification. As authors, we believe that it meets the learning outcomes in an active, interesting and enjoyable manner.

Good luck and enjoy!

Patrick Dundon, David King and Maria Sheehan, 2016

Features to Look Out For

Chapter and Topic Introductions

Each chapter begins with an introduction to some of the key topics you will be studying.

What you may already know gives examples of things you may have already encountered in primary school science, earlier chapters or in your everyday life. Check through them and see if there is anything you need to be reminded of.

What you will learn in this chapter provides a summary of the chapter you are about to study.

Learning Intentions tell you what you will be learning and doing in each topic. Once you finish a topic, you can visit the Check Your Learning section of your Portfolio to find out how well you have achieved each intention.

The **Key Words** in each topic are highlighted the first time they are used and are summarised in the key word box. The definition for each key word can also be found in your Key Words book.

Chapter 5

The Diversity of Life

What you may already know:

- There are many different living things.

What you will learn in this chapter:

- There are five groups of organisms – bacteria, protists, fungi, animals and plants.
- Bacteria are the most numerous type of organism on Earth and they have many roles.
- Viruses are not considered to be living things and can cause diseases.

Think BIG

- What was the first organism to appear on Earth?
- Are new organisms still evolving?

Puzzler

Can you pair the celebrity with the organism named after them? What language is used for the naming of organisms? Why? Try to say the names aloud!

1. David Attenborough
2. Steve Irwin
3. Bill Gates
4. Bob Marley
5. Angelina Jolie

a. *Trypanosoma irwini*
b. *Aptostichus angelinajolieae*
c. *Gnathia marleyi*
d. *Eristalis gatesi*
e. *Materpiscis attenboroughi*

82

The Diversity of Life **5.1**

The Five Kingdoms of Life

Learning Intentions

In this topic we are learning to:

- List the five kingdoms of life.
- Describe how organisms are classified.

Scientists believe that life first appeared on Earth 3,800 million years ago in the form of bacteria.

From these earliest organisms, millions of different species have evolved, including plants and animals.

It is thought that there are between 15 and 20 million different species on Earth today. This great variety of life is called **biodiversity**.

Classification

The system of grouping organisms together that share common characteristics is called **classification**.

Organisms are classified into five groups, or **kingdoms**.

These are:

1. Animals
2. Plants
3. Protists
4. Fungi
5. Bacteria

Homo sapiens

In the eighteenth century, Swedish scientist Carl Linnaeus introduced a system of naming organisms that is still used today. Linnaeus based his system on the physical similarities of organisms. Each organism was identified by two names: the first identified the genus of the organism and the second identified the species. This system of naming living things is called **binomial nomenclature**.

Using this system, humans are known as *Homo sapiens*. The word *sapiens* is Latin for 'wise'.

Key Words

Biodiversity
Classification
Kingdoms
Binomial nomenclature
Stimuli
Invertebrates
Vertebrates
Protists
Fungi
Decomposer

Definitions that are important to remember are underlined in each topic.

Animals

Protists

Fungi

Bacteria (earliest organisms)

⟳ Fig. 5.1.1
The five kingdoms of life

83

Think Big suggests some of the big ideas and important questions related to the area of science you are about to study. You should keep them in mind as you move through the chapter.

Each **Puzzler** is linked to something in the chapter. Can you crack them? If not, revisit them after you have finished the chapter.

Chapter Summary and Questions

The chapter summary sums up the main points you have learned in the chapter.
You can use this summary to check your understanding of the chapter and as a revision aid.

The **questions** at the end of each chapter test how well you know the topics in the chapter.

Each question is marked with a coloured thermometer to signify the level of difficulty:

These are the easiest questions.

These questions are getting harder.

These are the hardest questions.

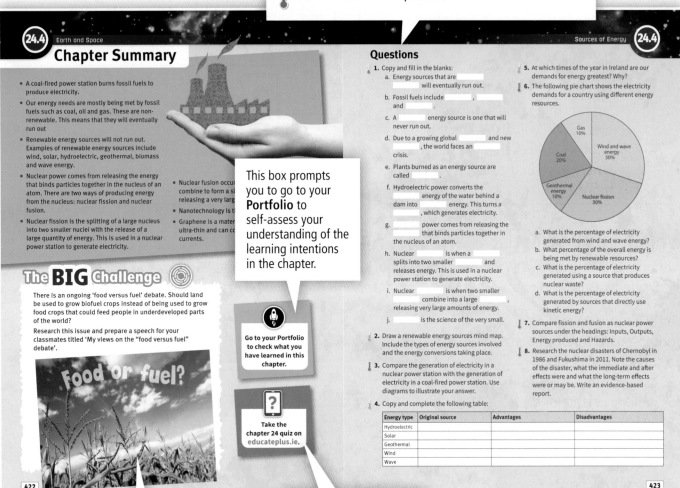

24.4 Earth and Space

Chapter Summary

- A coal-fired power station burns fossil fuels to produce electricity.
- Our energy needs are mostly being met by fossil fuels such as coal, oil and gas. These are non-renewable. This means that they will eventually run out
- Renewable energy sources will not run out. Examples of renewable energy sources include wind, solar, hydroelectric, geothermal, biomass and wave energy.
- Nuclear power comes from releasing the energy that binds particles together in the nucleus of an atom. There are two ways of producing energy from the nucleus: nuclear fission and nuclear fusion.
- Nuclear fission is the splitting of a large nucleus into two smaller nuclei with the release of a large quantity of energy. This is used in a nuclear power station to generate electricity.

- Nuclear fusion occur... combine to form a si... releasing a very larg...
- Nanotechnology is t...
- Graphene is a mater... ultra-thin and can c... currents.

The **BIG** Challenge

There is an ongoing 'food versus fuel' debate. Should land be used to grow biofuel crops instead of being used to grow food crops that could feed people in underdeveloped parts of the world?

Research this issue and prepare a speech for your classmates titled 'My views on the "food versus fuel" debate'.

Food or fuel?

422

This box prompts you to go to your **Portfolio** to self-assess your understanding of the learning intentions in the chapter.

Go to your Portfolio to check what you have learned in this chapter.

Take the chapter 24 quiz on educateplus.ie.

Sources of Energy **24.4**

Questions

1. Copy and fill in the blanks:
   a. Energy sources that are _____ _____ will eventually run out.
   b. Fossil fuels include _____, _____ and _____.
   c. A _____ energy source is one that will never run out.
   d. Due to a growing global _____ and new _____, the world faces an _____ crisis.
   e. Plants burned as an energy source are called _____.
   f. Hydroelectric power converts the _____ energy of the water behind a dam into _____ energy. This turns a _____, which generates electricity.
   g. _____ power comes from releasing the _____ that binds particles together in the nucleus of an atom.
   h. Nuclear _____ is when a _____ splits into two smaller _____ and releases energy. This is used in a nuclear power station to generate electricity.
   i. Nuclear _____ is when two smaller _____ combine into a large _____, releasing very large amounts of energy.
   j. _____ is the science of the very small.

2. Draw a renewable energy sources mind map. Include the types of energy sources involved and the energy conversions taking place.

3. Compare the generation of electricity in a nuclear power station with the generation of electricity in a coal-fired power station. Use diagrams to illustrate your answer.

4. Copy and complete the following table:

Energy type	Original source	Advantages	Disadvantages
Hydroelectric			
Solar			
Geothermal			
Wind			
Wave			

5. At which times of the year in Ireland are our demands for energy greatest? Why?

6. The following pie chart shows the electricity demands for a country using different energy resources.

Gas 10%
Wind and wave energy 30%
Coal 20%
Geothermal energy 10%
Nuclear fission 30%

   a. What is the percentage of electricity generated from wind and wave energy?
   b. What percentage of the overall energy is being met by renewable resources?
   c. What is the percentage of electricity generated using a source that produces nuclear waste?
   d. What is the percentage of electricity generated by sources that directly use kinetic energy?

7. Compare fission and fusion as nuclear power sources under the headings: Inputs, Outputs, Energy produced and Hazards.

8. Research the nuclear disasters of Chernobyl in 1986 and Fukushima in 2011. Note the causes of the disaster, what the immediate and after effects were and what the long-term effects were or may be. Write an evidence-based report.

423

This box reminds you to visit **educateplus.ie**, where you can complete an end-of-chapter quiz.

You can choose to attempt the **Big Challenge** that appears at the end of each chapter. These challenges give you the chance to use your scientific skills and knowledge to solve an interesting problem. You can write up your findings in your Portfolio.

Features Key

 Numeracy moments contain activities, hints and tips that will develop your scientific numeracy skills.

 Literacy moments help you to build your scientific reading, writing, listening and speaking skills.

 Plan, design and carry out **Scientific Investigations**. These investigations can be written up in your Portfolio.

 Use your scientific knowledge and research skills to investigate the role of **Science in Society**. You can write your findings up in your Portfolio.

 Sometimes a topic in one strand, such as Biological World or Earth and Space, will also feature in another strand. **Go links** tell you where to go in the book to find out more.

Digital Resources Key

As you work through the textbook, you will see the following icons. Each icon tells you where there is a digital resource related to what you are learning. These resources are available online at educateplus.ie.

 This icon indicates that there is an animated version of the illustration available to watch.

 This icon indicates there is an interactive version of the investigation that you can complete. The videos embedded in the investigation can also be viewed separately.

 This icon appears at the end of each chapter to remind you that you can complete an online quiz to test what you have learned in the chapter.

Working as a Scientist

Working as a Scientist tasks appear at the end of every chapter. Each one addresses an aspect of the work scientists do and relates that type of work to something you have learned about in the chapter.

The scientific areas addressed in Working as a Scientist tasks include:

- Asking questions and making predictions
- Investigation design
- Making and recording observations
- Presenting and analysing data
- Communicating science
- Responsible science.

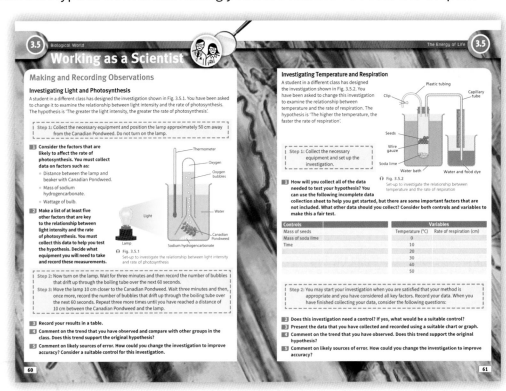

Introduction: Nature of Science

What is Science?

0.1

Learning Intentions

In this topic we are learning to:

- Consider science as a process that allows people to investigate natural occurrences (phenomena) that can be tested.
- Describe how science gives us a body of knowledge that is always changing.

Key Words

Scientific method
Hypothesis
Theory
Law
Principle

What is Science?

Science is the study of the world around us.

You have always been a scientist. Ever since you were a baby, crawling on the floor and putting things in your mouth, you have been doing scientific investigations – testing ideas, finding out information and making decisions based on that information.

Scientific Investigations

Scientists carry out investigations to answer questions about the natural world.

In this chapter, we will look at how and why scientific investigations are carried out. You can refer back to it as you carry out your own scientific investigations.

Fig. 0.1.1
We are all born as scientists, curious about the world around us

The Scientific Method

Observation: ask a question

Form a hypothesis

Test the hypothesis with investigations

Analyse the results

Form conclusions

Scientists work hard to solve problems in many different ways. One approach is to use what has become known as the scientific method.

The **scientific method** is a series of steps that scientists follow to investigate natural occurrences (phenomena) that can be tested. Figure 0.1.2 outlines these steps.

A natural occurrence is anything that happens in nature that is not controlled by humans. For example, an iceberg floating on water.

Fig. 0.1.2
The scientific method

Observation

To begin a scientific investigation you must ask a clear question that can be tested. For example, why do icebergs float?

This question will draw on scientific knowledge that already exists.

In science, each new discovery builds on the discoveries that have gone before. In the words of Isaac Newton, 'If I have seen further than others, it is by standing upon the shoulders of giants.'

You should find out as much information as possible about the problem you want to solve.

↻ **Fig. 0.1.3**
Science can test and attempt to explain natural phenomena such as 'Why do icebergs float?'

Hypothesis

Once research has been done and a question has been asked, a scientist will make an educated guess about what the answer might be. This is called a hypothesis.

A **hypothesis** is an idea that will be tested by an investigation.

For example, the question 'Why do icebergs float?' will become the hypothesis 'Icebergs float due to a lower density than liquid water'.

A hypothesis must be testable. For example, a hypothesis that can be tested is 'A dog pants in order to cool down'. An example of a hypothesis that cannot be tested is 'Putting your left sock on before your right sock will give you luck'.

A hypothesis cannot be tested if the technology needed does not yet exist. For example, at present it is impossible to test the hypothesis 'Life exists in other solar systems'.

Hypothesis or not?

In pairs, consider which of the following statements are hypotheses that could be tested in a scientific investigation:

- Diesel cars cause more air pollution than petrol cars.
- Orange is the nicest colour.
- A diet rich in sugary foods leads to high blood pressure.
- A die thrown with your left hand is more likely to turn up a six.
- The colour of the sky is blue.

Consider how you would develop investigations to test each of the reasonable hypotheses.

Scientists do not set out to prove that their hypothesis is true. They set out to show that, at this point in time, their hypothesis is not false. This seems like a small difference but a scientist must be willing to change their hypothesis based on new information.

Theories and Laws

A hypothesis that has been tested by scientists many times and has yet to be proven false may develop into a theory. Theories explain and predict natural phenomena. Examples include the Big Bang theory and Darwin's theory of evolution by natural selection (you will learn more about these theories later).

Scientists may also describe a natural phenomena as a law or principle. Laws and principles describe a natural phenomena that has been observed, but they do not explain how it works. For example, over 300 years after Newton's law of universal gravitation first described the effects of gravity, there is currently still not a theory to fully explain how gravity works.

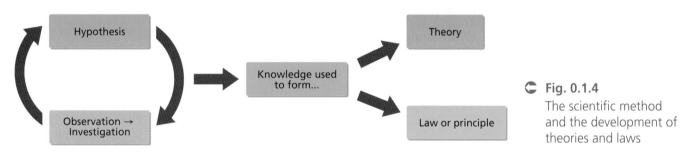

Fig. 0.1.4
The scientific method and the development of theories and laws

Asking questions and making predictions

As you use this book, you will carry out investigations in a number of ways, including the scientific method. Let's practise this method now, by working on the first two steps: asking a question and forming a hypothesis.

Investigation:

When you were younger, you may have played on the roundabout at the park. Do you remember feeling dizzy after getting off? Carry out an investigation into how spinning affects a person's reaction time.

Fig. 0.1.5
Children playing on a roundabout

Step 1. Observation: a reasonable question to ask would be 'Will I react slower after getting off the roundabout?'

Step 2. Form a hypothesis: how would you word this question as a hypothesis?

Now that you know how to ask questions and form a hypothesis, the following pages will look at the next steps of the scientific method. How to:

- Test the hypothesis with investigations.
- Analyse results.
- Form conclusions.

Investigation Design

Key Words

Variable
Control
Fair
Reliable
Reproducible
Repeatable
Risk assessment
Ethics

Learning Intentions

In this topic we are learning to:

- Distinguish between the different types of variables and a control.
- Explain how to produce a fair and reliable method to carry out an investigation.
- Discuss the importance of laboratory safety and ethics.

Once you have formed a hypothesis, you are ready to begin your investigation.

The investigation is the step of the scientific method that tests the hypothesis.

The first thing you must do before you carry out an investigation is make a plan. You must decide:

- What equipment to use.
- What method to follow.

In both cases, you should be able to give good reasons why you have made these decisions.

⊃ **Fig. 0.2.1**
Make a plan

Variables

The equipment you choose should be guided by the variables in your investigation.

A **variable** is any factor that can be changed, measured or controlled in an investigation.

There are three types of variable:

- An independent variable is a variable that you change.
- A dependent variable is a variable that changes as a result of changing the independent variable.
- Controlled (fixed) variables are all the other variables that are kept the same.

> **Example**
>
> A group of students want to investigate if water is needed for the growth of cress seedlings. The students place cotton wool in the base of two Petri dishes. Five cm³ of water is added to the cotton wool in dish A. No water is added to the cotton wool in dish B. Five cress seeds are added to both dish A and dish B. The students will then observe the growth of the cress seeds in both dishes for two weeks.
>
> The variables in this investigation are:
>
> 1. Independent variable: the availability of water for cress seeds (the variable that you change).
> 2. Dependent variable: the growth of the cress seeds (the variable that changes as a result of changing the independent variable).
> 3. Controlled (fixed) variables: the number of cress seeds, the amount of cotton wool and the laboratory conditions (these are the variables that are kept the same).

Control

A **control** is a copy of an investigation, where every factor is the same except the factor being investigated (independent variable).

A control is used for comparison. It helps you to find out if the independent variable has an effect on the dependent variable. It is important not to confuse a control with a controlled (fixed) variable.

> In the example above, dish B is the control set-up (since it lacks water, the factor under investigation). By comparing the growth of the cress seeds in dish A and dish B, the students can find out if water affects the growth of cress seedlings.

Designing a Method

The method you decide to follow should be **fair** and **reliable**.

To keep a test fair:

- Identify the independent variable.
- Identify the dependent variable.
- Identify the controlled (fixed) variables and have ways to keep these factors the same.

A reliable method should be:

- **Reproducible**: if somebody follows your method, they should be able to collect data similar to yours.
- **Repeatable**: if you repeat the investigation several times, or if you repeat a measurement in an investigation, you should collect and record similar data each time.

Your method should be described clearly, so that others can repeat it in a fair and reliable way using your description. Where necessary, include a diagram of how you set up your equipment.

Safety

An important part of investigation design is safety. You should be aware of the hazards of working in a science laboratory. You should also conduct a **risk assessment** of any investigation you plan to carry out.

A risk assessment should:

- Outline the hazards of carrying out your investigation.
- List the steps you can take to avoid these hazards.
- Identify the person responsible for minimising hazards.

Remember, a risk assessment is only useful if you act on it.

From the moment you plan an investigation, through setting up equipment and collecting data, you need to work in a safe and organised way. This will reduce the chance of damaging equipment and injuring yourself or your classmates.

Ethics

Ethics refers to the need to carry out investigations and give results in a responsible way.

You should consider the ethics of what you are trying to investigate, especially if your investigation involves living things (including humans). For example, an investigation to find out how mice react when they are exposed to electric shocks would be unethical because a living thing would be harmed.

⬥ **Fig. 0.2.2**
Laboratory safety is always the number one priority

Checklist for Investigation Design

Make sure you can answer 'yes' to all of the following questions before beginning an investigation.

1. Do I have a clear question and hypothesis that can be tested scientifically?
2. Have I made a prediction about what will happen and explained why?
3. Have I identified my independent and dependent variables?
4. Have I identified my controlled (fixed) variables and the ways to keep these factors the same?
5. Have I identified my equipment?
6. Have I conducted a risk assessment, including ethical considerations?
7. Do I know how to use the equipment safely and accurately?
8. Is my method described in a fair and reliable way?

Checklist

Choosing your equipment, designing a method to test your hypothesis and ensuring safety

Let's go back to our playground investigation and think about our equipment and method.

> **Step 3:** A suitable hypothesis may be 'The greater the number of times you are spun around, the slower your reaction time becomes'. Now that you have a hypothesis, you can design an investigation to test it.

Your equipment:

For this investigation, you will need a metre stick. The metre stick will be used to measure distance to an accuracy of the nearest centimetre. Catching the metre stick will test reaction time.

- The independent variable is the number of spins.
- The dependent variable is the distance the metre stick falls through a person's hands before being caught. The distance the metre stick falls before being caught is used as an indication of a person's reaction time.
- All other factors will be kept the same – these are your controlled (fixed) variables. The controlled (fixed) variables in this investigation may include holding the metre stick at the same height above the person's hands each time and always reading the distance on the metre stick from the bottom of the holder's clasped hands. Can you think of any other controlled (fixed) variables in this investigation?
- The control in this investigation is to measure the distance the metre stick falls through the student's hands before they are spun around. The only difference between this and future copies of the investigation is that in the control the student is not spun around, so that the factor being investigated (independent variable) is missing.

Your method:

- Working in pairs, one partner will spin themselves around a certain number of times with their arms held outstretched and the palms of both hands facing each other and held 5 cm apart.
- When that person stops spinning, the other member of the pair will hold the metre stick directly above the hands of the spinner.
- The person with the metre stick will call 'now' and then immediately release the metre stick.
- The person that has just been spun around clasps the metre stick between their two hands as fast as possible.

> **Risk assessment:**
> - Ensure that the person being spun around has enough space and that there is no water or items on the floor that are in the person's way.
> - The person spinning should stop immediately if they feel too dizzy. Do not exceed a safe number of spins or spin too quickly as the person may become disorientated and fall. Always err on the side of caution.
> - If a person feels unwell or nervous, do not insist that they participate.
> - Ensure there are no splinters on the metre stick.

Recording, Presenting and Analysing Data

Key Words

Data
Quantitative data
Qualitative data
Range
Error

Learning Intentions

In this topic we are learning to:

- Explain the difference between quantitative and qualitative data.
- Present data in tables and graphs.
- Interpret data and draw conclusions.

Analysing the results of your investigation is the fourth step of the scientific method. Before you can do this, you must understand what data is and how to present it.

Understanding Data

Data is numbers or words that can be organised to give information. There are two sources of data:

1. Primary data is collected by the person carrying out the investigation. For example, the roll call at the start of class is collected by the teacher.

2. Secondary data is collected by someone other than the person carrying out the investigation. For example, the public fill in a government census form and the data is used by a transport company to work out where new routes are needed.

There are two types of data:

1. **Quantitative data** is data recorded in numbers. It is also called numerical data. Quantitative data can be:
   - Continuous: it can have any value. For example, length or mass.
   - Discrete: it can have only certain values. For example, number of people or shoe size.

2. **Qualitative data** is data recorded using descriptive words. For example, eye colour or gender. It is also called categorical data.

Qualitative data can be:

- Ordinal: data is ranked. For example, how often you eat chocolate (never, rarely, sometimes).

- Nominal: data is not ranked. For example, the colour of a car.

Figure 0.3.1 shows the different types of data that can be collected about a person.

↻ **Fig. 0.3.1**
Types of data

Data for this girl

Qualitative
(Categorical)

Quantitative
(Numerical)

Nominal: blue eyes, brown hair

Ordinal: her grades in different subjects

Discrete: 2 legs, 2 eyes

Continuous: 1.52 m tall, 55 kg mass

When collecting data, it is important to set the range of values of the independent variable at the start. The **range** is the difference between the lowest and highest values.

It is important that the data we collect is accurate. If we do not measure in the correct way, we end up with inaccurate data. When this happens, it is known as an **error** in the measurement.

Recording Data

To help you organise your data, it should be clearly recorded in a results table (data collection sheet). This will help you to:

- Choose variables.
- Select a range of measurements.
- Think about the time between measurements.
- Spot patterns and relationships between variables.

Data may also be recorded using software such as Microsoft Excel. Such programs are especially useful when handling a large amount of data. They can generate a graph of the data electronically.

Presenting Data

Data must be organised to make it easier to understand. If data is presented clearly, it can be used as evidence to show that a hypothesis is false or not false.

To decide which type of graph or chart to use, you need to look at the type of variables in your investigation. The table below shows options for representing different types of data.

Type of data	Suitable graphs
Qualitative (nominal or ordinal)	Bar chart, line plot, pie chart
Quantitative (continuous)	Histogram, scatter plot
Quantitative (discrete)	Bar charts, pie charts, stem-and-leaf plots

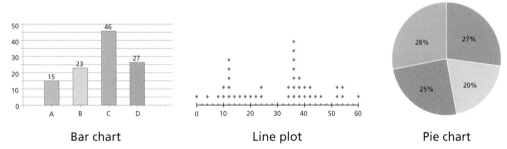

Bar chart   Line plot   Pie chart

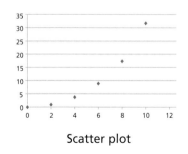

Scatter plot

When constructing a graph, you should:

1. Always put the quantity that you control on the *x*-axis.
2. Decide on a suitable scale for each axis.
3. Label the *x*-axis and the *y*-axis, and include the correct units.
4. Plot the points accurately.
5. Always make sure that the graph has a title and is dated.
6. Consider adding a line of best fit (a 'trend' line).

🎧 **Fig. 0.3.2**
Types of graph

Analysing Data

Once your data has been presented in a graph, you will need to work out what the graph is telling you. From the graph, you should be able to see the relationship between the two variables.

A graph will help you to see if or how the independent variable affects the dependent variable.

⮑ **Fig. 0.3.3**
Graphs of variables that are directly proportional (Graph 1) and inversely proportional (Graph 2)

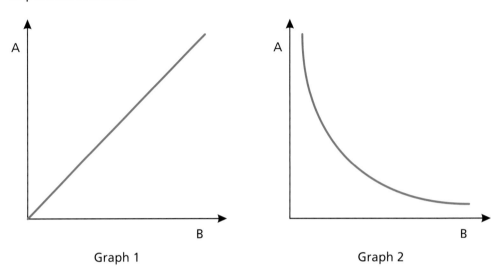

Graph 1   Graph 2

- Graph 1 shows a relationship that is directly proportional. If two quantities are directly proportional, as one increases, the other increases by the same factor.

- Graph 2 shows a relationship that is inversely proportional. If two quantities are inversely proportional, as one quantity increases, the other decreases by the same factor.

Forming Conclusions

The last step in the scientific method is forming conclusions. Conclusions are what you found out in the investigation.

Compare what you found out with your original hypothesis. Do your results support the original hypothesis or do they not support it? Either way, you should evaluate your investigation.

To evaluate your investigation, comment on its strengths and weaknesses.

- Method: consider sources of error in your method and suggest improvements to address these errors.

- Results: ask the following questions: Are the results valid? Do they measure what they were supposed to measure? Are the results repeatable and reproducible?

- Conclusion: your conclusions must be made based on the results of your investigation. You should not include statements that are not supported by the data you have collected.

Remember that there is no such thing as correct or incorrect data or right or wrong answers to scientific investigations. Each investigation generates new information, so even unexpected results have value.

Identifying, recording, analysing and evaluating your data

Now we can consider the data we will be collecting in our playground investigation.

The data you will collect:

The data collected during this investigation (the possible relationship between the number of times a person is spun around and reaction time) is primary data. The number of spins and the distance the metre stick falls before being caught are both quantitative data. The number of spins is discrete numerical data. The distance that the metre sticks falls through clasped hands is continuous numerical data.

As the investigator, you decide on the values of the independent variable (the number of spins), but you will have to measure and record the values of the dependent variable during the investigation (distance the metre stick falls before being caught). For example, the range of data for the number of spins might be between 0 and 10, increasing in increments (steps) of two each time. The range of data for the distance the metre stick falls before being clasped between hands may be calculated after the primary data has been collected.

Recording data during your investigation:

The data generated during this investigation was collected on the table to the right. From the data, it appears that as the number of spins increases, the distance the metre stick falls doubles each time.

A scatter plot will show that there is a positive relationship between the number of spins and the distance the metre stick falls before being clasped between hands.

Number of Spins	Distance (cm)
0	0
2	2
4	4
6	8
8	16
10	32

Analysing your results:

Step 4: The first graph shows that the positive relationship between the number of spins and the distance the metre stick falls before being clasped is not linear.

Fig. 0.3.4
Using graphs to analyse data

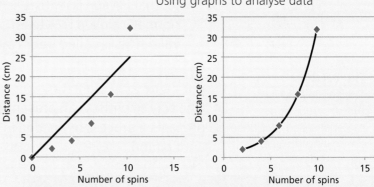

After taking away the first row of data, it would appear that the relationship between the number of spins and the distance the metre stick falls before being clasped is an exponential pattern (shown on the second graph), which means that the values are doubling each time.

Forming conclusions and reporting your results:

Step 5: The data collected during this investigation and its analysis indicates that as the number of spins increases, the distance the metre stick falls before being caught also increases. In light of these results, it would appear that our original hypothesis 'The more times you are spun around, the slower your reaction times will become' is not false.

Further investigations should be carried out to find out whether or not there are other factors that may also influence reaction times.

Communication, Teamwork and Responsible Science

Learning Intentions

In this topic we are learning to:

- Outline the different ways to communicate scientific knowledge.
- Review the role of models when communicating scientific information.
- Evaluate scientific information.
- Reflect on the importance of teamwork and responsibility in science.

◑ **Fig. 0.4.1**
We can read about scientific discoveries online

Communication

Science has a duty to produce new knowledge about the world around us. However, these new discoveries are of no use unless they are communicated to people in a way they can understand.

There are many ways to **communicate** scientific knowledge.

- Public events: scientific demonstrations, research conferences, competitions or student science fairs.

- The media: articles in newspapers, on the news, adverts on TV, science magazines or online. For example, an advert for a probiotic drink explains the science behind how it works in a way the general public can understand.

- Research articles: scientists can publish their research in scientific journals. When scientists send their work to journals for publication, it is normally judged by a team of other scientists to see if it is scientifically valid. This is called **peer review**.

◑ **Fig. 0.4.2**
This model represents the structure of a material called graphene that cannot be seen with the naked eye

Using Models

One way scientists can present concepts is by using models. A **model** presents a process or an idea in a simpler way, making it easier to understand.

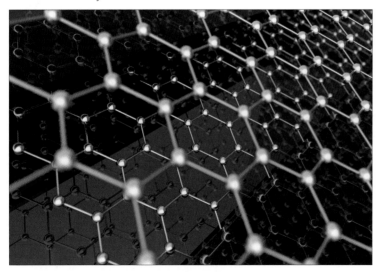

Models can be useful in representing:

- The structure of something.
- The way something works.
- The nature, characteristics or behaviour of something.

In *Catalyst*, you will learn about, develop and consider models that explain things such as the particle theory of matter, chemical reactions, electrical voltage and the cycling of matter.

Communicating eating habits

You and your classmates have completed an investigation into the eating habits of the students in your school. Come up with a list of ways of effectively communicating these findings to the following groups:

1. The students in the school.
2. Their parents.

Checklist for Evaluating Scientific Information

When scientific information is communicated to you, it is important to **evaluate** it so you can decide whether to accept or reject it. You should ask:

- Who is presenting the information?
- For what purpose is it being presented?
- Is the information up to date?
- Is it clear in its meaning?
- If there is data, has it been collected in a scientifically correct and ethical way?
- What is the scientific evidence for the claims being made?
- Are all opinions presented or is the information one-sided?
- Are all sources of information given?

Teamwork

Scientists often work in teams. For example, the research at CERN, a particle accelerator facility in Switzerland, is leading to some of the most exciting discoveries in the history of humankind. This is thanks to the joint effort of physicists, engineers, mathematicians and other scientists from over 20 countries around the world.

In class, you will likely work with a lab partner on investigations or work as part of a group when discussing scientific issues.

○ **Fig. 0.4.3**
A scientist in the control room at CERN, Switzerland

Responsible Science

Scientists serve science and society by carrying out fair investigations and communicating the results honestly.

Scientists must be free of bias. **Bias** is a strongly held personal opinion. It is based more on feelings than on fact.

Science does not always go in a straight line from asking a question to forming a conclusion. Along the way, scientists can make mistakes and have ideas that make them ask different questions and come up with new hypotheses. For this reason, it is important that scientists:

- Have inquiring minds.
- Have good reasoning skills.
- Are good communicators.
- Work well in a team.
- Are responsible.
- Appreciate the important role of science in past, present and future societies.

When we work and think as scientists, we have a responsibility to inform and improve society and show respect for our planet.

Scientific responsibility

With your lab partner, discuss the responsibilities of a team of scientists researching potential cures for cancer. Use a table to illustrate the people that scientists are responsible to and how they are responsible to them.

Chapter Summary

- Science is the study of the world around us.
- The scientific method is a series of steps that scientists follow to investigate natural occurrences (phenomena) that can be tested.
- A hypothesis is an idea that will be tested by an investigation.
- Scientists set out to demonstrate that their hypothesis is not false.
- Theories explain and predict natural phenomena.
- Laws and principles describe a natural phenomena that has been observed, but they do not explain how it works.
- An independent variable is a variable that you change.
- A dependent variable is a variable that changes when you change the independent variable.
- Controlled (fixed) variables are all the other factors that are kept the same.
- A control is a copy of an investigation. Every factor is the same except the factor being investigated (independent variable). A control is used for comparison.
- Data is numbers or words that is collected, organised and analysed to give information.
- There are two sources of data: primary data and secondary data.

- There are two types of data: quantitative and qualitative.
- Quantitative data is data recorded in numbers.
- Qualitative data is data recorded using descriptive words.
- The variables in an investigation will determine the type of graph or chart that needs to be constructed.
- At the end of an investigation, it is important to evaluate the method, the results and the conclusions.
- Scientific information can be communicated in various ways that are fit for purpose and audience, such as at public events, in the media and in research articles.
- Scientists can use models to communicate concepts or processes in a way that is easier to understand.
- When scientific information is communicated to you, it is important to evaluate it so you can decide whether to accept or reject it.
- Scientists often work in teams.
- Scientists serve science and society by carrying out fair investigations and communicating the results honestly.

The BIG Challenge

Test the following hypothesis: 'The type of surface a tennis ball is dropped onto will affect the height the ball will bounce.'

1. What types of data will you collect?
2. How will you carry out this test in a fair and reliable way?
3. Produce a table you can use to collect data in this investigation.
4. How will you present this data on a graph or chart?
5. Draw conclusions from the data you have collected.
6. Evaluate your method, results and conclusions. What are the limitations of this investigation?

Go to your Portfolio to check what you have learned in this chapter.

Take the Nature of Science quiz on educateplus.ie.

Questions

1. Copy and fill in the blanks:

   a. The _____ _____ is a series of steps that scientists follow to investigate natural occurrences (phenomena) that can be tested.

   b. A _____ is an idea that will be tested by an investigation.

   c. Scientists may describe a natural phenomena as a theory, a _____ or a _____.

   d. An _____ variable is a variable that you choose to change. A _____ variable changes when you change the _____ variable.

   e. To ensure that an investigation is safe a _____ _____ should be carried out.

   f. There are two types of data: _____ and _____.

   g. The type of _____ you choose will be guided by the _____ in the investigation.

   h. There are many ways to _____ scientific knowledge, such as at public events, in the media and in research articles.

   i. A _____ presents a process or idea in a simpler way, making it easier to understand.

   j. When scientific information is communicated to you, it is important to _____ it so that you can decide to _____ or _____ it.

2. Select the independent, dependent and controlled (fixed) variables for the following scientific questions:

   a. Do bigger magnets pick up more steel paper clips than smaller magnets?

   b. Does the temperature in an incubator affect the number of seeds that will germinate?

3. A survey of a herd of goats on a mountain and their position above sea level resulted in the collection of the following data: goat A (460 m), B (300 m), C (240 m), D (436 m), E (299 m), F (467 m), G (250 m), H (365 m), I (301 m), J (252 m), K (353 m), L (256 m).

   a. Draw a suitable table to present this data.

   b. Is there a range of heights in which more goats are found?

   c. How does a table make it easier to spot patterns compared to a list?

4. What types of data are the following?

   a. Favourite chocolate bar.

   b. Shoe size.

   c. Height in metres.

   d. Amount of time spent watching TV every day (1–2 hours, 3–4 hours, 5–6 hours).

   e. Types of plants in a field.

   f. Number of daisies in a field.

5. An investigation was carried out to find out the quantity of vitamin C in 100 cm^3 of different fruit juices. The data collected is as follows: kiwi fruit = 50 mg, apple = 5 mg, mango = 40 mg, grape = 12 mg, orange = 55 mg.

   a. What are the dependent and independent variables in this investigation?

   b. Plot this data on a suitable graph.

   c. What is the range of values in this investigation?

   d. Explain why it is easier to see the pattern using the graph rather than a list or a table.

6. Students investigated how the volume of a fixed mass of gas at 20 °C varied when the pressure of the gas was increased and decreased. They collected a range of data and made the following graph.

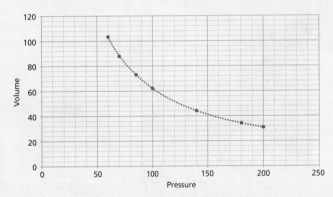

   a. What is missing from this graph?

   b. What are the dependent and independent variables?

   c. Is there a relationship between pressure and volume for this gas? Explain your answer.

Biological World

In Biological World, we will encounter many living things. These include the bacteria in our intestines, mushrooms in a field, trees in a forest, fish in the sea and birds in the air. Each of these things is different, yet they all share the spark of being 'alive'. Biology is the study of life.

In the study of life, it is only natural that we might want to focus on humans. After all, we are everywhere! But it is important to remember that fish, birds and even bacteria are made of energy and matter, just like humans are.

It is human nature to ask questions about the world we live in. In Biological World we will consider many interesting questions, such as 'Why do dogs pant?' and 'Why do human hands and bat wings have the same bone structure?'

The answers to such questions tell us something about how life developed so well on Earth.

Fig. 1
All living things are made of energy and matter

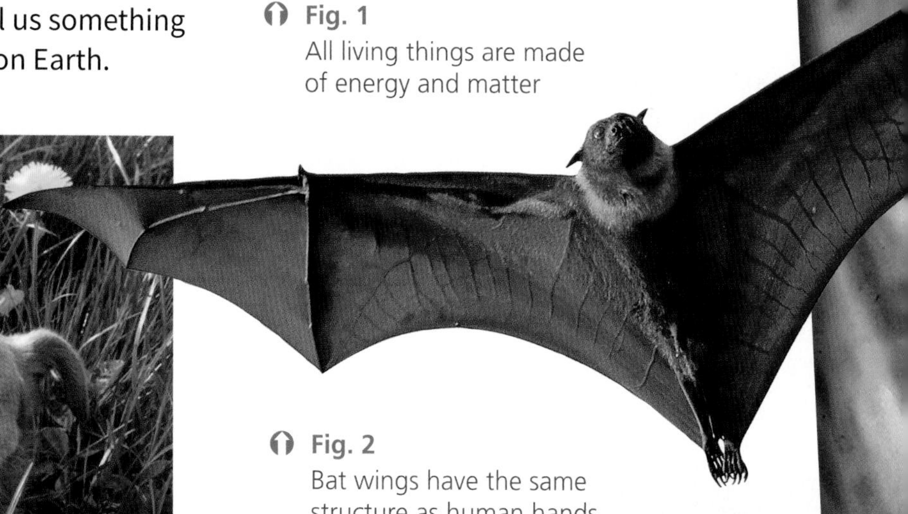

Fig. 2
Bat wings have the same structure as human hands

Fig. 3
Why do dogs pant?

What you may already know:

- Humans are born, grow, reproduce and die.
- Plants are green and can make their own food.
- Humans are related to chimpanzees.

Code Breaker

How many words or terms related to the biological world can you make using the letters in the following sentence?

I LOVE BIOLOGY BECAUSE IT IS THE STUDY OF LIFE

For example, 'cell'.

Use your Key Words booklet as a guide.

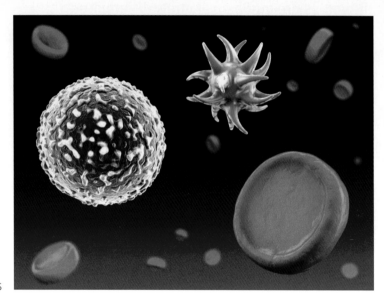

➲ Fig. 4
Blood cells

Think BIG

- What is life?
- Why do I have eyebrows?
- What is a thought?

In **Biological World** you will learn about:

Chapter 1   The characteristics of life, cells and microscopes.

Chapter 2   Biomolecules, balanced diet and how healthy eating can reduce the risk of disease.

Chapter 3   The energy of life, photosynthesis and respiration.

Chapter 4   DNA, genetics, variation and evolution.

Chapter 5   The diversity of organisms and the five kingdoms of life.

Chapter 6   Ecology, energy flow and habitat studies.

Chapter 7   Plant structures, processes and reproduction.

Chapter 8   Human structures, processes and reproduction.

Chapter 1

The Organisation of Life

What you may already know:

- There are many different plants and animals in the world.
- Our bodies are made up of many different parts.

What you will learn in this chapter:

- That living things differ from non-living things because of seven key characteristics.
- That living things are made up of cells.
- That cells are very small and we need some way of seeing them clearly.
- The differences between animal and plant cells.
- That living organisms are very organised.

Think BIG

- How did life begin?
- Can life exist on other planets?
- What are we made of?

Puzzler

Can you solve this puzzle?

Can you identify the two types of cells taking 'cellfies'?

(Hint: turn to topic 1.3 The Structure of the Cell.)

1. _____

2. _____

Defining Life

Learning Intentions

In this topic we are learning to:

- Identify seven characteristics common to living organisms.

Biology is the study of life. Every living thing is called an **organism**.

There are seven common features that help us tell the difference between living and non-living things.

The Characteristics of Life

A **characteristic** is a feature that helps identify a thing.

Each organism demonstrates all of the following characteristics of life:

1. Nutrition
2. Respiration
3. Excretion
4. Growth
5. Reproduction
6. Movement
7. Response

Key Words

Organism
Characteristic
Nutrition
Respiration
Excretion
Growth
Reproduction
Movement
Response

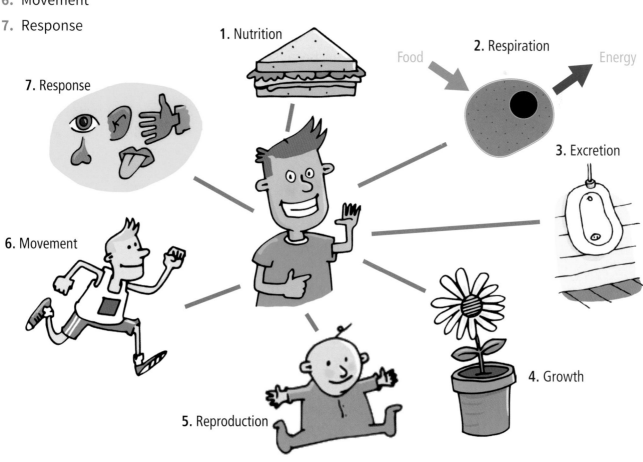

ᐱ **Fig. 1.1.1**
The seven characteristics of living organisms

1. Nutrition

- Nutrition is how organisms get their food.
- Plants are producers: they make their own food by photosynthesis.
- Animals are consumers: they eat other animals or plants.

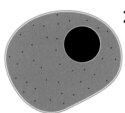

2. Respiration

- Respiration is the release of energy from food.
- It takes place in every cell of the body.
- Living things need energy to grow and reproduce.
- Respiration should not be confused with breathing.

3. Excretion

- Excretion is the removal of waste from cells.
- Waste must be expelled (excreted) from cells in case they become toxic.
- Excretion should not be confused with egestion (when waste food material leaves the body).

4. Growth

- All living things grow.
- Growth is an increase in the size of a living thing.
- Living things grow because their cells divide.

5. Reproduction

- Reproduction is the ability to produce new individuals (offspring).
- Reproduction ensures that a type of organism will not become extinct (die out).

6. Movement

- All living things move.
- Animals move their whole body to find food, mates and shelter or to escape danger.
- Parts of plants move to absorb more sunlight.

7. Response

- Response is the ability to react to a change in the environment.
- When an organism senses a change, it must respond fast in order to adapt and survive.

Characteristics of life

Using the first letter from each characteristic above, create a mnemonic to help you remember the seven characteristics of living organisms. For example, **N**o **R**eally **E**xcellent **G**iant **R**ates **M**y **R**oar.

'Classify'

When you classify things, you are putting them into different groups based on characteristics they share.

Classifying objects as living or non-living

1. Collect two plastic bags from your teacher. In pairs, label one bag 'Living' and the other 'Non-living'.

2. Under the supervision of your teacher, walk around the school grounds and collect three objects that you believe to be living and another three things that you believe to be non-living. If you cannot bring objects back to the laboratory with you, ask your teacher for permission to take photographs instead.

3. Back in the laboratory, classify the items as 'living' or 'non-living'. Explain your decisions to your classmates using the list of characteristics of living things. Remember that a living organism demonstrates all seven characteristcs of life. Record the findings of the class.

4. Following a class discussion, make a list of at least five characteristics that all living things have in common. (What about fire – is it alive?)

🔊 **Fig. 1.1.2**
Classifying objects as living or non-living

The Cell and Light Microscope

Key Words

Cells
Unicellular
Multicellular
Light microscope
Specimen
Lens

Learning Intentions

In this topic we are learning to:

- Identify cells as the 'building blocks' of all organisms and tell the difference between unicellular and multicellular organisms.
- Name the parts of a light microscope and explain what they do.
- Prepare slides using onion cells and view them under a light microscope.

All living things are made up of cells – life's building blocks.

Cells are tiny units that have all of the characteristics of life. All plants and animals are made of cells.

Some organisms, such as bacteria and yeast, may exist as a single cell. These organisms are **unicellular**.

Most organisms, such as earthworms, oak trees and humans, are made of millions of different cells. These organisms are **multicellular**.

The Light Microscope

As cells are tiny, they are difficult to study. Antonie van Leeuwenhoek's invention of the **light microscope** in the seventeenth century allowed biologists to study the details of cells for the first time.

You will use a light microscope in class to look at magnified images of small objects, including plant and animal cells. A sample studied under a microscope is called a **specimen**.

The Parts of a Light Microscope

Base: keeps the microscope stable.

Stage and stage clips: holds the slide in place.

Light source: a built-in light bulb or mirror that illuminates (lights up) the specimen.

Diaphragm: controls the amount of light passing through the specimen.

Objective lens: magnifies the specimen by different powers (x 4, x 10, x 40). Note: always start at the lowest power.

Eyepiece lens: magnifies the specimen, usually by a power of 10 (x 10).

Coarse focus wheel: brings the image into rough focus. Note: always adjust the coarse focus wheel before adjusting the fine focus wheel.

Fine focus wheel: brings the image into sharp focus.

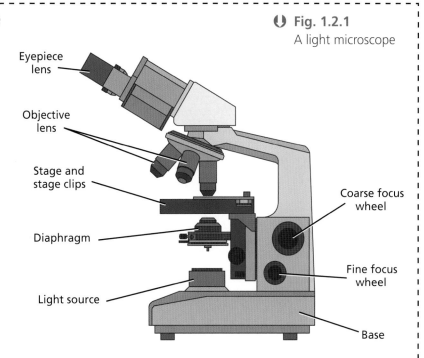

◑ Fig. 1.2.1
A light microscope

Eyepiece lens
Objective lens
Stage and stage clips
Diaphragm
Light source
Coarse focus wheel
Fine focus wheel
Base

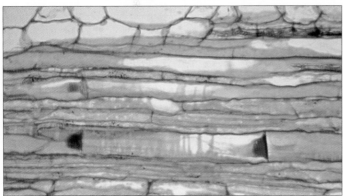

🎧 **Fig. 1.2.2**
A plant cell under a light microscope

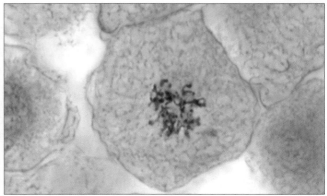

🎧 **Fig. 1.2.3**
An animal cell under a light microscope

Preparing a specimen of onion cells to view under a light microscope

1. Following the steps below, prepare a specimen of onion cells.

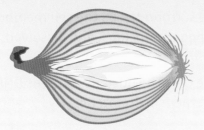

↻ **Fig. 1.2.4**
Preparing a slide of onion cells to view under a light microscope

① Cut an onion with a knife

② Remove an inner layer

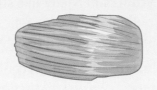

③ Peel off a thin layer of cells with tweezers

④ Place a drop of water on top of the slide and then place a thin layer of onion cells on top. Slowly add a cover slip. Mount on the stage and view under magnification x 40

↻ **Fig. 1.2.5**
Onion cells viewed under a light microscope

2. Look at the onion cells under the light microscope.

3. Draw and label what you see at each of the three total magnifications (x 40, x 100 and x 400), both with and without a stain (add 2–3 drops of iodine to your specimen with a dropper).

4. Describe the shape of plant cells. Why did you use a stain on your specimens?

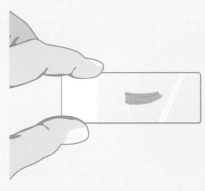

The Structure of the Cell

Key Words

Organelles
Cell membrane
Cytoplasm
Nucleus
Cell wall
Chloroplast
Vacuoles
Micrograph

Learning Intentions

In this topic we are learning to:

- Compare plant and animal cells.
- Outline the role of cell organelles, including the cell membrane, cytoplasm and nucleus.

Using a light microscope, we may also be able to see certain cell **organelles**. Organelles are small structures that carry out specific roles within the cell. Each organelle has a different job to do in the cell.

The three main organelles in both animal and plant cells are:

1. **Cell membrane:** surrounds the cell and controls which materials move into and out of the cell.

2. **Cytoplasm:** a jelly-like substance surrounded by the cell membrane. Contains other organelles, including the nucleus, and dissolved substances such as oxygen.

3. **Nucleus:** the control centre of the cell. The nucleus contains DNA (genes). We will learn more about them in Chapter 4.

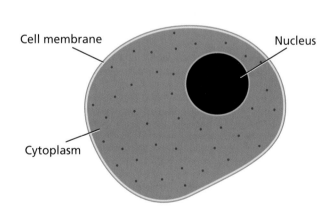

🎧 **Fig. 1.3.1**
An animal cell

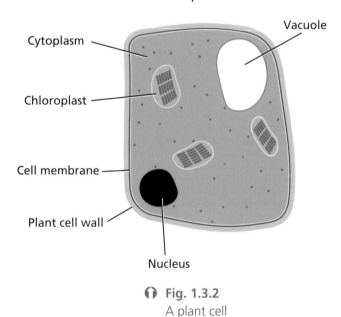

🎧 **Fig. 1.3.2**
A plant cell

Plant cells also have a cell wall and chloroplast. These two organelles are not found in animal cells.

1. **Cell wall:** strengthens the cell. Cell walls make plant cells stronger than animal cells.

2. **Chloroplast:** contain chlorophyll, which allows the plant cell to absorb sunlight energy for photosynthesis.

Vacuoles are membrane-bound structures that contain liquids. Animal cells contain small vacuoles. Plant cells often contain larger vacuoles full of water.

Electron Microscopes

Electron microscopes pass a beam of electrons through the specimen.
This allows a hugely magnified image to be formed (x 1,000,000).

GO Learn more about electrons in Chemical World 10.2

An image formed by an electron microscope is called a **micrograph**.
Micrographs are in black and white.

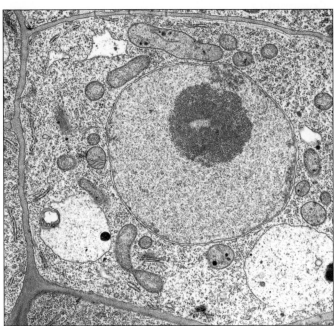

🎧 **Fig. 1.3.4**
Micrograph of a plant cell

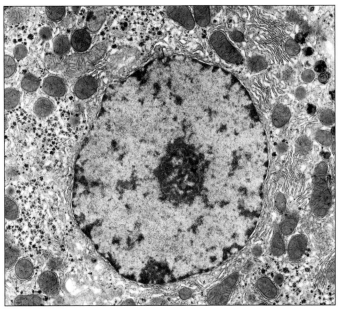

🎧 **Fig. 1.3.3**
An electron microscope

🎧 **Fig. 1.3.5**
Micrograph of an animal cell

Organisation of Life

Key Words

Organisation
Tissue
Organ
System
Population
Community
Ecosystem
Ecology

Learning Intentions

In this topic we are learning to:
• Outline the stages of organisation in living organisms.

All living organisms are made up of cells. Cells can work together to form tissues, organs and systems. This is called **organisation**.

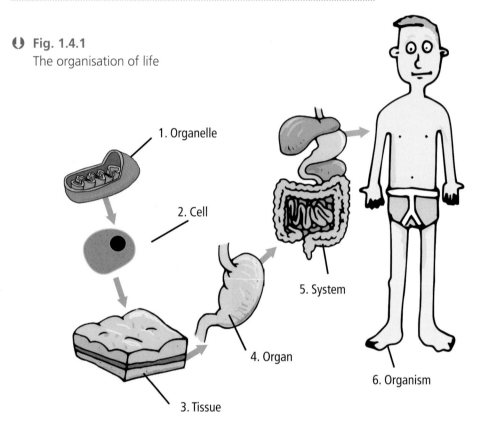

◑ **Fig. 1.4.1**
The organisation of life

1. Organelle
2. Cell
3. Tissue
4. Organ
5. System
6. Organism

All organisms are organised in the same way:

1. **Organelle**: the structures in cells.

2. **Cell**: the building block of life, made up of organelles. Different cells do different jobs. For example, white blood cells fight infection.

3. **Tissue:** a group of cells that work together. For example, blood is a tissue made up of red blood cells, white blood cells, platelets and plasma.

4. **Organ:** a group of tissues that work together. For example, the heart is an organ made up of cardiac muscle tissue, connective tissue in valves and fat tissue.

5. **System:** a group of organs that work together. For example, the heart is the organ at the centre of the circulatory system. It pumps blood around the body.

6. **Organism:** the result of all systems working together. For example, the circulatory system works with the breathing system to transport oxygen around the body.

Of course, no organism exists alone.

- Individual organisms of the same species form a **population**.
- Populations of different species that live close together are a **community**.
- Communities interact with their environment to form an **ecosystem**. The study of ecosystems is called **ecology**.

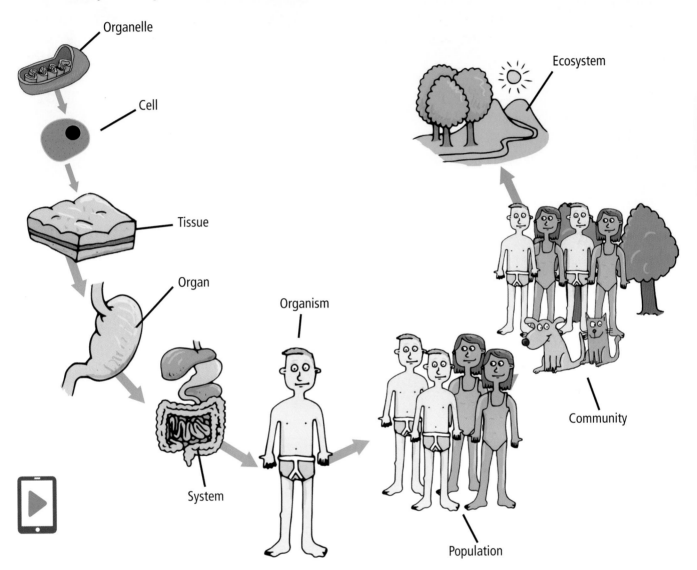

Fig. 1.4.2
The organisation of life, from organelle to ecosystem

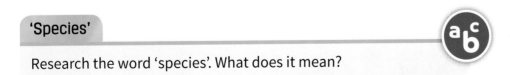

'Species'

Research the word 'species'. What does it mean?

We will learn more about how species interact in an ecosystem later in Biological World.

Chapter Summary

- Every organism shows the seven characteristics of life: nutrition, reproduction, respiration, excretion, response, growth and movement.

- All organisms are made up of cells.

- Some organisms are a single cell only (unicellular). Other organisms are made up of millions of cells (multicellular).

- We can use a light microscope to look at magnified images of cells.

- The key parts of a light microscope are: eyepiece lens, stage and stage clips, diaphragm, objective lens, coarse and fine focus wheels and the light source.

- Electron microscopes have made it possible to see cells in even greater detail.

- The structures within cells are organelles.

- The three main organelles in both animal and plant cells are the cell membrane, cytoplasm and the nucleus.

- Plant cells have two organelles that are not found in animal cells: the cell wall and chloroplasts.

- Organisms are very organised. The levels of organisation are: organelle, cell, tissue, organ, system and organism.

- Organisms of the same species form a population. Populations of different species that live close together are a community.

- Communities interact with their environment to form an ecosystem. The study of ecosystems is called ecology.

The **BIG** Challenge

Make a 3D model of an animal cell or a plant cell using common household items and arts and crafts materials (e.g. modelling clay, pipe cleaners, polystyrene balls, spaghetti, scissors, paper and paint).

Your model must include the organelles mentioned on page 24.

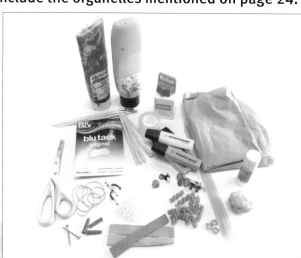

⊃ Fig. 1.5.1 Materials for building a cell model

Go to your Portfolio to check what you have learned in this chapter.

Take the chapter 1 quiz on educateplus.ie.

Questions

1. Copy and fill in the blanks:

a. Biology is the study of ▮▮▮▮▮.

b. ▮▮▮▮▮ are the building blocks of life.

c. ▮▮▮▮▮ is the removal of waste from cells.

d. ▮▮▮▮▮ is the release of energy from food.

e. ▮▮▮▮▮ cells have cell walls and chloroplasts. These are not found in ▮▮▮▮▮ cells.

f. The ▮▮▮▮▮ is the control centre of the cell.

g. Organisms made up of a single cell are ▮▮▮▮▮. Organisms made up of many cells are ▮▮▮▮▮.

h. When you look at a specimen under a light microscope, you should always adjust the ▮▮▮▮▮ focus wheel before adjusting the ▮▮▮▮▮ focus wheel.

i. The study of ecosystems is called ▮▮▮▮▮.

j. A ▮▮▮▮▮ is an image of a cell formed by an electron microscope.

2. Using the scale on the micrograph, estimate the diameter of each red blood cell. (Hint: refer to the *Formulae and Tables* booklet for information on units and prefixes.)

A

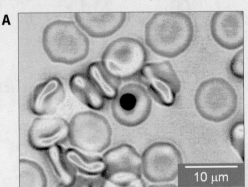

10 µm

B

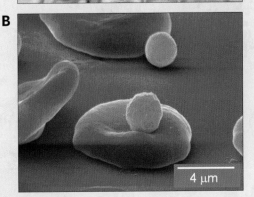

4 µm

3. Copy and label the diagram of the light microscope.

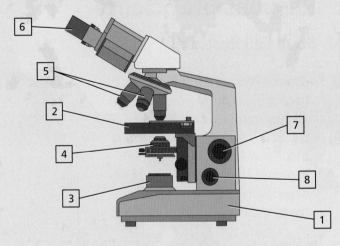

4. Arrange the following words in the correct order to describe how living organisms are organised: tissue, organelle, organism, cell, system, organ.

5. Biologists and chemists use the word 'nucleus' in two different ways. Research these uses and then clearly explain the different meanings of the word 'nucleus' in the biological world and in the chemical world.

6. Draw a labelled sketch of a plant cell and an animal cell.

7. Copy and complete the Venn diagram using these words: nucleus, cytoplasm, chloroplast, vacuole, cell membrane, cell wall.

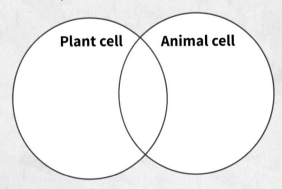

8. Identify three reasons why it is in the interests of all living organisms to be 'organised'.

29

Working as a Scientist

Responsible Science

Stem Cell Research

Stem cells are cells that can be used to make other types of cells, such as red blood cells and nerve cells. They can be taken from adult tissue and from embryos (unborn humans in the earliest stage of development). Stem cells can renew themselves.

Read the following extracts from a speech made by Barack Obama in support of the Stem Cell Research Enhancement Bill before he became President of the United States. Work in small groups to answer the questions that follow.

Fig. 1.6.1
Barack Obama

A few weeks ago I was visited by Mary Schneider and her son Ryan. When Ryan was just two years old, his parents and doctors noted severe delays in his motor and speech development, and he was diagnosed with cerebral palsy. His parents were devastated, as the prognosis for many children with cerebral palsy is quite grim, and given the severity of Ryan's condition, his doctors didn't have much hope for his improvement.

Yet, his parents had hope. Because when Ryan was born, his parents had saved his cord blood, a viable but limited source of stem cells. They found a doctor at Duke University who was willing to perform an experimental infusion with these cells to see if they might improve his condition. They did. In fact, they seem to have cured him. Within months of the infusion, Ryan was able to speak, use his arms, and eat normally, just like any other child – a miracle his family had once only dreamed of.

Ryan's story exemplifies the power and the promise of stem cells to treat and cure the millions of Americans who are suffering from catastrophic, debilitating and life-threatening diseases and health conditions…

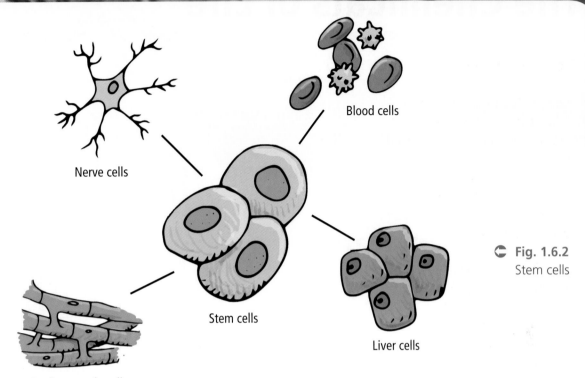

Nerve cells

Blood cells

Stem cells

Liver cells

Cardiac muscle cells

↻ **Fig. 1.6.2**
Stem cells

Recent developments in stem cell research may hold the key to improved treatments, if not cures, for those affected by Alzheimer's disease, diabetes, spinal cord injury and countless other conditions. Many men, women and children who are cancer survivors are already familiar with the life-saving applications of adult stem cell research…

By expanding scientific access to embryonic stem cells which would be otherwise discarded, this bill will help our nation's scientists and researchers develop treatments and cures to help people who suffer from illnesses and injuries for which there are currently none. But the bill is not without limits; it requires that scientific research also be subject to rigorous oversight.

I realise there are moral and ethical issues surrounding this debate. But I also realise that we're not talking about harvesting cells that would've been used to create life and we're not talking about cloning humans. We're talking about using stem cells that would have otherwise been discarded and lost forever – and we're talking about using those stem cells to possibly save the lives of millions of Americans…

1 **Why are stem cells thought to be one of the great hopes of medicine? Give at least one example to support your answer.**

2 **Embryonic stem cell research is controversial. In small groups, research the pros and cons and prepare a short presentation for your classmates outlining both sides of the debate.**

3 **Find out about stem cell research in Ireland. In your opinion, should the Irish Government fund research into the medical uses of embryonic stem cells? Give at least three reasons to support your answer.**

Chapter 2

The Chemicals of Life

What you may already know:

- Organisms need food for energy.
- Water is essential for all organisms.

What you will learn in this chapter:

- Organelles and cells are made from biomolecules and other minerals.
- Organisms need a balanced diet to supply energy for the growth and repair of cells, as well as for good health.
- The food pyramid, Reference Intake (RI) values and Body Mass Index help inform healthy eating.

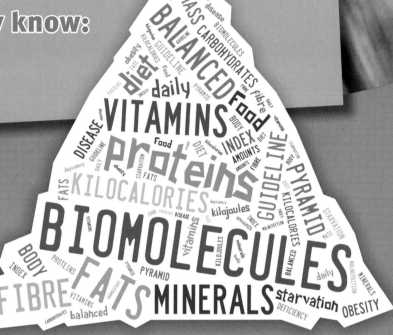

Think BIG

- Why do humans survive longer without food than without water?
- Why do we sometimes crave sugar and salt?
- What is a balanced diet?

Puzzler

Can you solve this puzzle?

Read the following labels that might appear on food packaging:

1. Sliced Irish bacon.
2. Irish-sliced bacon.

Are you being sold the same product in both cases? Explain your answer.

(Hint: consider where each pig was farmed and then processed.)

Biomolecules and Food Tests

Learning Intentions

In this topic we are learning to:

- Describe how food supplies organisms with the energy they need.
- Conduct investigations to find out the biomolecules present in different foods.

Key Words

Biomolecules
Carbohydrates
Proteins
Fats
Vitamins
Minerals

Biomolecules

Organelles and cells are made from **biomolecules**.

Plants can make biomolecules from raw materials in their environment. Animals must get biomolecules from the foods they eat. All of the foods consumed by an organism are referred to as its diet.

The four biomolecules that every organism needs are:

1. **Carbohydrates**
2. **Proteins**
3. **Fats**
4. **Vitamins**

The following table outlines the role of each biomolecule and which foods they come from.

Name	Role	Source
Carbohydrates Sugar Starch Fibre	• To provide a fast supply of energy • To provide a slow supply of energy • To prevent constipation	• Fruit, sweets • Potatoes, bread, pasta, rice • Brown bread, fruit, vegetables, cereals
Proteins	• For growth and repair of cells • To make muscle, hair and enzymes	Lean meat, fish, pulses and dairy products
Fats	• To provide a store of energy • To insulate and protect internal organs	Meats, dairy products, chocolate
Vitamins	• For healthy gums, teeth, joints and immune system	Fresh fruits and vegetables (vitamin C) and dairy products (vitamin D)

↻ **Fig. 2.1.1**
Can you match the foods pictured to the biomolecules they contain?

🎧 **Fig. 2.1.2**
Testing a potato for starch

Food Tests

Different tests can be performed to find out if a food contains a biomolecule. For example, iodine – an orange-brown chemical – is used to test for the carbohydrate starch:

- If a drop of iodine is placed on a potato, the iodine will turn blue-black. This colour change is a positive result for starch in potatoes.

- If a drop of iodine is placed in milk, the iodine will not change colour. This is a negative result for starch in milk.

The following table outlines the food tests that can be used to test for each biomolecule.

Name	Food test	Positive colour change
Carbohydrates	Starch: iodine	Orange-brown → blue-black
	Glucose: Benedict's reagent	Blue → brick red (needs heat)
Proteins	Biuret reagent (sodium hydroxide and copper sulfate)	Blue → purple/lilac
Fats	Brown paper	Opaque (not see-through) → translucent (see-through)

Other Nutrients

In addition to biomolecules, organisms also need **minerals** and water in their diet.

The following table outlines the roles and sources of these other important nutrients.

Name	Role	Source
Minerals	• To build biomolecules and to assist chemical reactions within cells. For example, animals need iron to produce red blood cells and plants need magnesium to produce chlorophyll	Lean meat, fresh fruit and vegetables, dairy products
Water	• Acts as a solvent • Helps transport materials in blood • Removes waste • Regulates temperature	Water and other liquids, fruits and vegetables

Food tests

1. Working in pairs, design an investigation to test some common foods (such as bread, milk, yoghurt, apples and fizzy drinks) for carbohydrates (starch and glucose), protein and fat. Consider the following questions:

   a. What should the blank table of results look like?

   b. What chemicals will you need to test each food?

   c. How will you prepare each food before the test?

   d. How will you make sure it is a fair test?

   e. What would be a suitable control for each test?

2. Following a class discussion, list foods that are good sources of starch, glucose and protein. Will this information influence what you eat?

Fig. 2.1.3
Common foods to be tested for biomolecules

Testing for the presence of water

1. In the presence of water, white anhydrous copper sulfate turns blue. Plan, design, carry out and write up an investigation to test for water using anhydrous copper sulfate.

2. Research the word 'anhydrous'.

3. Ask your teacher about another chemical test for water that was used up until very recently in Irish schools. Why do we no longer use this test? What does this suggest about scientists and the nature of scientific investigations?

Fig. 2.1.4
White anhydrous copper sulfate turns blue when it comes in contact with water

The Importance of a Balanced Diet

Key Words

Balanced diet
Kilojoules
Kilocalories
Reference Intakes
Food pyramid
Body Mass Index

Learning Intentions

In this topic we are learning to:

- Consider why one diet does not suit everyone.
- Interpret food labels.
- Plan a balanced diet to promote good health.

One diet does not suit everyone. Dietary choice has to account for a number of factors:

- Age
- Gender
- Genetics
- Health
- Physical activity.

A **balanced diet** provides carbohydrates, proteins, fats, vitamins, minerals, fibre and water in the correct quantities.

> **Fun Fact**
>
> A typical person requires approximately 2.5 litres of water a day. Of course, we need to drink more if we exercise or if it is a hot day.

Energy From Food

GO Learn more about energy and joules in Physical World 16.1

The quantities of biomolecules in food are given in grams (g). One gram is equal to one thousandth of a kilogram (kg).

Energy values for different foods can normally be found on a nutritional label on the food's packaging. As a joule is a small quantity of energy, the energy in foods is measured in thousands of joules, or **kilojoules** (kJ). On food labels, the energy content can also be given in **kilocalories** – 1 kcal is equal to 4.2 kJ.

🎧 Fig. 2.2.1
We need to drink more water when we exercise

➲ Fig. 2.2.2
A nutritional label showing the energy values of a typical food serving

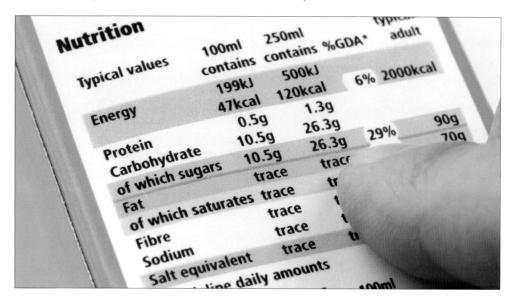

A person must eat foods that will supply them with the energy their body needs to do work, such as making the heart beat, breathing and replacing damaged and worn-out red blood cells. Further energy is needed to grow, fight infection and play sports.

- A typical teenage boy needs approximately 12,500 kJ of energy a day for work and growth.
- A typical teenage girl needs approximately 9,700 kJ of energy a day.
- A pregnant female needs more energy than a female who is not pregnant.

Fun Fact

If you yelled for eight years, seven months and six days, you would only produce enough energy to heat one cup of coffee.

Burn it off!

1. Imagine you have eaten a 100 g bar of chocolate that contains 2,176 kJ of energy. Using the information in Fig. 2.2.3, calculate how long you would have to walk for to burn off the energy in the bar of chocolate. Compare this to the amount of time it would take you to burn off the energy if you were sleeping.

↻ **Fig. 2.2.3** The amount of energy you need in a day depends on a number of factors. Typically, you need to …

- Wash and dress – 15 kJ a minute
- Walk – 13 kJ a minute
- Do school work – 10 kJ a minute
- Play sports – 65 kJ a minute
- Sleep – 5 kJ of energy a minute

2. Draw a suitable graph to compare the different energy values for the activities listed in Fig. 2.2.3.

Reference Intakes

We should be aware of the food we eat, especially of the quantities of energy, sugars, fats and salt that are in our food.

By law, companies must include a list of ingredients on food labels.

Food labels have to include **Reference Intake** (RI) values. RIs provide information about the amount of calories (energy), fat, sugars and salt needed for a healthy diet.

RIs help people make informed choices about what they are consuming.

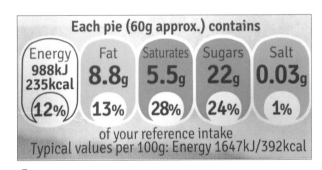

Each pie (60g approx.) contains

| Energy 988kJ 235kcal (12%) | Fat 8.8g 13% | Saturates 5.5g 28% | Sugars 22g 24% | Salt 0.03g 1% |

of your reference intake
Typical values per 100g: Energy 1647kJ/392kcal

↻ **Fig. 2.2.4** RI label

The following table lists the Reference Intake values for energy and other nutrients.

	REFERENCE INTAKE
Energy	8,400 kJ/2,000 kcal
Total fat	70 g
Saturates	20 g
Carbohydrates	260 g
Sugars	90 g
Protein	50 g
Salt	6 g

⮑ **Fig. 2.2.5**
Typical Reference Intake (RI) values

On food labels, RI values are given for an average adult female. This means they need to be adjusted to suit a person's own needs. For example, teenagers may need more protein and kilojoules of energy as they are growing fast.

The Food Pyramid

The **food pyramid** has been widely used in Ireland to promote healthy eating and to help people plan a balanced diet.

The general rule is that you eat the most servings of foods from the bottom of the pyramid and eat only small quantities of the foods from the top of the pyramid.

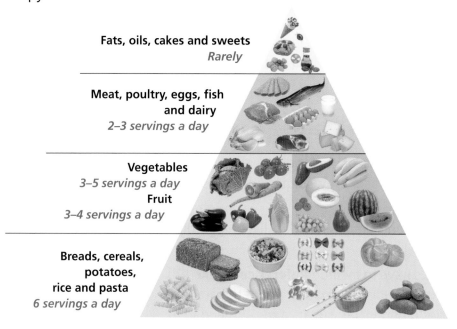

Fats, oils, cakes and sweets
Rarely

Meat, poultry, eggs, fish and dairy
2–3 servings a day

Vegetables
3–5 servings a day
Fruit
3–4 servings a day

Breads, cereals, potatoes, rice and pasta
6 servings a day

⮑ **Fig. 2.2.6**
The food pyramid

More Irish people are becoming overweight. In light of this worrying trend, the food pyramid has been reviewed. More emphasis is now being put on controlling portion size and reducing 'treat' foods such as crisps, sweets, chocolate and sugary drinks.

Body Mass Index

Body Mass Index (BMI) provides people with quantitative (numerical) information about their weight and whether or not it is healthy. It also helps people to measure how successful a new exercise regime or healthy diet has been over a period of time.

BMI can be calculated using the following formula:

$$BMI = \frac{Mass\ (kg)}{Height^2\ (m^2)}$$

BMI is not always reliable. It does not tell the difference between fat mass and muscle mass, so a healthy person, such as an athlete, might show as overweight or obese on the BMI scale.

Daily energy intake

Using the two meals in Fig. 2.2.7, answer the following questions:

1. Which meal has the most energy?
2. How could you reduce the energy in Meal 1 to make it healthier? How many kilojoules did you 'save'?

	Male (kJ)	Female (kJ)
8-year-old	7,200	7,200
Teenager (14)	10,700	8,300
Adult office worker	9,400	8,400
Adult manual worker	12,900	10,700
Pregnant woman		8,600
Breastfeeding mother		9,900

The table above shows suggested daily energy intakes for different people.

3. Why do you think that males typically need more energy than females? How many more kilojoules does a male teenager need than a female teenager?
4. Why do you think the difference in energy requirements of males and females becomes so noticeable in teenage years? Explain your answer.
5. Why do manual workers need more energy than office workers?
6. If a female adult office worker becomes pregnant, how many more kilojoules do you think she should start to consume? Compare your value to similar data online.
7. Why does a breastfeeding mother need more energy than a pregnant woman?

Meal 1:
1 roast chicken breast with skin (808 kJ)
3 boiled potatoes (1,556 kJ)
10 tablespoons of carrots (126 kJ)
1 cup of boiled green peas (561 kJ)
250 ml freshly squeezed orange juice (490 kJ)
Total = 3,541 kJ

Meal 2:
1 hamburger (2,301 kJ)
150 g of French fries (2,092 kJ)
355 ml of Coca Cola (598 kJ)
Total = 4,991 kJ

🎧 Fig. 2.2.7
Nutritional information for two meals

Malnutrition

Key Words

Malnutrition
Starvation
Disease
Deficiency diseases
Obesity

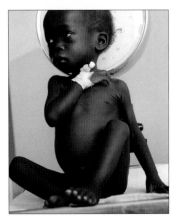

🎧 **Fig. 2.3.1**
A malnourished child being weighed in Uganda

'Mal'

a b c

Look up the prefix 'mal'. What language does it come from? Now explain the term 'malnutrition' in your own words.

Learning Intentions

In this topic we are learning to:

- Justify the importance of a balanced diet, regular exercise and rest.
- Discuss how malnutrition and poor lifestyle choices may lead to health problems.
- Identify the causes and symptoms of various dietary and lifestyle diseases.

Malnutrition is a diet that is not balanced.

When most people hear the word malnutrition, they think of the food shortages that lead to **starvation**. Unfortunately, this is still a problem in some developing countries.

Malnutrition can also mean too much food. In developed countries, processed foods with too much sugar and low nutritional value have led to an increase in malnutrition and its related health problems.

Deficiency Diseases

A **disease** is a condition that affects an organism's ability to work normally.

Diseases caused by a lack of a particular nutrient are called **deficiency diseases**. For example, scurvy is caused by a lack of vitamin C, which leads to bleeding gums, loose teeth and joint problems.

The following table outlines some of the diseases caused by malnutrition.

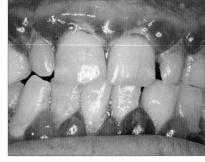

🎧 **Fig. 2.3.2**
Swollen and bleeding gums caused by scurvy

Disease	Dietary and lifestyle cause(s)	Symptom(s)
Obesity	• Consuming too many calories in diet (sugars and fats) • Not getting enough exercise	• Weight gain • Makes it more difficult to move • Can make underlying health problems worse
High blood pressure	• Too much saturated fat in diet, leading to high cholesterol • Too much salt in diet	• Increases heart rate • Increases risk of heart disease, stroke and blood clots
Type 2 diabetes	• Too much sugar and fat in diet	• May shorten life expectancy • May result in kidney failure, heart disease, stroke • May require limb amputation
Osteoporosis	• Not enough calcium and vitamin D in diet	• More likely to suffer bone fractures, particularly in females
Anaemia	• Not enough iron in diet	• Red blood cells cannot carry oxygen • Tired and listless

Obesity

If you consume more energy than your body needs, this energy will be stored as fat. In extreme cases, this may lead to **obesity**.

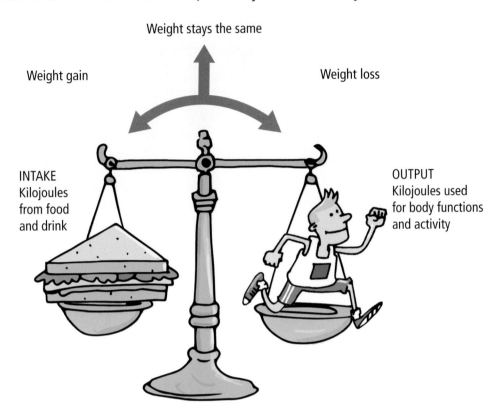

Weight stays the same

Weight gain

Weight loss

INTAKE
Kilojoules
from food
and drink

OUTPUT
Kilojoules used
for body functions
and activity

⟲ **Fig. 2.3.3**
Energy balance

Carrying too much fat puts the body under pressure. The heart has to work harder, which leads to increased blood pressure. High blood pressure increases the risk of stroke and heart disease.

Obesity is also linked to an increase in the disease type 2 diabetes. Diabetes affects how the body uses glucose, the main type of sugar in blood.

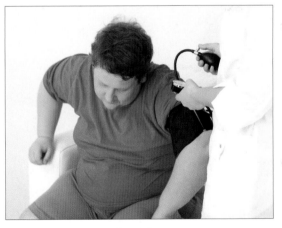

⟲ **Fig. 2.3.4**
Obesity
causes health
problems

Lifestyle Choices

To keep healthy, a balanced diet must be combined with other good lifestyle choices, such as:

- Exercise
- Regular periods of rest
- Drinking lots of water
- Limiting alcohol
- Avoiding cigarettes and recreational drugs.

⟲ **Fig. 2.3.5**
Avoid smoking
to keep healthy

Chapter Summary

- The four biomolecules in food are carbohydrates, proteins, fats and vitamins. Other key nutrients in food are minerals, fibre and water.

- Carbohydrates and fats provide energy. Proteins are key for the growth and repair of cells and enzymes.

- Vitamins and minerals are needed in small quantities to promote health.

- Fibre keeps our digestive system in good working order.

- Water has many key roles, including transport, controlling temperature and the removal of waste. Water must be consumed throughout the day.

- A balanced diet supplies an organism with all the biomolecules and nutrients in the correct quantities.

- Each person's balanced diet will be slightly different due to factors such as age, gender, genetics, health and physical activity.

- Food labels provide a list of ingredients and nutritional information. Reference Intake (RI) values are given to help consumers make informed decisions about healthy-eating choices and portion size.

- The food pyramid and Body Mass Index may also provide valuable information to consumers and medical professionals regarding diet and health, but they have limitations.

- Malnutrition is a diet that is not balanced. Starvation is still too common in countries where there are food shortages.

- In more developed countries, malnutrition may be caused by a diet that is too high in sugar, leading to weight gain. In extreme cases, this develops into obesity and leads to health problems, such as high blood pressure and type 2 diabetes.

- Deficiency diseases are caused by a lack of a particular nutrient in the diet. For example, scurvy is caused by a lack of vitamin C.

- A balanced diet must be combined with a healthy exercise regime, regular periods of rest, drinking lots of water, limiting intake of alcohol and avoiding cigarettes and recreational drugs.

The BIG Challenge

Design a balanced menu for your school canteen. The canteen will offer a choice of three meals at lunchtime:

Consider the following:

- Are your meals nutritionally balanced?

- Will your meal offer a drink?

- Is there enough choice to meet all students' tastes?

- Are your prices fair and competitive? Be sure to research all supply costs for each menu.

- Will you offer snacks or treats? Will you cater for customers who are vegetarian, vegan, coeliac, diabetic or lactose intolerant?

Go to your Portfolio to check what you have learned in this chapter.

Take the chapter 2 quiz on educateplus.ie.

Questions

1. Copy and fill in the blanks:
   a. All of the foods consumed by an organism are referred to as its _____ .
   b. Potatoes, pasta and rice are all good sources of _____ .
   c. The roles of _____ in the body include transport, controlling temperature and the removal of waste.
   d. _____ is used to test for the presence of starch in food.
   e. The units used to describe the energy content of food are _____ (kJ) or _____ (kcal).
   f. A _____ _____ contains the correct quantities of all key biomolecules and nutrients for good health.
   g. The food pyramid and _____ _____ (RI) values help consumers to make informed decisions about their diet.
   h. _____ is a diet that is not balanced.
   i. If a person's diet lacks sufficient quantities of a particular nutrient, then a _____ _____ may develop.
   j. _____ is a growing problem in developed countries and is leading to more cases of high blood pressure and type 2 diabetes.

2. Use the data in the table below to answer the following questions:
   a. Which food contains the most carbohydrates? Why do we need carbohydrates?
   b. Which food contains the least iron? Why do we need iron?
   c. Which food supplies the most energy?
   d. Why do you think cabbages and apples are so much lower in protein?
   e. How much protein is there in 200 g of chicken?
   f. How much fat is there in 75 g of milk?

3. Why do you think people choose to follow a vegetarian or vegan diet? Compared to a traditional diet, are there likely to be any key nutrients missing in a vegetarian or vegan diet? What can vegans and vegetarians do to make up for any deficiencies in their diet?

4. Why do professional rugby players sometimes drink protein shakes after training sessions?

5. Diabetes is sometimes referred to as 'sweet urine' disease. The urine of a diabetic patient returns a positive result for glucose.
   a. What test may be used to examine urine for the presence of glucose?
   b. What is the colour change of a positive result?
   c. How do diabetics test for blood sugar levels? Research Clinistrips and explain how they work.
   d. What type of biomolecule is glucose?

6. List three ways that water is important to all living organisms.

7. Explain the following statements:
   a. People sometimes take a vitamin C supplement during the winter.
   b. Teenagers need more calcium and vitamin D than adults do.
   c. Constipation may be avoided by including more wholegrain cereals in your diet.

8. What is your favourite meal?
   a. List the biomolecules and nutrients in this meal.
   b. Do you believe it is a healthy meal? Could you substitute other foods or cooking techniques to make it more healthy and balanced?

9. Research BMI and prepare a short report explaining why it is sometimes considered an unreliable indicator of weight status.

Food	Energy (kJ/100 g)	Protein (%)	Fat (%)	Carbohydrate (%)	Fibre (%)	Iron (mg/100 g)	Vitamin C (mg/100 g)
Milk	273	3.4	3.7	4.6	0	0.1	3
Sausage	1,515	10.8	31.9	9.7	0	1.1	0
Chicken	602	26.4	4.1	0	0	0.6	0
Cabbage	64	1.8	0	2.5	56	0.6	25
Apples	198	0.4	0	12.1	21	0.3	6

Working as a Scientist

Presenting and Analysing Data

Healthy Eating in School Canteens

After the initial buzz and excitement, the school's new canteen has had a fall-off in business. It appears that many of the 850 students in the school have gone back to bringing in their own lunches from home or buying food from the vending machines.

Each of the canteen's three meal deals is priced at €3.50. The manager of the canteen shows you the sales figures for the last six weeks.

🎧 **Fig. 2.5.1**
The school canteen

Week number	UNITS SOLD PER WEEK		
	MEAL 1 Soup, brown roll, piece of fruit and water	MEAL 2 Toasted sandwich, piece of fruit and orange juice	MEAL 3 Lasagne and a smoothie
1	127	145	230
2	127	148	234
3	125	138	214
4	115	133	207
5	111	123	199
6	107	120	186

1 What is the general trend over the first six weeks for sales of each of the three meal deals?

2 The canteen manager has a meeting with the school's principal at the end of the week. Instead of using the table of data, the manager asks you to come up with a suitable chart that will clearly show the trend in sales. Create this chart. Make sure to include a title and label all axes.

3 In your opinion, is this trend in sales nothing much to worry about or does it suggest the beginning of the end for the school's canteen? Explain your reasons.

The manager would like to know the reasons why students are staying away from the canteen. She asks you to design a short questionnaire to gather useful information about the students, their preferred foods and their opinions on value for money. The canteen manager intends to analyse the data you collect and use it to change the menu, pricing structure, special offers and advertising.

4 Design and produce the questionnaire, keeping in mind length (maximum 10 questions), anonymity, ease of analysis and how to avoid bias.

5 Consider how and where you will conduct the survey. What is the best option? Explain your choice. How large do you think your sample should be? Explain why.

In science, we are often interested in the relationships between different factors. If the factor that you choose to measure can take different values, it is called a variable. If another factor is not allowed to change value and instead is kept fixed at all times, it is called a controlled variable.

The school's PE teacher is concerned that more and more students are purchasing sugary sweets, crisps and fizzy drinks from the vending machines. Word has reached the PE department that your survey was excellent. Your PE teacher asks you to design a simple investigation to see if there is a link between the energy content of the foods bought in the vending machine and the BMI of the students purchasing items from the machine.

🎧 **Fig. 2.5.2**
Student at vending machine

6 **Design and produce a simple data collection table to record all of the key information. The answers to the following questions will help inform the design of your data collection table and how you will then collect and analyse your data:**

a. What is the PE teacher's hypothesis?

b. What three pieces of background information should you collect from each student?

c. What measurements will you need to take from each student?

d. How will you protect their anonymity?

e. How will you collect data regarding energy content of food? (Hint: all labels should quote kJ/100 g.)

f. How will you use this data to calculate BMI values?

g. What are the two variables in this investigation?

h. Were there any controlled (fixed) variables? Is this a strength or weakness of your investigation? Explain.

i. What is a control group? Would it be possible to include a control group in this investigation?

j. Can you think of any sources of error that may occur during the investigation? How might you reduce their effect?

k. Select a suitable chart that you could use to see the trend between your variables. Consider the title and labels that you will put on your chart.

l. Would you have any ethical concerns about carrying out this investigation?

What you may already know:

- Food gives organisms the energy they need.
- Animals must consume their food but plants can make their own food.

What you will learn in this chapter:

- Enzymes are proteins that control the rate of chemical reactions in cells.
- Organisms have different ways of making sure that cells are always kept under the same conditions.
- Photosynthesis is a chemical reaction that allows plants to make their own food.
- Respiration allows organisms to change the chemical energy in food into more useful forms.

Think BIG

- What is the ultimate source of energy on Earth?
- Why do the leaves of many plants turn reddish-brown in autumn?
- Which three chemical reactions play a key role in controlling the balance between oxygen and carbon dioxide in the Earth's atmosphere?

Puzzler

Can you find the following key terms in the word search?

Carbon dioxide

Water

Sunlight

Chlorophyll

Glucose

Oxygen

Energy

Homeostasis

Metabolism

Respiration

Photosynthesis

Enzymes

I	R	E	S	P	I	R	A	T	I	O	N	D	S	V	F
V	H	C	C	O	C	A	A	K	B	A	G	I	K	E	M
B	O	R	V	A	C	Y	K	T	Y	X	S	D	S	W	E
W	M	E	N	E	R	G	Y	M	G	E	M	O	H	K	T
B	E	F	T	Q	W	B	M	S	H	X	C	Q	W	X	A
F	O	A	H	M	F	I	O	T	Z	U	B	D	E	R	B
T	S	C	P	A	Q	O	N	N	L	B	K	R	W	I	O
N	T	G	Q	O	Z	Y	U	G	D	K	T	V	Q	S	L
I	A	G	Q	W	S	G	Q	L	D	I	H	B	E	A	I
M	S	E	Q	O	N	V	W	H	O	O	O	M	L	X	S
S	I	L	T	E	U	W	W	I	V	X	Y	X	M	B	M
Q	S	O	J	B	R	C	D	H	R	Z	Y	F	I	W	J
Y	H	O	O	E	A	N	K	U	N	F	F	G	N	D	I
P	E	H	T	S	D	E	V	E	J	E	L	B	E	G	E
P	S	A	S	U	N	L	I	G	H	T	E	O	A	N	M
P	W	H	K	E	C	H	L	O	R	O	P	H	Y	L	L

Metabolism, Enzymes and Homeostasis

Learning Intentions

In this topic we are learning to:

- Explain the role of energy and its changes in living organisms.
- Describe the role of enzymes in controlling chemical reactions in cells.
- Explain how organisms achieve homeostasis.

Key Words

Metabolism
Enzyme
Substrate
Product
Homeostasis

Metabolism

Thousands of chemical reactions must take place within living things to give them the energy they need to grow, reproduce and respond to their environment.

Together, all of the chemical reactions that take place in the cells of organisms are known as **metabolism**.

Enzymes

In Chemical World we learn that chemicals that control the rate of a reaction are called catalysts. An **enzyme** is a biological catalyst that speeds up the chemical reactions in cells.

There are thousands of different enzymes. Each enzyme controls a specific step in a chemical reaction.

- The substance an enzyme acts on is called a **substrate**.
- The enzyme acts on the substrate and changes it into a **product**.

For example, the enzyme maltase acts on the substrate maltose and changes it into the product glucose.

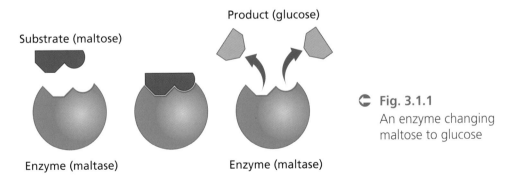

Substrate (maltose)

Product (glucose)

Enzyme (maltase)

Enzyme (maltase)

⟳ Fig. 3.1.1
An enzyme changing maltose to glucose

'Enzyme'

Eduard Buchner, a German scientist, discovered that when he added an extract from yeast to sugar, the sugar turned into alcohol. As a result, he coined the term 'enzyme' from the Greek words *en* meaning 'in' and *zyme* meaning 'yeast'.

Can you think of any commercial uses for changing sugar into alcohol?

Enzymes in action

1. Under the supervision of your teacher, add cubes of potato to a hydrogen peroxide solution.

2. Describe what happens when you add potato to a mixture of hydrogen peroxide and washing-up liquid. Explain what is causing this change.

3. Identify the enzyme, substrate and product of this reaction.

4. What were your controlled (fixed) variables? Why is it necessary to use a water bath?

5. During your research of enzymes, did you notice anything interesting about their names? (Hint: suffix and substrate.)

6. Following a class discussion, come up with a list of controlled variables for this investigation. Consider the environmental factors that may affect the reaction.

Fun Fact

Have you ever wondered how chocolates with caramel centres are made?

To start with, the caramel is actually a solid mixture of sucrose and an enzyme. Chocolate is poured over this solid mixture. The trapped enzyme then gets to work breaking down the sucrose into two other sugars that are far more soluble and even sweeter: glucose and fructose. By the time you eat the sweet, it is soft and gooey!

Fig. 3.1.2
A caramel chocolate

Homeostasis

Enzymes are proteins. Proteins are very sensitive to changes in their environment, such as temperature and pH. If an enzyme changes, it may stop working and no longer turn a substrate into a product.

For this reason, organisms must make sure that the conditions inside them stay the same, even though outside conditions change. This quest for 'sameness' is called **homeostasis**.

The enzymes in our bodies work best at 37 °C. Our body works to keep our cells at this temperature, no matter what the temperature outside is.

Think about how your body reacts on a hot day and on a cold day. Sweating and shivering are both ways of maintaining homeostasis.

- On a hot day we sweat to remove heat from the skin. Our blood vessels dilate (become wider) to allow more heat to be lost.
- On a cold day we shiver and these small movements create warmth. Our blood vessels constrict (become narrower) to keep heat in the body.

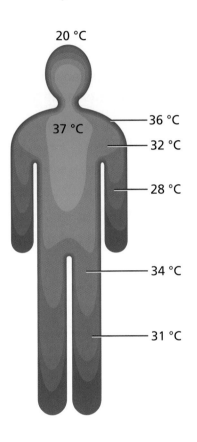

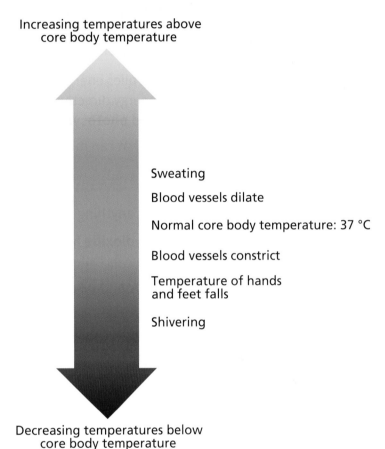

Increasing temperatures above core body temperature

Sweating

Blood vessels dilate

Normal core body temperature: 37 °C

Blood vessels constrict

Temperature of hands and feet falls

Shivering

Decreasing temperatures below core body temperature

🎧 **Fig. 3.1.3**
How our bodies regulate temperature

Fun Fact

Homeostasis is the reason dogs pant on a hot day. Unlike humans, dogs do not have sweat glands, so they have to stick out their tongues to control their temperature instead!

🎧 Fig. 3.1.4

Photosynthesis

Key Words

Photosynthesis
Producers
Carbon dioxide
Water
Chlorophyll
Sunlight
Glucose
Oxygen

Learning Intentions

In this topic we are learning to:

- Outline the role of photosynthesis in controlling the flow of energy and cycling of matter through the Earth.
- Formulate a word equation for photosynthesis.
- Investigate the environmental factors that affect the rate of photosynthesis.

The Sun supplies energy to the Earth in the form of light. Plants can use this light energy directly to make their own food. The way plants make their food is called **photosynthesis**.

Organisms that can make their own food are called **producers**.

Reactants of Photosynthesis

A reactant is anything that is needed for a chemical reaction to take place.

1. **Carbon dioxide** from the air enters the plant through small openings in the leaves called stomata.
2. **Water** from the soil enters through the plant's roots.
3. **Chlorophyll** is the green pigment found in the chloroplast of plant cells. It absorbs light energy and changes it into chemical energy.
4. **Sunlight** is the energy absorbed by the leaves.

GO Learn more about reactants and products in Chemical World 12.1

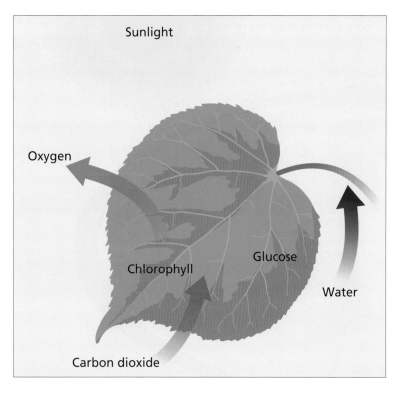

Products of Photosynthesis

A product is anything that is produced in a chemical reaction.

1. **Glucose** is the food made by the plant. It can be used to provide energy for the plant. Many plants store excess glucose in the form of starch.
2. **Oxygen** can be used to provide energy for the plant. It is released into the air through stomata. The oxygen released by photosynthesis is important as it then becomes available to all other plants and animals for respiration.

↻ **Fig. 3.2.1**
Photosynthesis

Equation for Photosynthesis

$$6CO_2 \quad + \quad 6H_2O \quad \xrightarrow[\text{chlorophyll}]{\text{sunlight}} \quad C_6H_{12}O_6 \quad + \quad 6O_2$$

$$\text{Carbon dioxide} \quad + \quad \text{water} \quad \xrightarrow[\text{chlorophyll}]{\text{sunlight}} \quad \text{glucose} \quad + \quad \text{oxygen}$$

'Photosynthesis'

Photo means 'light' and synthesis means 'to make with'.
Together, photosynthesis means 'to make with light'.

Confirming photosynthesis by testing for starch in leaves

The excess glucose produced during photosynthesis is stored as starch. Remember that iodine changes colour from orange-brown to blue-black if starch is present. As a result, iodine is a simple way to test if photosynthesis has taken place.

1. Before you start this investigation, consider the following:

   a. If you use a plant that has been left on a windowsill, how can you be sure that the starch in this plant is actually the result of photosynthesis? (Hint: starch needs to be removed from the plant before this investigation to make sure the starch produced is the result of photosynthesis. How could starch be removed from the plant?)

   b. What would be a suitable control to use in this investigation? (Hint: how might you stop a plant from photosynthesising?)

   c. Before you test a leaf for starch, you will need to remove the chlorophyll. Why do you think it is necessary to remove the chlorophyll before testing for starch?

   d. How long should you leave a plant to photosynthesise before testing for starch?

2. Consider changing this investigation to test for glucose. Is there any valid reason to test a leaf for glucose? Explain your answer.

3. Does this investigation confirm that sunlight is needed for photosynthesis? Explain your answer and mention the other controlled variables you would need for this to be a valid investigation.

⊂ **Fig. 3.2.2**
Testing for the presence of starch

Stripy leaves

If you have been in a hotel lobby or in an office, you have probably seen spider plants and geraniums. These plants are popular because of their stripy leaves. These stripes are quite rare in nature as most leaves are entirely green.

1. Plan, design, carry out and write up an investigation to confirm which of these four statements is correct:

   a. The entire leaf surface can photosynthesise.

   b. Only the green parts of the leaf surface can photosynthesise.

   c. Only the creamy-white parts of the leaf surface can photosynthesise.

   d. None of the leaf surface can photosynthesise.

Fig. 3.2.3
A spider plant

2. Why is there a difference in colour between the green and creamy-white parts of the leaf surface?

3. Are such leaves common in nature? Do you think humans may have a role to play in developing these plants? Explain your answer.

4. What term do gardeners use to describe plants with stripy leaves?

5. Could you change this investigation to test if carbon dioxide is needed for photosynthesis?

6. Do you think it would be possible to design an investigation to confirm that water is needed for photosynthesis? What are the challenges you might have to consider?

Photosynthesis and Industry

Fig. 3.2.4
Cows grazing

Photosynthesis is a very important biological process.

The farming industry relies on photosynthesis to produce food for humans, such as cereals, fruits and vegetables.

Photosynthesis is also used to make food for cattle to eat. For example, grass is grown as a crop to feed cattle and the cattle then produce milk and beef.

In Ireland, we are lucky that our land and climate provide the right conditions for photosynthesis, so that we can grow a range of crops and rear livestock:

- Lots of sunlight.
- Plenty of rain.
- The soil and air temperatures allow plant enzymes to work normally for most of the year.
- Carbon dioxide is freely available from our atmosphere.

However, there are a couple of factors that limit how well photosynthesis takes place:

- The lack of nutrients in the soil, such as nitrates, phosphates and potassium.
- Our outdoor temperatures are too low to grow some crops.

Glasshouses or polytunnels are often used to grow crops that would not naturally grow in Ireland. Crops that do grow outdoors in Ireland, such as tomatoes, can also be produced more quickly in these structures.

↻ Fig. 3.2.5
Tomato plants being grown in a glasshouse

It is possible to adjust the conditions in glasshouses and polytunnels to increase photosynthesis:

- Artificial light provides increased light around the clock.
- Burning kerosene increases carbon dioxide concentration.
- Plants are irrigated and fertilised to ensure they get enough water and nutrients.
- Temperature can be increased to suit plants that need higher temperatures to grow.

By increasing photosynthesis in these ways, more crops can be grown and sold.

Fun Fact

Some scientists are researching ways to make fuels using photosynthesis. One of the ideas is an 'artificial leaf', which is a type of solar cell that can turn sunlight energy into a chemical fuel.

When it is exposed to sunlight, the 'leaf' generates oxygen and hydrogen bubbles. These bubbles can be collected and used to deliver power.

53

Respiration

Key Words

Respiration
Consumers
Heat
Mitochondria
Building reaction
Breaking reaction
Combustion

Learning Intentions

In this topic we are learning to:

- Recognise that all organisms respire and explain the role of energy for organisms.
- Formulate a word equation for respiration.
- Evaluate the role of respiration and photosynthesis in the flow of energy and cycling of matter through the Earth.

All organisms need energy to do work. Work takes many forms – making new cells, replacing damaged or worn-out cells, physical activity, thinking and even sleeping.

⏻ **Fig. 3.3.1**
Types of work

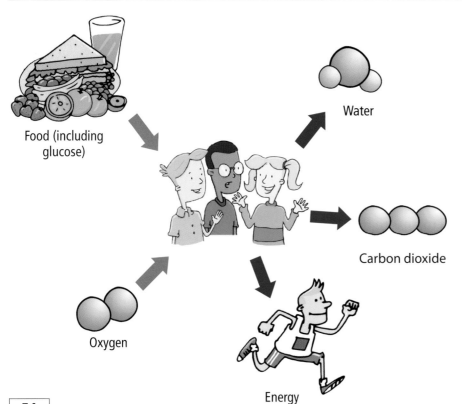

Food (including glucose)

Water

Carbon dioxide

Oxygen

Energy

Organisms get their energy from food.

The release of energy from food is called **respiration**.

As we know, plants make their own food. Animals, including humans, get their food by eating plants or other animals.

Organisms that must eat food because they cannot make their own are called **consumers**.

↻ **Fig. 3.3.2**
Respiration

Reactants of Respiration

1. Oxygen is needed by most living things for respiration. This is called aerobic respiration.
2. Glucose releases energy. This energy is changed into other forms – kinetic energy when you run, sound energy when you talk, or stored as chemical energy in the form of fat if a person consumes more energy than they need.

GO Learn more about forms of energy in Physical World 16.1

Factorising glucose

The chemical formula for glucose, a six-carbon sugar, is $C_6H_{12}O_6$.

1. Using your knowledge of algebra, factorise glucose so that it takes the following form: $(C_xH_yO_x)_n$ where x, y and n are all natural numbers. The trick is to select the smallest possible values for x, y and n. This will give you the general form of all six-carbon sugars.
2. Research the term used to describe all six-carbon sugars.

Products of Respiration

1. Carbon dioxide is a waste product of respiration. It passes out of the body through the lungs.
2. Water is also a waste product of respiration.

Note that some of the energy produced by respiration will be 'lost' as **heat**.

Respiration in Cells

Respiration takes place inside most plant and animal cells.

Mitochondria are tiny organelles in the cytoplasm. Respiration reactions take place in the mitochondria of cells.

Enzymes carefully control these reactions.

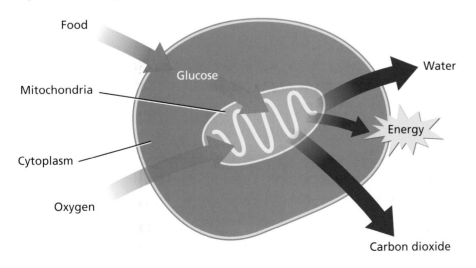

↻ **Fig. 3.3.3**
Respiration in a cell

Equation for Respiration

$$C_6H_{12}O_6 + 6O_2 \xrightarrow[\text{mitochondria}]{} energy + 6CO_2 + 6H_2O$$

$$Glucose + oxygen \xrightarrow[\text{mitochondria}]{} energy + carbon\ dioxide + water$$

Photosynthesis and Respiration

 GO Learn more about how carbon cycles through the Earth in Earth and Space 22.2

Only some organisms photosynthesise, but all organisms respire.

Photosynthesis and respiration help control the balance between carbon dioxide and oxygen in the atmosphere.

The equations that describe both processes are almost the reverse of one another:

- The reactants of respiration (glucose and oxygen) are the products of photosynthesis.
- The products of respiration (water and carbon dioxide) are the reactants of photosynthesis.

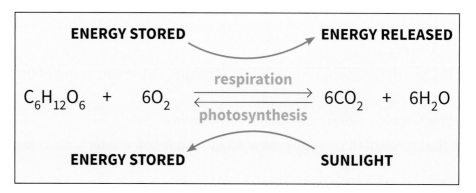

- Photosynthesis is a **building reaction**. This means that it temporarily stores energy.
- Respiration is a **breaking reaction**. This means that it releases stored energy.

Confirming that living organisms respire and dead organisms do not respire

1. Plan, design, carry out and write up an investigation to show that respiring organisms release energy as heat. This set-up should also allow you to confirm if carbon dioxide is produced as a waste product by respiring organisms.

   Before you start this investigation, consider the following:

   a. What should you use as a control?

   b. What chemical is used to test for the presence of carbon dioxide? What is the positive result for this test? Ask your teacher if there are carbon dioxide sensors in the school laboratory that could be used.

   →

2. Consider changing this investigation to test if:

   a. Sunlight is needed for respiration.

   b. Oxygen is needed for respiration.

   c. Water is produced as a waste product of respiration.

   (Hint: there are many different 'oxygen scavengers' in the products we buy. These are made up of iron powder and sodium chloride that will be useful for testing b, and anhydrous copper sulfate may be useful for testing c.)

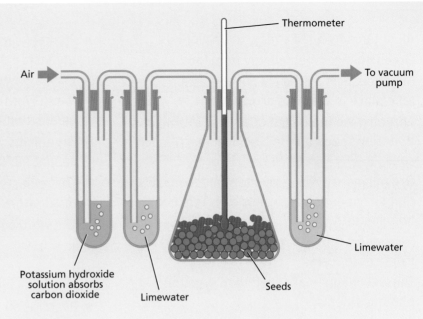

○ **Fig. 3.3.4**

Germinating seeds produce heat and release carbon dioxide during respiration

Respiration and combustion analogy

An analogy means using similarities between different things to help us understand new ideas. For example, we can use the similarities between respiring food and burning wood or coal in a fire to help develop our understanding of respiration.

Combustion

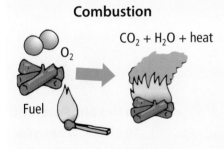

Respiration

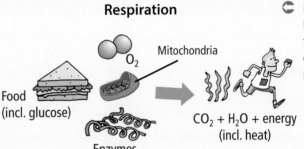

◑ Fig. 3.3.5

Using an analogy to consider combustion and respiration

1. Using the image above, see if you can come up with statements to describe the analogy between these processes. Consider the following:

   » fuel
   » products
   » reactants
   » energy transformations.

   Start each statement: 'In respiration the [fuel/reactant/product/energy transformation] is _____; in combustion the [fuel/reactant/product/energy transformation] is _____.'

2. Are there any weaknesses in this analogy? (Hint: consider the rate of energy release and the control of energy release.)

GO Learn more about combustion reactions in Chemical World 14.1

Chapter Summary

- All organisms need energy to do work.
- Organisms get their energy from food.
- Metabolism is all the chemical reactions that take place in the cells of organisms.
- Enzymes are biological catalysts. This means that they speed up the chemical reactions in cells.
- Organisms strive to stay the same to make sure that enzymes will work properly. This is called homeostasis.
- Organisms that can make their own food are called producers.
- The way plants make their food is called photosynthesis.
- The word equation for photosynthesis is:

Carbon dioxide + water $\xrightarrow[\text{chlorophyll}]{\text{sunlight}}$ glucose + oxygen

- Farmers can boost production by controlling the factors that affect photosynthesis in glasshouses and polytunnels.
- Photosynthesis is a building reaction. This means that it temporarily stores energy.
- Organisms that must eat food because they cannot make their own are called consumers.
- The release of energy from food is called respiration.
- The word equation for respiration is:

Glucose + oxygen $\xrightarrow{\text{mitochondria}}$ energy + carbon dioxide + water

- Respiration is a breaking reaction. This means that it releases stored energy.
- Photosynthesis and respiration help control the balance between carbon dioxide and oxygen in the atmosphere.

The BIG Challenge

In the 1640s, the Dutch scientist Jan Baptist van Helmont suggested that a willow tree grown in a pot gained 74 kg in mass. Curiously, the mass of the soil in the pot decreased by only 57 g. Van Helmont believed that the increase in mass was due to regularly adding water to the pot over the five years.

Working in small groups, design a similar investigation that may be completed over a period of between one month and six months. (Hint: van Helmont seemed to be aware of water but what other substances should he also have tracked? Consider both sides of the equation for photosynthesis and respiration.) Best of luck – hopefully it won't take you five years!

The tree when van Helmont planted it

The tree in its pot after 5 years

The tree out of its pot after 5 years

🎧 **Fig. 3.4.1**
Van Helmont investigation

Go to your Portfolio to check what you have learned in this chapter.

Take the chapter 3 quiz on educateplus.ie.

Questions

1. Copy and fill in the blanks:

   a. All organisms need energy to do _____.

   b. _____ is all the chemical reactions that take place in the cells of living things.

   c. _____ are biological catalysts.

   d. The environment is constantly changing but organisms strive to keep things the same. This is called _____.

   e. Normal human body temperature is _____ °C.

   f. Plants are producers. Animals are _____.

   g. Photosynthesis is a building reaction. _____ is a breaking reaction.

   h. Only some organisms photosynthesise, but all organisms _____.

   i. Complete the word equation for photosynthesis:

Carbon dioxide	+	water	sunlight → chlorophyll	_____	+	_____

   j. Complete the word equation for respiration:

_____	+	oxygen	→ mitochondria	energy	+	_____	+	water

2. Copy and complete the following table.

	Photosynthesis	Respiration
Select from list: producers only, consumers only, both producers and consumers		
Select from list: building reaction, breaking reaction		
Organelles involved are …		
Reactants are …		
Products are …		
Select from list: energy is stored temporarily in food, energy is released in a readily usable form		

3. Consider the following statement: 'Photosynthesis is essential for the survival of animals.' Do you agree or disagree? Give at least three points to support your answer.

4. List three ways that plants are adapted to maximise photosynthesis? (Hint: think about the structure of leaves.)

5. Boxers and endurance athletes often train at high-altitude camps before a competition. Research this training strategy. Pay particular attention to respiration, circulatory and breathing systems.

6. Research and explain why some plants are considered to be 'shade-loving'. Give at least two points to support your answer.

7. Do warm-blooded animals need to consume more food than cold-blooded animals? Give three points to support your answer.

8. Complete the following paragraph: 'I want to grow cress seeds that I bought in my local supermarket. To grow (germinate), the seeds will need...'

9. The following graph shows the relationship between the concentration of carbon dioxide and the rate of photosynthesis in Canadian Pondweed.

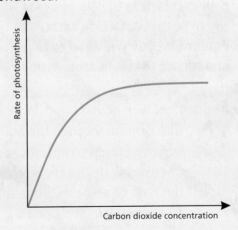

   a. Identify (i) the independent variable, (ii) the dependent variable, (iii) at least three controlled (fixed) variables to make this a fair investigation.

   b. Why does the graph increase to begin with?

   c. Why does the graph then level off?

Working as a Scientist

Making and Recording Observations

Investigating Light and Photosynthesis

A student in a different class has designed the investigation shown in Fig. 3.5.1. You have been asked to change it to examine the relationship between light intensity and the rate of photosynthesis. The hypothesis is 'The greater the light intensity, the greater the rate of photosynthesis'.

> **Step 1:** Collect the necessary equipment and position the lamp approximately 50 cm away from the Canadian Pondweed. Do not turn on the lamp.

1 **Consider the factors that are likely to affect the rate of photosynthesis. You must collect data on factors such as:**

- Distance between the lamp and beaker with Canadian Pondweed.
- Mass of sodium hydrogencarbonate.
- Wattage of bulb.

2 **Make a list of at least five other factors that are key to the relationship between light intensity and the rate of photosynthesis. You must collect this data to help you test the hypothesis. Decide what equipment you will need to take and record these measurements.**

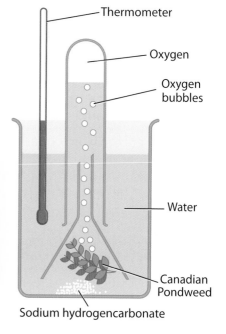

Fig. 3.5.1
Set-up to investigate the relationship between light intensity and rate of photosynthesis

> **Step 2:** Now turn on the lamp. Wait for three minutes and then record the number of bubbles that drift up through the boiling tube over the next 60 seconds.
>
> **Step 3:** Move the lamp 10 cm closer to the Canadian Pondweed. Wait three minutes and then, once more, record the number of bubbles that drift up through the boiling tube over the next 60 seconds. Repeat three more times until you have reached a distance of 10 cm between the Canadian Pondweed and the lamp.

3 **Record your results in a table.**

4 **Comment on the trend that you have observed and compare with other groups in the class. Does this trend support the original hypothesis?**

5 **Comment on likely sources of error. How could you change the investigation to improve accuracy? Consider a suitable control for this investigation.**

Investigating Temperature and Respiration

A student in a different class has designed the investigation shown in Fig. 3.5.2. You have been asked to change this investigation to examine the relationship between temperature and the rate of respiration. The hypothesis is 'The higher the temperature, the faster the rate of respiration'.

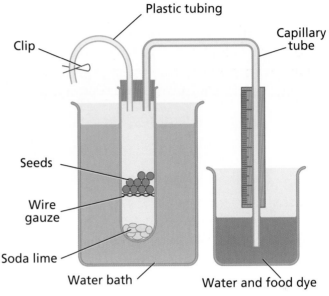

Step 1: Collect the necessary equipment and set up the investigation.

1 How will you collect all of the data needed to test your hypothesis? You can use the following incomplete data collection sheet to help you get started, but there are some important factors that are not included. What other data should you collect? Consider the independent, dependent and controlled (fixed) variables needed to make this a fair test.

🎧 **Fig. 3.5.2**
Set-up to investigate the relationship between temperature and the rate of respiration

Independent variable	Dependent variable	Controlled (fixed) variables	
Temperature (°C)	Rate of respiration (cm)	Mass of seeds	
0		Mass of soda lime	
10		Time	
20			
30			
40			
50			

Step 2: You may start your investigation when you are satisfied that your method is appropriate and you have considered all key factors. Record your data. When you have finished collecting your data, consider the following questions:

2 Does this investigation need a control? If yes, what would be a suitable control?

3 Present the data that you have collected and recorded using a suitable chart or graph.

4 Comment on the trend that you have observed. Does this trend support the original hypothesis?

5 Comment on likely sources of error. How could you change the investigation to improve accuracy?

Chapter 4

The Continuity of Life: Genetics and Evolution

What you may already know:

- The nucleus is the control centre of the cell.
- You have inherited features, such as hair colour, from your parents.
- Humans are closely related to chimpanzees.

What you will learn in this chapter:

- DNA contains the information needed to make up every part of our bodies.
- Parents pass on genes to their offspring.
- The technology now exists to alter genes. This is called genetic engineering.
- Genes can mutate. This introduces variation to the population but it can also cause some diseases.
- Darwin's theory of evolution by natural selection.

Think BIG

- Are you unique?
- Are Olympic gold medalists a product of nature, nurture or both?
- Should we clone humans?

Puzzler

Can you solve this puzzle?

Use the pictures to work out a key term that you will come across in this chapter.

Genetics

Learning Intentions

In this topic we are learning to:

- Distinguish the difference between inherited and acquired characteristics.
- Recognise that a gene is the basic unit of inheritance.
- Appreciate the role of Gregor Mendel in developing our understanding of inheritance and consider a simple genetic cross.

Genetics is the study of how characteristics are passed on from one generation to another.

There are two types of characteristics:

1. **Inherited characteristics** are passed on from parents to their children by genes. For example, eye colour, blood type and curly or straight hair.

2. **Acquired characteristics** are not inherited from our parents. They are learned throughout our life. For example, the accent we speak in or being able to ride a bike.

Characteristics are also known as **traits**.

Key Words

Genetics
Inherited characteristics
Acquired characteristics
Traits
Chromosomes
DNA
Gene
Gametes
Sperm
Egg
Zygote
Fertilisation
Dominant
Recessive
Genetic cross

⟳ **Fig. 4.1.1**
Curly hair is an inherited characteristic

⟳ **Fig. 4.1.2**
Being able to ride a bike is an acquired characteristic

Chromosomes and Genes

Chromosomes are thread-like structures found in the nucleus of an animal or plant cell. They are made up of protein and a chemical called **DNA** (deoxyribonucleic acid).

A **gene** is a short section of the DNA in a chromosome. Each gene contains the information needed to make a different protein in a cell. Proteins make up everything in our bodies, such as enzymes, muscles, bones, hair and teeth.

There are approximately 20,500 genes in each cell in the human body.

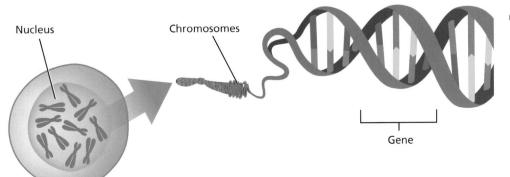

Nucleus

Chromosomes

Gene

⟳ **Fig. 4.1.3**
The organisation of genetic material

63

People and Science

We have known for a long time that characteristics are passed from parents to their children. But science has only recently discovered exactly how this information passes between generations.

In 1953, **James Watson and Francis Crick** showed that DNA is shaped like a spiral staircase, commonly known as the double helix. This is an efficient way of storing the huge quantity of genetic information in each cell and it also helps cells to divide correctly. In 1962, Watson and Crick, along with Maurice Wilkins, won a Nobel Prize for their discovery.

⊃ Fig. 4.1.4
Watson and Crick

Chromosome Numbers

The DNA race

The race to understand DNA was long and eventful.

Research the controversy surrounding the race to understand DNA and prepare a short multimedia presentation for your classmates.

Every human body cell contains 46 chromosomes, except gametes. **Gametes** are the cells involved in reproduction.

- The male gamete is a **sperm**. It contains 23 chromosomes.
- The female gamete is an **egg**. It contains 23 chromosomes.

During human reproduction the male sperm and the female egg fuse and a single cell called a **zygote** is produced. This is called **fertilisation**. We will learn more about how fertilisation takes place later.

The zygote contains 46 chromosomes. Twenty-three of these chromosomes come from the father and the other 23 come from the mother.

The new zygote has a unique combination of genes inherited from both the male and female parent and shares certain characteristics with both.

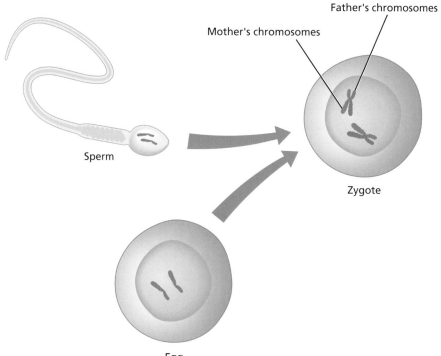

Father's chromosomes

Mother's chromosomes

Sperm

Zygote

Egg

⊃ Fig. 4.1.5
A sperm and egg produce a zygote

Dominant and Recessive Genes

In some cases, one gene for a trait is **dominant** over another gene for that same trait. The non-dominant gene is called the **recessive** gene.

- A dominant trait will show in a child even if only one parent has the dominant gene.
- A recessive trait will only show if both parents pass the recessive gene on to the child.

For example, the gene for the presence of the skin pigment melanin is dominant over the gene for the absence of melanin (recessive). When an individual has one or both dominant genes, they will produce skin with the pigment melanin.

The recessive trait will show only if the individual has two recessive genes for that trait. In this case, the individual will produce skin without melanin, a condition known as albinism.

 'Dominant' and 'recessive'

The meanings of the words 'dominant' and 'recessive' outside of biology can help us remember how they are used when talking about inheritance.

'Dominant' means having power over others. A dominant trait has power over a recessive trait.

'Recessive' can be used to describe something that is moving back. A recessive trait may stay in the background.

○ Fig. 4.1.6
A young boy with albinism

People and Science

During the mid-nineteenth century, Augustinian monk **Gregor Mendel** carried out a series of breeding studies of pea plants, tracking how characteristics such as flower colour and seed shape were inherited.

Mendel discovered that when he bred purple-flowered plants with white-flowered plants, all the new plants produced had purple flowers. This is because the gene for purple flowers is dominant, and the gene for white flowers is recessive.

Mendel used his data to describe a 'particulate mechanism of inheritance', which forms the basis of how we study inheritance today. Mendel's work came before the discovery of genes and DNA. Mendel believed that a particle was passed on from parents to children during reproduction. Later it became obvious that Mendel's 'particle' was a gene.

○ Fig. 4.1.7
Gregor Mendel

Fun Fact

Red-green colour blindness is a quite common recessive trait in humans. Approximately 10 per cent of males have some form of colour blindness. However, it is unusual for females to have this condition.

Opticians use Ishihara test plates to determine colour blindness. What numbers can you see in the following test plates? Colour blind people will not see the same numbers as people with normal vision.

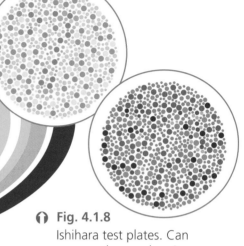

🎧 **Fig. 4.1.8**
Ishihara test plates. Can you see the numbers?

Genetic crosses

Scientists use genetic crosses to study the inheritance of different traits. Figure 4.1.9 shows a simple **genetic cross** that describes the inheritance of sex (gender) in humans.

⮕ **Fig. 4.1.9**
A simple genetic cross

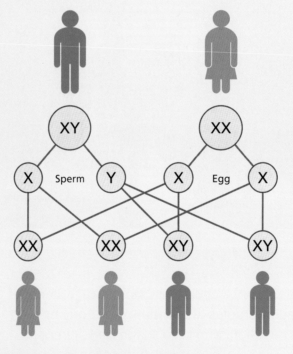

- Males are represented as 'XY' as they have a single X chromosome and a single Y chromosome.
- Females are represented as 'XX' as they have two X chromosomes.

Working in pairs, answer the following questions:

1. Research Irish census data online. Calculate the ratio of males to females for each census. Do you see a trend emerging? Can you explain this trend using the genetic cross shown in Fig. 4.1.9?

2. Interpret the simple genetic cross in Fig. 4.1.9 to answer this question: who determines the sex of a human child – the father or mother?

Nature versus Nurture

Nature versus nurture is one of the longest running debates in science. How much do the genes we are born with or the environment we live in affect who we are? For example, how smart we are, how good at sports we are and how likely we are to put on weight.

The reality is that all of these traits are the result of our genes *and* our environment – genes offer potential, the correct environment allows this potential to be realised.

Nature versus nurture

Look closely at the following image. In small groups, discuss your initial response to this image.

◔ Fig. 4.1.10

What scientific message is this image attempting to deliver? Do you think that the image is helpful and fair or is it simply for shock value? Could you use this image in a campaign to raise awareness of childhood obesity?

Variation and Evolution

Key Words

Species
Variation
Natural selection
Evolution
Artificial selection

Learning Intentions

In this topic we are learning to:

- Analyse the role of environmental and genetic factors in variation.
- Use Darwin's theory of evolution by natural selection to explain the diversity of organisms.

Variation

A **species** is a group of similiar organisms that can breed with each other to produce fertile offspring. We all belong to the human species. Yet, if you look around your classroom you will see lots of differences in height, hair colour and eye colour, for example.

Variation describes all of the differences in traits that exist in members of the same species.

Variation is caused by two things:

1. Environment (where and how we live). For example, our body fat is caused by how much we eat and how much exercise we do.

2. Inheritance. For example, the colour of our eyes is caused by the genes we get from our parents.

Often these two factors interact with each other. For example, how tall a person grows may be influenced by their diet as well as their genes.

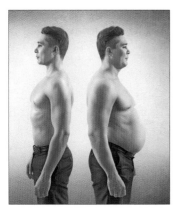

🎧 **Fig. 4.2.1**
Body shape is an example of variation due to environment

Survival

A species needs variation to survive. For example, in the 1950s a virus called myxomatosis almost wiped out rabbits in the United Kingdom.

The disease killed most of the rabbits that caught it. However, a very small number of rabbits were genetically different and had a natural resistance to the disease.

Over time, the rabbit population grew from the few resistant individuals, meaning that genetic variation saved UK rabbits from extinction.

🎧 **Fig. 4.2.2**
Eye colour is an example of variation due to genes

Natural Selection

Natural selection is the process by which the members of a species who are best suited to their environment are most likely to survive and reproduce.

Any useful changes that take place in a species will be passed on to future generations. A well-known example is the change in the colour of peppered moths close to cities:

- In areas where air quality is good, the light-coloured wings are an advantage, so the gene for this colour is dominant in the gene pool (all the genes in a population).

- In areas where trees and buildings are covered in dust and dirt, light-coloured moths become more visible and are in danger of being eaten by predators, so a darker wing colour becomes an advantage and is passed on to future generations.

Evolution

Natural selection explains **evolution**.

Evolution is the gradual change in the inherited characteristics of a species over time. Evolution can lead to new species.

The theory of evolution by natural selection was introduced by Charles Darwin.

Fig. 4.2.3
A light-coloured moth on a white wall

People and Science

Charles Darwin developed one of the greatest and most controversial ideas in science: the theory of evolution by natural selection.

The belief that humans are created by God was, and still is, widely held. It was against this backdrop that Darwin proposed that, like all other species, humans had evolved from earlier forms.

In December 1831, Darwin boarded HMS *Beagle* at Plymouth, England, and set sail across the globe on an almost five-year voyage that would take him to many faraway places, including South America, Africa, Asia and, famously, the Galápagos Islands in the middle of the Pacific Ocean. This voyage gave Darwin the opportunity to observe and collect thousands of different specimens.

Fig. 4.2.4
Charles Darwin

1. Geospiza magnirostris.   2. Geospiza fortis.
3. Geospiza parvula.   4. Certhidea olivacea.

Fig. 4.2.5 Darwin's finches

Darwin was interested in the small differences between birds on the Galápagos Islands. He collected 26 specimens. Of these specimens there were 25 different species. These birds became known as 'Darwin's finches'.

Darwin suggested that the variation in the beaks of these otherwise similar birds was evidence of how they had evolved to get access to different food sources on the separate islands. The individuals with the best beak structure would get the most food and so survive to reproduce. Nature was selecting the genes that coded for the best beak and deselecting the genes that coded for less useful beak types.

In 1859, Darwin published his famous book, *On the Origin of Species by Means of Natural Selection*. The book divided opinion in the scientific community and among the general public.

Today, Darwin's theory is widely accepted in the scientific community. Further evidence of evolution comes from fossils and DNA research.

The five-digit limb

Look closely at the following image.

Human hand   Bat wing   Whale fin

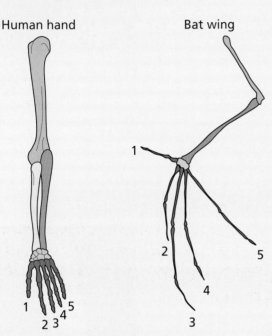

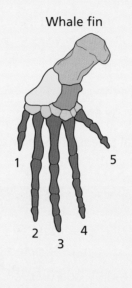

↺ **Fig. 4.2.6**
Similar bone structure in the forelimbs of different animals

In pairs, consider the following questions:

1. Where does each of these organisms live?
2. How does each of these different organisms move?
3. What does this suggest regarding the inheritance of a five-digit limb?
4. Does the inheritance of this five-digit limb type provide any evidence for Darwin's theory?

Evolution, still dividing opinion 150 years on

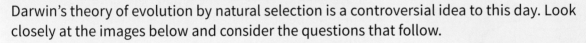

Darwin's theory of evolution by natural selection is a controversial idea to this day. Look closely at the images below and consider the questions that follow.

1. What is your first reaction to image A? Is it balanced or biased to favour one viewpoint?
2. Do you think image B is an accurate representation of Darwin's theory?
3. Image C hints at the controversy between two groups of people that have very different opinions on Darwin's theory. Identify these groups and outline the difference in their viewpoints.

Selective Breeding

Over thousands of years, humans have changed plants and animals through careful breeding to improve their useful characteristics. This is known as **artificial selection** because the changes do not take place naturally.

For example:

- Breeding programmes are common in the livestock industry, where cows are bred to produce large volumes of milk and beef.
- The racehorse industry develops traits such as speed, hurdling ability and endurance.
- All dogs are descended from the grey wolf. Hundreds of breeds of domestic dog have been bred over the last 15,000 years or so.

🎧 **Fig. 4.2.7**
Racehorses are selectively bred for speed and endurance

Grey wolf (common ancestor)

🎧 **Fig. 4.2.8**
All dog breeds are descended from the grey wolf

71

Mutation

Key Words

Mutation
Tumour
Benign
Malignant
Mutagen

Learning Intentions

In this topic we are learning to:

- Examine how mutation introduces variation into a population.
- Explain the causes and treatments for certain cancers.
- Consider the role of mutation and inheritance in common genetic disorders.

Mutation is a change in a gene or chromosome.

Like other causes of variation, mutation can be inherited or influenced by an organism's environment.

Mutation can also happen randomly. Mutations may be useful to an organism, but they can also be harmful.

Cancer

Cells are constantly dividing. Mutated cells divide much more quickly than normal cells. This can cause a mass of cells called a **tumour** to form.

- **Benign** tumours do not move to other parts of the body.
- **Malignant** tumours can spread and are more of a concern.

The group of diseases resulting from this type of mutation is called cancer. There are approximately 200 different cancers.

Most cancers are not inherited. Certain cancers become more common as people age, such as prostate cancer in males and ovarian cancer in females.

It is important that people are aware of the signs and symptoms of cancer. The earlier the disease is diagnosed, the less likely it is to spread and the sooner treatment can start. This greatly improves the chances of recovery.

Treatments

Current treatments for cancer include surgery, radiotherapy, chemotherapy, biological therapies or a combination of these treatments. Research these treatments and prepare a short report on each for your classmates.

Causes of Mutation

While most mutations are completely random, they can also happen because of certain environmental factors.

For example:

- Smokers are at far greater risk of developing lung cancer than non-smokers.
- Ultraviolet (UV) rays in sunlight destroy the DNA of skin cells. People who spend too long in the sun without applying sunscreen and those who use sunbeds increase their risk of skin cancer.
- Exposure to gamma rays or X-rays can cause mutation.

Any environmental factor that increases the likelihood of mutation is called a **mutagen**.

🎧 **Fig. 4.3.1**
A man wearing a protective anti-radiation suit

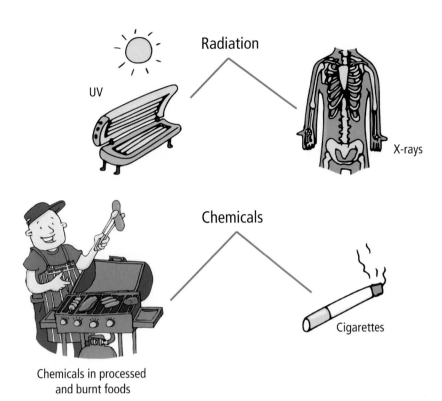

C **Fig. 4.3.2**
Common mutagens

People and Science

Marie Curie made understanding radioactivity her life's work. She pioneered the first ever trials of radiation therapy to treat cancer.

Curie herself died from a disease of the bone marrow brought on by overexposure to radiation.

Curie shared the 1903 Nobel Prize in Physics with her husband Pierre Curie and the physicist Henri Becquerel. She also won the Nobel Prize in Chemistry in 1911.

⊃ **Fig. 4.3.3**
Marie Curie

GO Learn more about radiation in Earth and Space 24.2

Effects of Mutation

Mutations can alter the genes in gametes. These mutations and faulty genes may be passed on to an individual's children.

At fertilisation, if a zygote receives a faulty gene for a particular trait through the male sperm and a similarly faulty gene for that same trait through the female egg, then the offspring will not have a working copy of that gene.

For example, haemophiliacs do not have a working copy of the gene that makes the blood-clotting protein. As a result, they are at risk of excessive bleeding.

'Karyotype'

A karyotype is an organised picture of a person's chromosomes that helps scientists to identify certain genetic disorders.

The chromosomes are shown in pairs and numbered. The last two chromosomes are marked to show the person's gender: XY for male and XX for female.

Down Syndrome

We know that normal body cells have 46 chromosomes. If a zygote receives the wrong number of chromosomes from the sperm or egg cells (gametes) during fertilisation, it leads to a genetic disorder.

The most common example of this form of mutation is Down syndrome, where the offspring receives an extra copy of chromosome number 21.

Figure 4.3.4 shows the karyotype for a male with Down syndrome. Note the extra copy of chromosome 21.

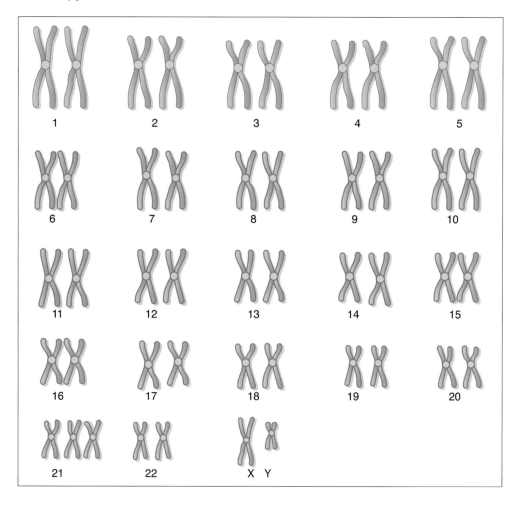

⮕ Fig. 4.3.4
Chromosomes from a male with Down syndrome

Down syndrome and mother's age

In pairs, look carefully at the graph in Fig. 4.3.5 and consider the following questions:

1. What trend, if any, is emerging in this graph?

2. What other information would you need before you could make a balanced judgment on the data?

3. Research the terms 'correlation' and 'causation'. Does either of these terms apply to this data?

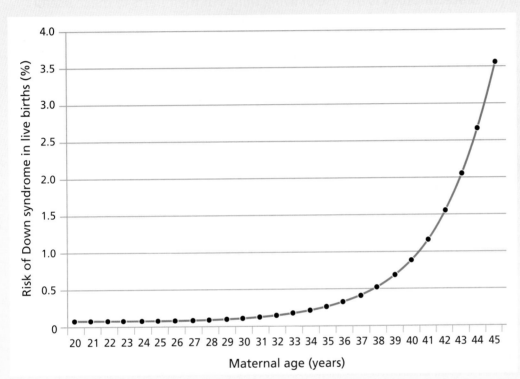

↺ **Fig. 4.3.5**
Down syndrome
and mother's age

Debating genetics

Advances in our understanding of genetics have forced society to ask some very big questions. Have a class debate about one of the following issues:

- The availability of gastric bypass surgery for morbidly obese patients.
- The pros and cons of genetic screening.
- The use of embryonic tissues for stem cell research and therapies.

Genetic Engineering and Cloning

Learning Intentions

In this topic we are learning to:

- Research the arguments for and against genetic engineering.

Biotechnology is the use of living things or their parts to make useful products and to perform useful services.

An early example of biotechnology is the use of microorganisms to make food such as cheese and bread.

The discovery of DNA marked the beginning of modern biotechnology. Since then, biotechnology has made huge changes in industries such as medicine, farming and food science.

Genetic Engineering

Genetic engineering is deliberately changing genes to produce desirable characteristics.

Genetic engineering is also called genetic modification (GM).

Genetically altered genes can be used in medicine or to produce new types of plants or animals.

Insulin

An example of genetic engineering in medicine is the treatment of the disease diabetes. Our bodies naturally produce a protein hormone called insulin to control the levels of glucose in our blood. However, a person who has diabetes may need insulin from an external source to keep them healthy.

Most of the insulin needed for the treatment of diabetes is now made using genetically engineered bacteria.

The human gene that controls insulin production is inserted into the bacteria *E. coli*. This bacteria is then grown in huge numbers to mass-produce insulin.

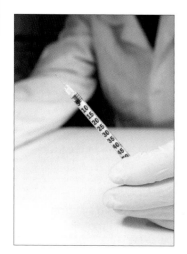

◯ **Fig. 4.4.1**
An insulin injection

◔ **Fig. 4.4.2**
'Golden' rice

Golden Rice

Genetic engineering also allows scientists to produce a slightly different form of a gene. As a result, the new gene will produce a slightly different protein.

For example, a common species of rice was genetically engineered to produce large quantities of beta-carotene. Humans need beta-carotene to make vitamin A.

This new rice – known as golden rice because of its colour – offered the hope of reducing vitamin A deficiency in parts of the world where a lack of vitamin A in the diet is common.

The **Human Genome Project** was set up during the 1990s to map all 20,500 (approx.) human genes. The project was completed in 2003. The data collected opened up many avenues for further research across the sciences, as well as informing advances in biotechnology.

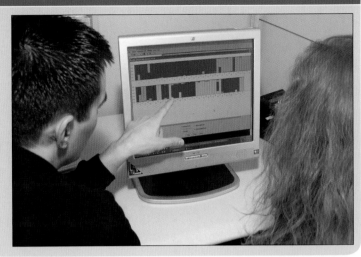

⮕ **Fig. 4.4.3**
Researchers at the National Human Genome Research Institute

Cloning

Genetically identical individuals are called clones. **Cloning** can happen in nature. For example, some twins are genetically identical.

Whereas genetic engineering produces altered forms of a gene, cloning produces exact copies of genes. Cloning can also produce exact copies of animals and plants.

In 1996, Dolly the sheep became the world's first deliberately cloned animal – identical in every way to the sheep whose tissue cells were used in the cloning process. Dolly was euthanised in 2003 because of arthritis and lung disease.

The easiest way to clone a plant is by taking a cutting. We will learn more about this method when we look at how plants reproduce.

🎧 **Fig. 4.4.4**
Identical twins

DNA and the future

To understand how genetic engineering can serve society in a responsible way, we must get information and data from reliable sources.

Prepare a short report outlining the ethical issues surrounding each of the following:

- GM foods
- Cloning
- Centralised DNA databases

Carry out your research using trustworthy sources.

🎧 **Fig. 4.4.5**
Dolly the sheep

Chapter Summary

- Genetics is the study of how characteristics are passed on from one generation to another.

- Inherited characteristics are passed on from parents to their children by genes. Acquired characteristics are learned throughout our life.

- Chromosomes are found in the nucleus of a cell. They are made up of protein and a chemical called DNA.

- A gene is a short section of the DNA in a chromosome.

- All human body cells contain 46 chromosomes, except gametes. Gametes contain 23 chromosomes.

- The male gamete is a sperm. The female gamete is an egg.

- Traits can be dominant or recessive.

- A species is a group of organisms that can breed with each other to produce fertile offspring.

- Variation describes all of the differences in traits that exist in members of the same species. In most cases, variation is due to a combination of environmental and genetic factors.

- Natural selection is the process by which the members of a species who are best suited to their environment are most likely to survive and reproduce.

- Evolution is the gradual change in the inherited characteristics of a species over time. Evolution can lead to new species. The theory of evolution by natural selection was introduced by Charles Darwin.

- Mutation is a change in a gene or chromosome. It can introduce useful variation in genes but may also cause certain genetic diseases.

- Biotechnology is the use of living things or their parts to make useful products and to perform useful services.

- Genetic engineering is deliberately changing genes to produce desirable characteristics.

The BIG Challenge

In groups, look through newspapers and magazines and find a photograph of a famous family that includes a mother, a father and their children. (The children can be grown-ups!)

Stick the picture to a piece of card and label the characteristics that the children have inherited from their parents. Suggest which parent the trait was inherited from. What does it tell you about the parents' genes?

Remember that some visible traits might be acquired rather than inherited. Maybe someone has dyed their hair!

Present your poster to the rest of the class.

Go to your Portfolio to check what you have learned in this chapter.

Take the chapter 4 quiz on **educateplus.ie**.

Questions

1. Copy and fill in the blanks:

   a. _____ is the study of how characteristics are passed on from one generation to another.

   b. _____ characteristics are passed on from parents to their children by genes. _____ characteristics are learned throughout our life.

   c. Chromosomes are found in the nucleus and are made up of _____ and protein.

   d. All human body cells contain _____ chromosomes, except gametes which contain _____.

   e. The male gamete is a _____. The female gamete is an _____.

   f. Genes are either dominant or _____.

   g. Scientists use _____ _____ to study the inheritance of different traits.

   h. Charles Darwin is famous for his theory of _____ by natural selection.

   i. The breeding of racehorses for speed or hurdling ability is an example of _____ selection.

   j. _____ is the use of living things or their parts to make useful products and to perform useful services.

2. Explain the difference between these terms and give examples:
   a. Inherited characteristics and acquired characteristics.
   b. Dominant and recessive.

3. Describe three ways that variation can be introduced to a population.

4. Research one example of genetic engineering in each of the following organisms:
   a. Bacteria
   b. Plants
   c. Animals

5. Following the approach of the genetic cross on page 66, attempt a similar cross between a male bird (ZZ) and a female bird (ZW). Which of the parents in this ZW system determines the sex (gender) of the offspring? Explain your answer.

6. Explain the meaning of the expression 'survival of the fittest' in evolution.

7. Explain how Darwin's finches helped him to develop his theory of evolution by means of natural selection.

8. Darwin first wrote about evolution in 1858 with another British scientist. Find out who this scientist was and briefly explain why his contribution to this key idea in the biological world has almost been forgotten.

9. Mules and hinnys are produced as a result of a cross between a donkey and a horse. Using your understanding of genetics and sexual reproduction, explain why mules and hinnys are not considered as separate species, whereas donkeys and horses are separate species.

10. The alphabet is made up of 26 letters. Different combinations of these letters can form thousands of words. Likewise, there are thousands of different genes, yet the DNA molecule that makes up these genes is written in a code of only four different 'letters'. These are called bases. Find out what these bases are and try to explain how they can account for so many different genes.

Working as a Scientist

Asking Questions and Making Predictions

Investigating Inheritance: 'Softmeats'

Your teacher has just created the new species *Mallow vulgaris*, more affectionately known as 'softmeat'. Using softmeat, you will develop a model to explain the formation of gametes and also genetic crosses.

Step 1: Investigation design

To make your model, you will need: marshmallows (round and square), thumbtacks (two different colours), toothpicks, pipe cleaners, lollipop sticks, modelling clay, markers, elastic bands and plastic cups.

You will track the inheritance of gender (sex) and also four other characteristics that vary on an either/or basis. The traits (and symbols for genes) are as follows:

Gender (sex): two lollipop sticks, female – red x 2; male – 1 blue + 1 red. Colour both sides of each lollipop stick.

Body shape: round – R; square – r. Label one lollipop stick 'R' and another lollipop stick 'r'. You will use a round marshmallow and a square marshmallow to build softmeats of different body shapes.

Height: tall – T; short – t. Label one lollipop stick 'T' and another lollipop stick 't'. You will use a whole toothpick or half a toothpick to build softmeats of different heights.

Eye colour: blue – B; white – b. Label one lollipop stick 'B' and another lollipop stick 'b'. You will use blue and white thumbtacks to build softmeats of different eye colours.

Tail shape: straight – S; curly – s. Label one lollipop stick 'S' and another lollipop stick 's'. You will use a straight piece of pipe cleaner and a curly piece of pipe cleaner to build softmeats of different tail shapes.

1 Why did you use both uppercase and lowercase versions of the same letter? What do the letters represent?

2 What do the lollipop sticks represent?

Each person should now have 10 lollipop sticks. Join the lollipop sticks for a particular trait together with a piece of modelling clay, so those labelled 'B' and 'b' will be together and so on. Some softmeats will be female (red lollipop stick x 2), others male (blue x 1 and red x 1). You should now have five pairs of lollipop sticks. Secure them together with an elastic band. These are all the genes needed to build your softmeat.

> **Step 2: Making and recording observations**
> Now you will start breeding your softmeats! In pairs, place five empty paper cups on the desk. Label the paper cups 'Sex', 'Body shape', 'Height', 'Eye colour' and 'Tail shape'. Each person should then put their pair of lollipop sticks into the appropriate cup. You should now have two pairs of lollipop sticks in each cup.

3 **For your model to work, is it necessary to always breed a female and male? Explain your answer.**

Each person will now take two lollipop sticks from each cup, but only on the conditions that you do not look when you are picking and only take one lollipop stick from a pair. You must mix up the pairs.

4 **What does this step of your model represent? Is there any limitation to this part of the model?**

5 **Why is it important that this step happens randomly? In nature, what property does this step introduce into a population?**

6 **Why is it necessary that the pairs are split apart? Consider what would happen during fertilisation if this did not occur.**

Each person should now have ten lollipop sticks again. Recombine the lollipop sticks for the same trait. For example, you should have two lollipop sticks for height but they could be any of the following combinations: TT, Tt or tt. Your job is to build your own softmeat using the materials supplied by your teacher.

After completing your individual breeding programmes, consider the following questions as a class.

7 **What traits were most common for:**
    a. Sex (gender)?
    b. Height?
    c. Eye colour?

What conclusion can you draw from these observations?

8 **Collect all of the data from the class for:**
    a. Body shape
    b. Tail shape

Write the number of individuals with each version of the trait as a ratio. For example, if there were 16 straight tails and 8 curly tails, this would be written as 16:8 or, more simply, 2:1. Consider the other traits. Do you see a trend? Is the ratio for sex the same?

9 **This type of genetic cross is described as a monohybrid cross. Why? Research the famous law that Mendel developed using all of his data from monohybrid crosses. Prepare a short report for your classmates.**

Chapter 5

The Diversity of Life

What you may already know:

- There are many different living things.

What you will learn in this chapter:

- There are five groups of organisms – bacteria, protists, fungi, animals and plants.
- Bacteria are the most numerous type of organism on Earth and they have many roles.
- Many scientists do not consider viruses to be living things. Viruses can cause diseases.

Think BIG

- What was the first organism to appear on Earth?
- Are new organisms still evolving?

Puzzler

Can you pair the celebrity with the organism named after them? What language is used for the naming of organisms? Why? Try to say the names aloud!

1. David Attenborough

2. Steve Irwin

3. Bill Gates

4. Bob Marley

5. Angelina Jolie

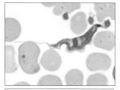

a. *Trypanosoma irwini*

b. *Aptostichus angelinajolieae*

c. *Gnathia marleyi*

d. *Eristalis gatesi*

e. *Materpiscis attenboroughi*

The Five Kingdoms of Life

In this topic we are learning to:
- List the five kingdoms of life.
- Describe how organisms are classified.

Scientists believe that life first appeared on Earth 3,800 million years ago in the form of bacteria.

From these earliest organisms, millions of different species have evolved, including plants and animals.

It is thought that there are between 15 and 20 million different species on Earth today. This great variety of life is called **biodiversity**.

Classification

The system of grouping organisms together that share common characteristics is called **classification**.

Organisms are classified into five groups, or **kingdoms**.

These are:

1. Animals
2. Plants
3. Protists
4. Fungi
5. Bacteria

Homo sapiens

In the eighteenth century, Swedish scientist Carl Linnaeus introduced a system of naming organisms that is still used today. Linnaeus based his system on the physical similarities of organisms. Each organism was identified by two names: the first identified the genus of the organism and the second identified the species. This system of naming living things is called **binomial nomenclature**.

Using this system, humans are known as *Homo sapiens*. The word *sapiens* is Latin for 'wise'.

Key Words

Biodiversity
Classification
Kingdoms
Binomial nomenclature
Stimuli
Invertebrates
Vertebrates
Protists
Fungi
Decomposer

Animals

Plants

Protists

Fungi

Bacteria (earliest organisms)

↻ **Fig. 5.1.1**
The five kingdoms of life

Animals

Animals live in almost every environment on Earth. The majority of animals live in water. However, many live on land.

Fig. 5.1.2
Animals

Animals are multicellular organisms. They can respond to changes in their environment and move about in search of food, water, shelter and mates.

All of the changes in an organism's environment are called **stimuli**.

Animals are consumers. This means that they must find and eat their food.

There is huge variety within the animal kingdom – some animals have wings, others have arms; some have lungs and others have gills.

Animals can be divided into two groups:

- **Invertebrates** are animals that do not have a backbone. For example, insects, snails, crabs and starfish.

- **Vertebrates** are animals that do have a backbone. For example, humans, crocodiles, fish and birds.

Fig. 5.1.3
Invertebrates

Fig. 5.1.4
Vertebrates

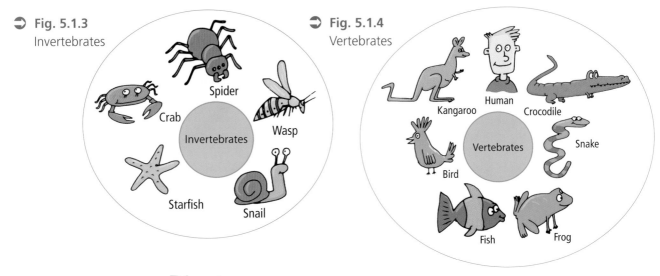

Plants

Fig. 5.1.5
Plants

Plants are multicellular. They have chlorophyll and are able to produce their own food by photosynthesis. They in turn provide food for other living things.

Plants remove carbon dioxide from the air, which is important in keeping the oxygen and carbon dioxide in the Earth's atmosphere balanced.

Plants cannot move as easily as animals. However, they can change the direction they grow in to respond to stimuli.

There are many types of plants. In general, they have leaves, stems and roots. Many also have flowers, fruits and seeds. We will learn more about the structure of plants and their processes later in Biological World.

Protists

There are many different kinds of **protists**. This kingdom includes plankton, algae, slime and water moulds.

Protists were the first organisms to evolve a nucleus. Most are unicellular, but some live in colonies. The majority of protists live in water.

The way protists get their food varies, including plant-like photosynthesis and animal-like eating.

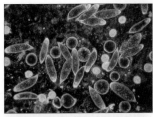

🎧 **Fig. 5.1.6**
Protists

Looking at amoebae

Amoeba proteus is an example of a unicellular protist that is found in standing bodies of water, such as ponds, puddles and water troughs.

Mount a sample of pond water on a slide and see if you can locate an amoeba. Record your method and findings. Draw a diagram of the amoeba. Describe its movement or, if you can, record its movement on video.

➲ **Fig. 5.1.7**
Amoeba proteus

Fungi

Fungi are more closely related to animals than they are to plants. This is because they do not contain chlorophyll and so cannot produce their own food.

Fungi can be unicellular, such as yeast, or made up of long threads, such as mushrooms and the moulds that cause bread to spoil.

Fungi are **decomposers**. Decomposers feed on dead plant and animal material.

We can eat some fungi (e.g. mushrooms) or use them to make other products, such as alcohol and bread. However, others are poisonous and some can cause diseases, such as athlete's foot.

🎧 **Fig. 5.1.8**
Fungi

Looking at black bread mould

Black bread mould (*Rhizopus stolonifer*) is a mould often found on bread. Bring some slices of fresh bread and toasted bread into school. You will also need a plastic sandwich bag.

Plan an investigation to see if the quantity of water in bread affects how quickly the bread goes mouldy. Follow your teacher's instructions at all times and do not eat any mouldy bread.

🎧 **Fig. 5.1.9**
Black bread mould

Bacteria and Viruses

Key Words

Microorganisms
Bacteria
Binary fission
Culturing
Antibiotics
Virus
Parasites
Pathogen
Vaccine
Vaccination

Learning Intentions

In this topic we are learning to:

- Describe the defining features of bacteria and viruses.
- Consider the important role that bacteria play as producers and decomposers.
- Discuss the role of bacteria and viruses as disease-causing organisms.

Microorganisms

Microorganisms are very small living things. They cannot be seen by the human eye alone and must be viewed using microscopes.

Bacteria and viruses are microorganisms.

Bacteria

Bacteria are the most common organisms on Earth.

They can survive in environments that are too harsh for other organisms to live in. For example, bacteria can be found living in geysers, salty rock pools and the human body.

All bacteria are made up of only one cell (unicellular). They do not have a nucleus.

Kingdom Monera

Kingdom Bacteria is also referred to as Kingdom Monera, as the prefix 'mono' means 'one' and all members of this kingdom are composed of a single cell. The prefix 'uni' also means 'one'.

 Learn more about fission in Earth and Space 24.2

Binary Fission

Bacteria reproduce by a process called **binary fission**. This means that one bacteria cell divides in two and the number of bacteria doubles with each generation.

Some bacteria can reproduce every 20 minutes. This means that a lot of bacteria are produced in a very short period of time.

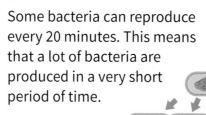
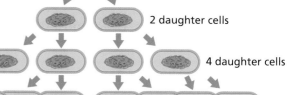

Parent cell

2 daughter cells

4 daughter cells

8 daughter cells

🎧 **Fig. 5.2.1**
Binary fission

Binary fission

$1_2{}^3$

We can model the number of bacteria present after a certain number of generations using the function $y = 2^n$, where y is the number of bacteria and n is the number of the generation ($n = 0, 1, 2$, etc.). For example, when $n = 2$, then $y = 2^2 = 4$.

1. Why do we start with 2^0?
2. How many bacteria are there after 10 generations?
3. What assumptions are made in this model?
4. What are some of the limitations of this model?

Culturing microorganisms

Bacteria can be grown in large numbers in the laboratory. This is called **culturing**. Your teacher will supply you with some sterile nutrient agar media in Petri dishes. These dishes should be sterile or free of all microorganisms. Nutrient agar contains all the nutrients bacteria require in order to grow.

1. You will attempt to culture bacteria from five separate sources: soil, air, water, skin and hair. It is very important that you follow your teacher's instructions, as culturing bacteria in large numbers can create a risk of infection.

2. Monitor the growth of bacteria by taking pictures of sealed, unopened plates every 24 hours.

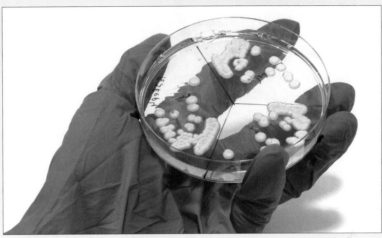

🎧 **Fig. 5.2.2**
A scientist culturing microorganisms

The Importance of Bacteria

Bacteria play a very important role in cycling matter through the Earth:

- Some bacteria can photosynthesise. This means that they take in carbon dioxide from the air, which helps reduce global warming.

- The majority of bacteria are decomposers. By breaking down dead organisms, bacteria release the nutrients back into the environment for other organisms to use.

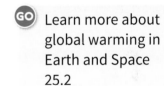 Learn more about global warming in Earth and Space 25.2

GO Learn more about the cycling of matter in Earth and Space 22.2

The following table outlines other benefits of bacteria.

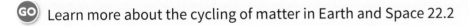

Use	Example
Food	Bacteria can be used to make yoghurt and cheese from milk. Probiotics contain living cultures of bacteria that help keep the gut healthy
Vitamins	Bacteria in the large intestine produce vitamins B and K
Antibiotics	Bacteria produce antibiotics that can be used to treat certain diseases
Biotechnology	*E. coli* has been genetically engineered to produce insulin, which is used to treat diabetes
Natural gas	Bacteria can be used in piggeries to break down waste organic matter, reducing the amount of waste and producing natural gas as a fuel

⮕ **Fig. 5.2.3**
Probiotic products contain living cultures of bacteria

◐ **Fig. 5.2.4**
Streptomyces scabies on a potato

The Negative Effects of Bacteria

Although most bacteria are harmless, some can have negative effects:

- Food spoilage: *Flavobacterium* causes food products with a high sugar content to spoil.

- Livestock and crop diseases: some bacteria live on or in another organism and cause it harm. For example, *Streptomyces scabies* causes scabs on potato tubers.

- Human diseases: a small number of bacteria also cause human diseases. For example, *Streptococcus mutans* causes tooth decay.

Antibiotic Resistance

An **antibiotic** is a chemical produced by microorganisms that is used as a drug to treat certain diseases caused by bacteria and fungi.

The speed at which bacteria reproduce can help them evolve a resistance to antibiotics. This makes it more difficult to treat diseases caused by bacteria.

The way we use antibiotics has added to this problem. The following table outlines how humans have encouraged antibiotic resistance and how we might prevent it in future.

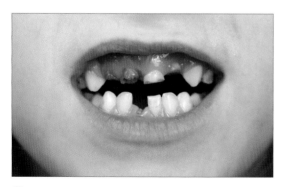

◐ **Fig. 5.2.5**
Tooth decay

Causes	Prevention
The use of antibiotics to treat viral infections – antibiotics have no effect on viruses	Do not prescribe antibiotics for viral diseases such as colds and flu
Patients not completing the full course of antibiotics	Finish full course of antibiotics
The widespread use of antibiotics in agriculture	Regulation of the use of antibiotics in farming

Viruses

Viruses are even smaller than bacteria. A **virus** is simply a protein coat surrounding a small quantity of genetic material, such as DNA.

Although they are often grouped with microorganisms, many scientists do not consider viruses to be living things. This is because viruses cannot reproduce by themselves. Unlike bacteria, viruses can only reproduce by attaching themselves to the cells of other organisms. For this reason, they are known as **parasites**. Parasites live off or in another living thing.

Viruses cause diseases in animals and plants. Viruses also cause diseases in humans, including:

- Cold sores
- Common cold
- Influenza (flu)
- Measles
- Chickenpox
- Ebola

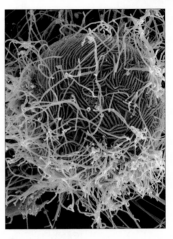

Fig. 5.2.6
The Ebola virus in an infected cell

Vaccination

Any organism that causes disease is called a **pathogen**.

A **vaccine** is a treatment that protects the body from a particular disease. It is made from a weak or dead specimen of the pathogen that causes the disease.

The process of providing vaccines on a large scale is called **vaccination**.

The vaccination controversy

Vaccination can be a very controversial topic. In groups, research the results of vaccination programmes for diseases such as measles, common cold, influenza and Ebola. Consider information and data from different sources.

Based on your research, justify your position on the widespread use of vaccination programmes.

People and Science

Edward Jenner, an eighteenth-century English doctor and scientist, is famous for developing the world's first vaccine. Smallpox was a major cause of death during the period and Jenner realised that milkmaids, who had contact with cowpox, did not get smallpox. Based on this observation, Jenner infected people with the pus from cowpox patients and found that this stopped them getting the far-more-serious smallpox. It is said that Jenner's discovery has saved more lives than the work of any other human.

Louis Pasteur also helped to develop vaccination as a way of protecting humans against disease. Pasteur also invented pasteurisation, which is a way to kill the pathogens in substances such as milk to make them safe to consume.

'Vaccination'

The word 'vaccination' was coined by Jenner. It is derived from the Latin word *vacca*, meaning 'cow'.

Fig. 5.2.7
Edward Jenner

Fig. 5.2.8
Louis Pasteur

Chapter Summary

- All living things are thought to have evolved from bacteria, the first organisms that appeared on Earth.

- Organisms are classified into five kingdoms: animals, plants, fungi, protists and bacteria.

- All animals are consumers. The two major groups of animals are invertebrates (do not have a backbone) and vertebrates (do have a backbone).

- Plants can make their own food by photosynthesis.

- Protists were the first organisms to evolve a nucleus. The majority of protists are unicellular and live in water.

- Fungi are decomposers. This means they help break down dead plant and animal material. Some can be eaten or used in making foods. Others are poisonous or cause disease.

- Bacteria are the most common organisms on Earth. All bacteria are unicellular and have no nucleus.

- Bacteria reproduce by binary fission. This means that their numbers double with every generation.

- Bacteria play a very important role in cycling matter through the Earth. They are also used to make foods and antibiotics.

- Bacteria also cause some negative effects, including food spoilage and disease.

- Viruses are usually not thought of as living things as they cannot reproduce by themselves. Viruses cause many diseases.

- Viruses are known as parasites because they live off or in another living thing.

- Organisms that cause disease are called pathogens.

- A vaccine is a treatment that protects the body from a particular disease. It is made from the pathogen that causes the disease.

The BIG Challenge

Your task is to research four modern food preservation methods and four methods from the past.

Use your knowledge of the biological world to explain how each method stops microorganisms from spoiling food.

Your report on each should take the form of a poster with lots of images and no more than 100 words.

Go to your Portfolio to check what you have learned in this chapter.

⮌ Fig. 5.3.1
Preserved foods

Take the chapter 5 quiz on educateplus.ie.

Questions

1. Copy and fill in the blanks:

   a. The great variety of life on Earth is called _____ .

   b. _____ is the system of grouping living things that share common characteristics.

   c. There are five _____ of life: _____ , plants, fungi, protists and _____ .

   d. Animals are divided into two main groups, _____ and vertebrates.

   e. Plants can make their own food by _____ .

   f. _____ were the first organisms to evolve a nucleus.

   g. Bacteria reproduce by binary _____ .

   h. Viruses are known as _____ because they live off or in another living thing.

   i. A _____ is a treatment that protects the body from a particular virus.

   j. The common cold and influenza are both caused by a _____ .

2. Viruses have been described as being 'on the margins of life'. Research and report on the characteristics of viruses that are considered lifelike and those characteristics that are not considered lifelike.

3. Copy and complete the following table to compare each of the five kingdoms. Note: there may be more than one answer in each cell of the table.

4. Consider the following statement: 'Antibiotic resistant bacteria are an example of evolution by natural selection.' Do you agree or disagree with this statement? Provide evidence to explain your answer.

5. Research the common name of each of the following organisms:

   a. *Fraxinus excelsior*

   b. *Apis mellifera*

   c. *Quercus petraea*

   d. *Bos taurus*

   e. *Salmo salar*

   f. *Troglodytes troglodytes*

6. Give two activities of humans that have increased the spread of antibiotic resistance amongst bacteria and two ways we can help slow it down.

7. Research Alexander Fleming's discovery of the antibiotic penicillin. Prepare a short summary explaining why Fleming's work is often held up as an example of 'productive failure' in science.

8. In 2014 and 2015, the Ebola virus became a significant public health problem in Africa, receiving lots of media attention. Research the Ebola virus under the following headings:

   a. Cause(s)

   b. Symptom(s)

   c. Treatment(s)

   d. Prevention measures

   Prepare a short summary and present it to your classmates.

Characteristic	Bacteria	Protists	Fungi	Animals	Plants
Unicellular or multicellular					
Producer, consumer or decomposer					
Binary fission, sexual or asexual reproduction					
Example x 3					

Working as a Scientist

Asking Questions and Making Predictions

Bioremediation of Old Mine Sites

Acid mine drainage (AMD) is acidic water that flows from metal or coal mines. It has a low pH and contains metals, such as zinc (Zn). Too much zinc causes soil and water pollution and can be dangerous to plants and animals.

Dr Siobhán Jordan and Laura Holland are researchers at the Dundalk Institute of Technology (DkIT). They are working on an Environmental Protection Agency (EPA) funded project examining the use of organic materials such as spent mushroom substrate (SMS) as a way of treating AMD.

🎧 **Fig. 5.4.1**
Spent mushroom substrate (SMS)

The use of organisms or organic materials to treat pollution in soil or water is called bioremediation.

🎧 **Fig. 5.4.2**
Wetland trial

Over a 207-day trial, the pH of the AMD rose successfully from 3.0 towards neutral and upward of 99 per cent of zinc particles (mg/l) were also removed from the AMD.

Look closely at the following data collected during the trial:

| | pH | | Zn | | Temperature |
Day	AMD	Remediated AMD	A AMD (mg/l)	B Remediated AMD (mg/l)	°C
35	3.13	7.63	93.53	0.10	7.7
50	3.16	7.67	90.35	0.05	8.0
63	3.19	6.74	91.35	0.04	5.8
76	3.10	7.10	93.33	0.02	2.3
92	3.17	6.74	91.24	0.03	0.9
106	3.05	7.56	89.45	7.42	7.0
119	3.10	7.76	89.41	5.57	4.1
132	3.12	7.69	91.62	0.06	5.3
148	3.01	7.80	92.14	0.00	5.8
160	3.27	7.82	94.50	0.01	9.4
183	3.15	7.78	98.54	0.06	9.5
195	3.16	7.87	94.50	0.06	10.3
210	3.20	7.78	97.22	0.12	12.8

1 **What type of data is:**
- Day?
- pH?
- Zn?
- Temperature?

2 **Calculate the average pH and Zn levels recorded over the course of the trial.**

3 **Calculate the percentage removal rate of Zn from the AMD solution for each day using the following equation: $(A - (\frac{B}{A}) \times 100)$. Add this column of data to the table above.**

4 **Select a suitable chart or graph and plot the percentage removal rate of Zn against temperature over time. If possible, use a package such as Excel or GeoGebra to plot the data.**

5 **Comment on the trend in your chart or graph. Do you think the data supports the use of spent mushroom substrate as a viable option to treat AMD? Explain your answer.**

6 **In your opinion, what effect does the low temperature have on the ability of spent mushroom substrate to remove zinc from the AMD? Explain your answer.**

Chapter 6

The Interactions of Life: Ecology

What you may already know:

- All living things share the planet.
- Living things need energy from their environment to survive, grow and reproduce.
- Changes in the environment cause organisms to change. This leads to new species evolving by natural selection.

What you will learn in this chapter:

- An ecosystem is all organisms interacting with each other and their environment.
- How organisms adapt in an ecosystem.
- Feeding relationships describe the flow of energy through an ecosystem.
- How to gather information about ecosystems through habitat studies.

Think BIG

- Why do tigers have stripes and camels have humps?
- Why are animals tagged by ecologists?
- Why is it important that individuals of the same species are not identical?

Puzzler

Can you identify the organism Einstein was describing when he said:

'If the _____ disappeared off the surface of the globe, then man would have only four years of life left. No more _____, no more pollination, no more plants, no more animals, no more man.'

The Structure of an Ecosystem

Key Words

Ecology
Habitat
Population
Community
Ecosystem
Balance of nature
Biome
Biosphere

Ecology

Living things are affected by where they live. Their survival depends on the food and shelter available, as well as the other living things in the area.

Ecology is the study of how living things interact with their environment and each other.

Habitats

The place where an organism lives is its **habitat**. For example, a pond, a hedge or a meadow.

A **population** is a group of organisms of the same species living in the same habitat. For example, a population of frogs might live along a stretch of river.

A **community** is all of the different populations that live in a habitat. For example, the stretch of river may also provide a habitat for a population of willow trees and kingfishers.

Ecosystem

An **ecosystem** is all the communities interacting with each other, and with their environment.

Over time, the number and types of species in an ecosystem reaches a steady state. This steady state is known as the **balance of nature**.

An ecosystem that extends over a very large area is called a **biome**. Rainforests, coral reefs and deserts are biomes.

The activity of organisms in one ecosystem will affect those in neighbouring ecosystems.

All of the Earth's ecosystems together form one large ecosystem known as the **biosphere**. The biosphere extends from the bottom of the deepest ocean to the top of the highest mountain.

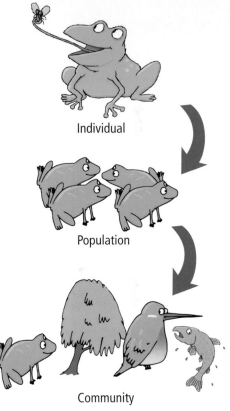

Individual

Population

Community

Ecosystem

🎧 **Fig. 6.1.1**
The organisation of an ecosystem

Interactions of Organisms in an Ecosystem

Key Words

Abiotic
Biotic
Competition
Predation
Predator
Prey
Symbiosis
Interdependence

Learning Intentions

In this topic we are learning to:

- Identify how organisms interact with the non-living environment.
- Consider how organisms also interact with each other in different ways.

Every living thing depends on its habitat to meet its needs, including food, water, shelter and mates.

Two types of factors affect the plants and animals living in a habitat:

1. Non-living: such as the temperature and the type of land. These are called **abiotic** factors.

2. Living: the types of organisms that live there and how they affect each other. These are called **biotic** factors.

Together, these factors affect the type and number of organisms that live in a habitat.

Abiotic (Non-living) Factors

The three most important abiotic factors are:

- Weather
- Soil
- Type of landscape

1. Weather factors include temperature, light intensity, rainfall and wind. For example, cacti grow in low rainfall regions and woodlice live in damp, humid conditions.

🎧 **Fig. 6.2.1**
Cacti grow in ecosystems with low rainfall

Ireland's south-westerly winds

The most common wind in Ireland blows from between the south and the west. The wind travels over the Atlantic Ocean, collecting lots of moisture before it reaches the southwest coast of Ireland. How might the weather conditions differ between the west and east coasts of the country? What impact might the south-westerly wind have on ecosystems in these regions? (Hint: consider things such as the shape of trees.)

2. Soil factors include pH and moisture. If soil conditions are good, there will be plant life. An area with plants is also likely to attract animals as they can eat the plants.

3. Physical factors define the type of landscape. For example, the direction the habitat faces and whether the ground is sloped or flat.

🎧 **Fig. 6.2.2**
Soil conditions affect plant life

Biotic (Living) Factors

The three most important biotic factors are:

- Competition
- Predation
- Symbiosis

1. **Competition** is the struggle between organisms for things that are in short supply, such as food, space, oxygen, water, light and mates.

   Competition can take place between two organisms of the same species. For example, male deer lock horns to compete for mates. It can also take place between different types of organisms. For example, grass and weeds compete for space and light in a garden.

🎧 **Fig. 6.2.3**
Male deer lock horns to compete for female mates

2. **Predation** controls the number of organisms in an ecosystem.

   A **predator** is an organism that hunts and kills another animal as a source of food. The organism being hunted is the **prey**. For example, ladybirds eat greenfly and lions eat zebras.

3. **Symbiosis** is a relationship between organisms of different species where at least one benefits. The other organism may be unaffected, harmed or also benefit.

   For example, cleaner fish eat parasites out of the mouths of Moray eels, meaning the eel is kept healthy and the cleaner fish get food. Because it is benefiting from the relationship, the eel will not eat the fish.

Interdependence

When two organisms depend on each other for an important aspect of their survival it is called **interdependence**.

The relationship between flowering plants and insects is an example of interdependence. Bees collect pollen from a flower as a source of food. They then transfer the pollen to a different flower of the same species so that fertilisation can take place. Both species play a role in the survival of the other.

All such interactions help maintain the balance of nature.

'Flora' and 'Fauna'

'Flora' is the term used to describe the plant life in an ecosystem. In Roman mythology, Flora was the goddess of plants, flowers and fertility. 'Fauna' is the term used to describe the animal life in an ecosystem. Faunus was the god of the forest, plains and fields in Roman mythology.

🎧 **Fig. 6.2.4**
A ladybird (predator) eating greenfly (prey)

🎧 **Fig. 6.2.5**
A cleaner fish in the mouth of a Moray eel

🎧 **Fig. 6.2.6**
A bee carrying pollen

97

Adaptations of Organisms in an Ecosystem

Learning Intentions

In this topic we are learning to:

● Compare the adaptations of different organisms to suit their habitats.

In order to survive, organisms must adapt to their habitat.

Adaptation is when an organism develops characteristics that make it better suited to its habitat. Adaptation is the result of evolution. For example, seaweeds can survive on rocky seashores because they have developed holdfasts, slimy mucus and air bladders that allow them to live in and out of water.

There are two main types of adaptation:

1. Physical adaptations: features of an organism's body that help it survive.

2. Behavioural adaptations: what the organism does to help it survive.

Examples of Physical Adaptations

● A cheetah's powerful limbs and sharp teeth makes it an excellent predator.

● A gazelle's long limbs allow it to run away from predators.

Fig. 6.3.1
Seaweed can survive in and out of the water

Fig. 6.3.2
A cheetah chasing a gazelle

● A grasshopper is the same colour and shape as a blade of grass for camouflage.

● Snakes produce venom that kills and digests prey.

● A nettle stings to prevent it being eaten by grazing animals.

Fig. 6.3.3
A camouflaged grasshopper

Examples of Behavioural Adaptations

- Field mice are nocturnal. They are only active at night, which improves their chances of not being eaten by owls.
- Squirrels, bats and bears hibernate. The animal enters a deep sleep to conserve energy over the winter, when food is harder to find and temperatures are very low.

🎧 **Fig. 6.3.4**
Hibernating bats

- Swallows and buffalo migrate to areas with better weather, feeding and breeding conditions.
- Sunflowers can turn to follow the movement of the Sun in order to maximise photosynthesis.

Safety in numbers

Many organisms live in large groups. For example, shoals of fish, packs of wolves and herds of buffalo. Why do you think they do this? Consider the phrase 'safety in numbers'. What do you think it means? Give an example of its use in everyday conversation.

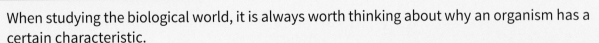

Considering adaptations

When studying the biological world, it is always worth thinking about why an organism has a certain characteristic.

Research the adaptations of each of the following organisms: brown kelp, black bread mould, camels, polar bears, holly and humans.

1. Identify at least one physical and behavioural adaptation of each organism.
2. Explain how each of these adaptations suits the organisms to their habitats.

Niche

All of a species' adaptations allow it to play a special role in the ecosystem.
A **niche** is the role of an organism within a habitat.

No two organisms may occupy the same niche.

Feeding Relationships in an Ecosystem

Key Words

Feeding relationship
Herbivores
Carnivores
Omnivores
Food chain
Food web
Biomass

Learning Intentions

In this topic we are learning to:

- Model the flow of energy through an ecosystem using a food chain and a food web.
- Review the importance of decomposers to the cycling of key nutrients through the living and non-living parts of the Earth.

A **feeding relationship** is the way energy and nutrients are passed from one organism to another through an ecosystem.

- Producers make their own food. For example, plants photosynthesise.
- Consumers must get their food by eating plants or other animals.

There are three types of consumer:

1. **Herbivores** are animals that eat plants only. For example, cattle and rabbits.

2. **Carnivores** are animals that eat animals only. For example, sparrowhawks and ladybirds.

3. **Omnivores** are animals that eat both plants and animals. For example, foxes and humans.

- Decomposers feed on dead plant and animal material. By breaking down this material, they recycle nutrients back into the soil. For example, bacteria, fungi and earthworms.

There are two ways to describe feeding relationships:

- Food chain
- Food web

'Biomass' ⓐⓑⓒ

The quantity of matter in an organism is called its **biomass**.

The biomass of individual organisms increases as you move towards upper feeding levels in food chains. Predators are usually bigger than their prey.

Food Chain

A **food chain** describes feeding relationships using arrows to show which organism eats another.

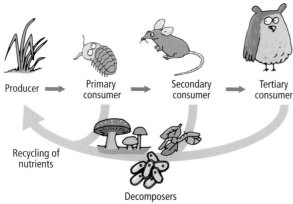

🎧 **Fig. 6.4.1**
A food chain showing decomposers

1. Food chains usually start with a plant, the producer.

2. The organism that eats the producer is the primary consumer. Primary consumers are usually herbivores.

3. Primary consumers are eaten by a secondary consumer. Secondary consumers are carnivores or omnivores.

4. Secondary consumers may be eaten by a tertiary consumer. Tertiary consumers are the top predators in an ecosystem.

5. In all feeding relationships, the dead plant and animal material is broken down by decomposers.

Food Web

Feeding relationships are not usually as simple as food chains suggest. Organisms usually feed on many different food sources and may also be eaten by more than one consumer. Feeding relationships are better shown using a food web. A **food web** is made up of interconnected food chains.

Food webs clearly show that all the organisms in an ecosystem depend on each other for survival. For example:

1. If a disease killed large numbers of rabbits, removing them from the food chain, more grass would grow.

2. More grass would mean more food for grasshoppers and their numbers would increase.

3. Badgers would have more grasshoppers to eat and so the number of badgers would also grow.

4. On the other hand, fewer rabbits would mean less food for foxes, so their numbers would decrease.

GO Learn more about the cycling of matter in Earth and Space 22.2

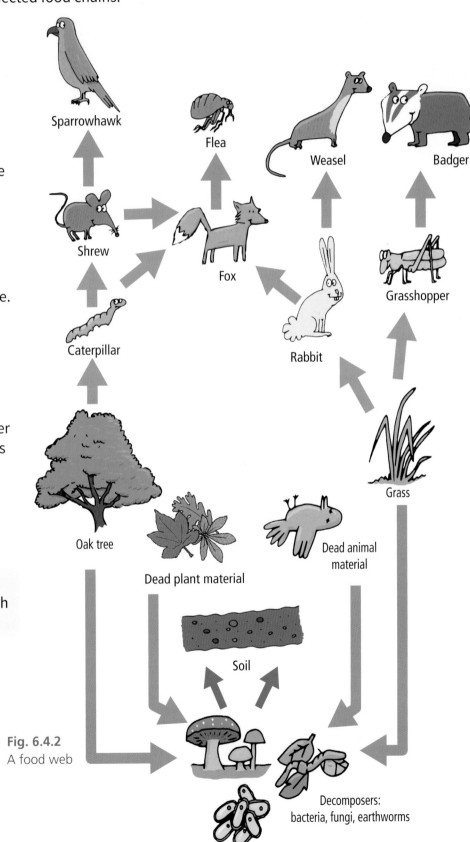

⬦ Fig. 6.4.2
A food web

Conducting a Habitat Study

Key Words

Qualitative survey
Quadrat
Identification key
Quantitative survey
Frequency
Percentage cover
Distribution
Line transect
Abundance

Learning Intentions

In this topic we are learning to:

- Choose the appropriate equipment and techniques to safely survey a habitat.
- Conduct a local habitat study.

When you carry out a habitat study, it is very important to be sensitive to the ecology of the area. Remember the motto: 'Take only memories, leave only footprints.'

Steps in a Habitat Study

> **Step 1:** Selection and general description of the habitat

Before beginning your habitat study, it is important to select a suitable site. You should think about:

- Likely weather conditions and suitable clothing.
- Landowner permission.
- Potential hazards. For example, deep river beds or a bull in a field.
- Packing enough food, drink, dry clothing, an Ordnance Survey map and first aid supplies.

After arriving on-site, the first task is to record a general description of the habitat. This can take the form of a labelled map.

> **Step 2:** Qualitative survey of species in the habitat

A **qualitative survey** is a list of the different species in the habitat. It does not provide the numbers of each species present.

Collecting and Identifying Plants and Animals

A **quadrat** can be used to survey plants in a habitat. A quadrat is a square frame made of metal, plastic or wood. A person throws a pen randomly over their shoulder and the quadrat is then placed over the pen. The area enclosed by the quadrat is then checked for the animal or plant being surveyed.

◔ **Fig. 6.5.1** A quadrat

A qualitative survey of plants is easier because plants do not move from place to place. Of course, this is not the case for animals. It is necessary to select suitable equipment to collect animals before any attempt is made to identify them.

The following table describes examples of equipment that may be used:

Equipment	What it looks like	How it works	What it collects
Pooter		Operator inhales through the shorter tube and sucks the insects into the jar using the longer tube. Plastic mesh prevents the operator inhaling the insect	Spiders and small insects from leaf litter on the ground or from the bark and leaves of plants
Pitfall trap		A jar or tin is buried level with the ground surface. The opening is covered by a piece of wood or flat rock that keeps rain out and protects trapped animals. Bedding or bait may be placed in the trap. The position of the traps should be recorded on the map and they should be inspected regularly	Small animals that move along the surface of the ground, such as beetles and snails
Cryptozoic trap		A sheet of wooden board on the ground. The animals are attracted by the high humidity under the board and take shelter. Natural cryptozoic traps include stones, fallen branches and leaf litter. These traps can be inspected simply by turning them over	Cryptozoa are animals that hide by day and are normally active only at night, such as slugs and woodlice
Sweep net		There are many types of nets that vary in mesh size depending on the organism to be collected. These include sweep nets (swept over long grass), insect nets (to catch flying insects) and plankton and fish nets	Insects, small animals and fish

Other animals are too big to be caught in traps or they remain hidden. Be aware of signs of animal activity, including faeces, footprints, remains of prey, dens, burrows and birdsong.

When you are unsure of a species, an **identification key** can be used. Look carefully at the characteristics of the organism and then begin answering the questions on the key. Keep going until you identify the organism. Identification keys are available for all types of plants and animals.

'Dichotomous' a b c

An identification key is also known as a dichotomous key. The word 'dichotomous' means 'divided or dividing into two parts'. This name reflects that at each stage in the process of identifying a species, you are always given two choices.

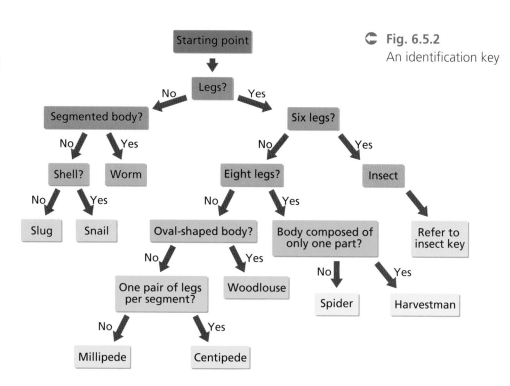

Fig. 6.5.2
An identification key

All the species identified during the qualitative survey are put into a list.

> **Step 3:** Quantitative survey of species present in the habitat

A **quantitative survey** collects numerical data about the species in the habitat. Quantitative surveys are always conducted for a single species at a time. The following techniques can be used to collect this data.

- **Frequency** is the percentage chance of a species being present in a randomly chosen standard quadrat. Mark out the area under survey and select at least ten quadrats at random. Record if the species is present or absent using a single tick for present and a single cross for absent. Percentage frequency is calculated using the following formula:

$$\text{Percentage frequency} = \left(\frac{[\text{No of ticks}]}{[\text{Total no. of quadrats}]}\right) \times \frac{100}{1}$$

It is important to use enough quadrats to give a reasonable idea of the frequency of a species in a habitat.

- **Percentage cover** is the area of ground covered by plants or by animals. Percentage cover can be measured using a grid quadrat with a wire grid stretched across it to form smaller sample squares. A record is kept of the number of squares the species under survey is found in.

Percentage cover is calculated using the following formula:

$$\text{Percentage cover} = \left(\frac{[\text{No. of squares species found in}]}{[\text{Total no. of small squares}]}\right) \times \frac{100}{1}$$

Percentage cover is a useful way of finding out the most dominant plant or animal in a habitat.

Calculating the area covered by a quadrat 1 2 3

The length of each side of a standard quadrat is 0.5 m. Calculate the area covered by a single quadrat. How many quadrats must be positioned side by side to cover an area of 1 m²?

● **Distribution** records the area(s) within a habitat where a species is found.

The distribution of organisms in a habitat is investigated using a **line transect**. A rope is laid out across the habitat and marked with a knot at every metre. Each knot is checked to see if the species under survey has touched the line transect. For example, the types and numbers of species of plant will change as you move further away from a hedgerow because of increased light.

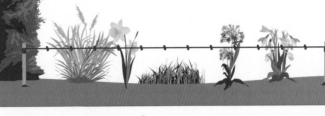

🎧 **Fig. 6.5.3**
A line transect

● **Abundance** refers to the size of a population of a species. The abundance of a plant species is measured using standard quadrats. The quadrats are thrown at random. The number of times the species is found in each quadrat is recorded. Results are then scaled up to estimate the number of plants in the entire habitat.

All of the numerical data collected during the quantitative survey is compiled in tables.

> **Step 4:** Measurement of abiotic (non-living) factors in the habitat

If a species is present in a habitat, it shows that it is adapted to the abiotic factors in that habitat. If a species is absent from a habitat, it is likely that some factor, either abiotic or biotic, is outside the range that species can survive in.

Abiotic factors that might be investigated include soil pH and light intensity.

All of the abiotic data is collected in tables.

GO Learn more about testing pH in Chemical World 13.2

> **Step 5:** Observations of interactions in the habitat

The data collected during qualitative and quantitative surveys should be used to provide examples of the following interactions:

● Variation within and between species
● Interdependence
● Competition
● Predator–prey relationships
● Adaptations
● Feeding relationships

> **Step 6:** The final report

All of the data collected during the course of your habitat study must be analysed and evaluated. The final report may include:

● Maps
● Tables
● Bar charts, histograms, scatter plots, pie charts, etc.
● Simple statistics, such as means, ranges, correlations, etc.

The report should also comment on sources of error, possible future work and any recommendations you might have.

Chapter Summary

- The place where an organism lives is its habitat. For example, a pond or hedgerow.

- A population is a group of organisms of the same species living in the same habitat. A community is all of the different populations that live in a habitat.

- An ecosystem is all the communities in a habitat interacting with each other, and with their environment.

- An ecosystem that extends over a very large area is called a biome. For example, a rainforest or desert.

- Two types of factors affect the plants and animals living in a habitat: abiotic (non-living) and biotic (living).

- Abiotic factors include weather, soil and type of landscape. Biotic factors include competition, predation and symbiosis.

- Competition is the struggle between organisms for limited resources.

- The predator catches, kills and eats the prey.

- Symbiosis is a relationship between two different species where at least one benefits.

- When two organisms depend on each other for an important aspect of their survival, it is called interdependence.

- Adaptation is when an organism develops characteristics that make it better suited to its habitat. There are two main types of adaptation: physical and behavioural.

- A niche describes the role of an organism within a habitat.

- A feeding relationship is the way energy and nutrients are passed from one organism to another in an ecosystem. Feeding relationships can be described by food chains and food webs.

- There are six stages to a habitat study: 1. Selection and general description of the habitat; 2. Qualitative survey of species in the habitat; 3. Quantitative survey of species present in the habitat; 4. Measurement of abiotic factors in the habitat; 5. Observations of interactions in the habitat; 6. The final report.

- A qualitative survey is a list of the different species in a habitat. An identification key helps you to identify unknown species. Animals can be collected or observed using pooters, pitfall traps, cryptozoic traps and sweep nets.

- A quantitative survey provides numerical data of species in a habitat. The data can be collected using quadrats, grid quadrats and line transects. The data includes frequency, percentage cover, distribution and abundance.

The BIG Challenge

The lichens that grow on trees and rocks can be used as an indicator of air pollution as they are very sensitive to excess sulfur dioxide in the air. Your task is to conduct a survey of lichens in your school grounds. Consider using a video camera to record your work in the field.

1. With the assistance of a suitable identification key, collect qualitative and quantitative lichen data. All data should then be transferred onto a map of the habitat.
2. Evaluate the data for evidence of air pollution, if any.
3. Prepare a report and suggest recommendations to improve air quality in the school environment.

Go to your Portfolio to check what you have learned in this chapter.

Take the chapter 6 quiz on educateplus.ie.

Questions

1. Copy and fill in the blanks:

   a. The relationship between organisms and their environment is called an _____ .

   b. A _____ is a group of organisms of the same species living in the same habitat. A _____ is all of the different populations that live in a habitat.

   c. The non-living factors that affect the types and numbers of species that live in a habitat are _____ . Living factors are biotic.

   d. _____ is the struggle between organisms for things that are in short supply.

   e. _____ are characteristics that suit an organism to their environment.

   f. A _____ is the role of an organism within a habitat.

   g. Feeding relationships can be described by food _____ and food _____ .

   h. A qualitative survey is a _____ of the species in a habitat.

   i. Unfamiliar species can be identified using an _____ _____ .

   j. A _____ survey of plant and animal species collects _____ data, including frequency, percentage cover, distribution and abundance.

2. Prepare a short report to explain how foxes are adapted to survive in both the countryside and in cities. Your report should include reference to physical and behavioural adaptations.

3. Consider this Einstein quote: 'If the bee disappeared off the surface of the globe, then man would have only four years of life left. No more bees, no more pollination, no more plants, no more animals, no more man.' Do you agree with this statement? Give at least three reasons to support your answer.

4. Explain why parasitism is important in ecosystems. Why it is rare for a parasite to kill its host?

5. Explain how to operate a pooter with the aid of a labelled sketch.

6. A student surveyed a woodland habitat (25 m x 10 m) for woodrush. The following data was collected.

Quadrat number	Presence or absence	Percentage cover
1	✓	20
2	✗	0
3	✓	35
4	✓	40
5	✗	0
6	✗	0
7	✓	15
8	✗	0
9	✗	0
10	✓	45

   a. Is this data qualitative or quantitative?

   b. What type of quadrat was used to collect the data in column 2? How was the data collected? Use this data to calculate the percentage frequency of woodrush. Why do you think woodrush was absent in some of the quadrats sampled?

   c. What type of quadrat was used to collect the data in column 3 of the above table? How was the data collected? Use this data to calculate the percentage cover of woodrush. Using the dimensions of the habitat, calculate the area of habitat covered by woodrush.

   d. State one advantage of each method. Give an example of a situation when it is appropriate to use one method instead of the other.

7. 'No two species may occupy the same niche.' Give three reasons to explain this statement.

8. Research predator–prey relationships, then sketch a graph illustrating the relationship between populations of both ladybirds (predators) and greenfly (prey) over time.

Working as a Scientist

Presenting and Analysing Data

Conducting a Habitat Study

Over the course of two lessons, a class of students planned a habitat study of the local park. The teacher told the students to follow the six steps of a habitat study.

The students were asked to carry out a quantitative study of rushes and calculate abundance. Each pair randomly selected ten sample sites within the habitat and recorded the number of rushes at each site using a quadrat. At each sample site, the students also collected a small sample of soil from a depth of 5 cm using a trowel. Each soil sample was stored in a separate plastic specimen bag and returned to the laboratory for analysis.

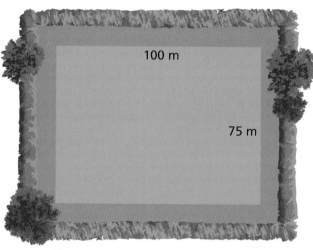

🎧 **Fig. 6.7.1**
The area under study

1 **Calculate the total area of the habitat under study by the students in Fig. 6.7.1.**

2 **Calculate the area of the quadrat used by the students in Fig. 6.7.2.**

3 **Calculate the number of individual quadrats needed to scale up to the total area of the habitat.**

4 **Why is it important that the sample sites were chosen randomly and were well distributed throughout the habitat?**

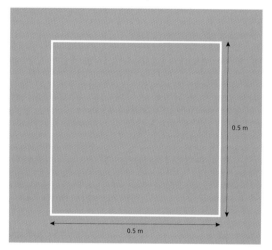

🎧 **Fig. 6.7.2**
Quadrat used during habitat study

When the students began their survey, they realised it was not always easy to count the rushes, as some of them were only partially inside the quadrat. The teacher told them to count only those plants that were halfway or more inside the quadrat.

5 **How many rushes are recorded in the quadrat in Fig. 6.7.3?**

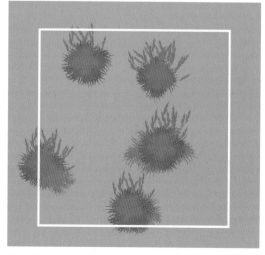

🎧 **Fig. 6.7.3**
Rushes in a quadrat

6 Do you think this method introduces a source of error? If so, how might the error be reduced?

The following data was collected by one group of students:

Quadrat number	Number of rushes
1	2
2	4
3	3
4	0
5	0
6	2
7	1
8	3
9	2
10	1

7 Calculate the mean number of rushes per quadrat. Calculate the range of rushes per quadrat.

8 Using your answer to question 3, calculate an estimate of the total number (abundance) of rushes in the habitat.

Over the next week, the students analysed the percentage moisture content of each of their fresh soil samples. The raw data is recorded in the table below.

Quadrat number	Mass of fresh soil (g)	Mass of oven-dried soil (g)
1	2.04	1.29
2	2.03	1.10
3	2.09	1.30
4	1.97	1.48
5	2.01	1.47
6	2.14	1.48
7	1.87	1.33
8	2.05	1.19
9	2.05	1.37
10	2.03	1.44

9 Using this data, calculate the percentage soil moisture for each quadrat using the following formula:

$$\text{Percentage soil moisture} = \left(\frac{[\text{Mass of fresh soil} - \text{mass of oven-dried soil}]}{[\text{Mass of fresh soil}]}\right) \times \frac{100}{1}$$

10 With the aid of a labelled diagram, describe the steps taken in the measurement and calculation of soil moisture content.

11 Produce a scatter plot of soil moisture content (x-axis) versus number of rushes (y-axis). Do you see any trend in the data? If yes, explain why you think this is the case.

12 Could the results of this survey be used to assess the effects, if any, of a drainage scheme within the park? Would a similar follow-up study be necessary?

Chapter 7

Structures and Processes of Life: Plants

What you may already know:

- Plants can make their own food by photosynthesis.
- Plants play an important role in controlling the levels of oxygen and carbon dioxide in the atmosphere.

What you will learn in this chapter:

- There are many different types of flowering plants, but they all have the same four organs: roots, stems, leaves and flowers.
- Many plants can reproduce without a mate (asexually), both naturally and under the control of humans.
- The flower is adapted to allow plants to reproduce sexually.

Think BIG

- Why can you tell the age of a tree by counting the number of rings in the trunk?
- Why would the fruit and veg aisle in the supermarket be much barer if there were no bees?

Puzzler

Can you solve this puzzle?

Mia is visiting her local garden centre and needs to use the bathroom. The owners of the garden centre have extended the plant theme to the signs on the bathroom doors.

Help Mia choose the right option!

(Hint: turn to topic 7.4 Sexual Reproduction in Flowering Plants.)

The Structure of Flowering Plants

Key Words

Bud
Root
Stem
Leaf
Flower

Learning Intentions

In this topic we are learning to:

- Classify the four plant organs: root, stem, leaf and flower.
- Explain how plant organs are adapted to perform special roles.

Flowering plants are the most recently evolved type of plant on Earth. There are many different species of flowering plants, including magnolias, water lilies, horse chestnut and wheat. Although there are many types of flowering plants, they all have the same basic structure.

↻ **Fig. 7.1.1**
Varieties of flowering plants

Figure 7.1.2 shows the main parts of a flowering plant.

- The part of the plant that grows above the ground is the shoot.
- The part of the plant that grows in the soil is the root.

All species of flowering plants have four organs:

1. Root
2. Stem
3. Leaf
4. Flower

A flowering plant may also have buds, fruits and seeds.

A **bud** produces new growth. It can develop into a side branch, leaf or flower.

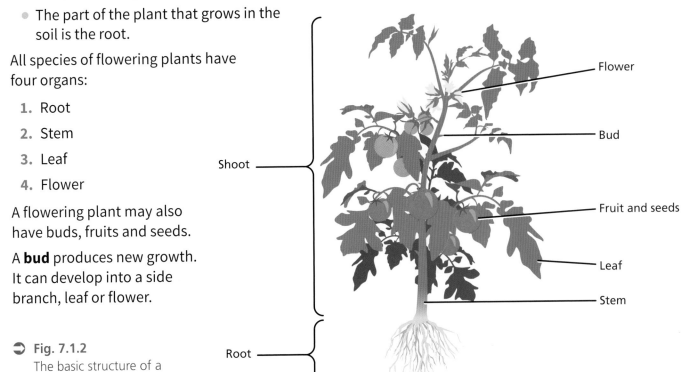

● **Fig. 7.1.2**
The basic structure of a flowering plant

Shoot

Root

Flower

Bud

Fruit and seeds

Leaf

Stem

The Root

The **root** has the following roles:

- Anchors and supports the plant in the soil.
- Absorbs water and minerals from the soil.
- Some roots can store food and water. For example, carrots store food in the form of sugar.

Fun Fact

Under one hectare of winter wheat, there may be up to 300,000 km of roots. This increases the surface area available for the absorption of water and mineral nutrients from the soil into the plant.

Fig. 7.1.3
A carrot is a root

Fig. 7.1.4
Fibrous roots of wheat

The Stem

The **stem** has the following roles:

- Supports the buds, leaves and flowers.
- Carries water and minerals from the roots to the leaves and flowers.
- Carries food from the leaves to the roots and other parts of the plant.
- Some stems store food and water. For example, potatoes store food in the form of starch.

The Leaf

🎧 **Fig. 7.1.5**
The wide variety of leaves shows how adaptable plants are to different habitats

The **leaf** has the following roles:

- Produces food by photosynthesis.
- Some leaves store food. For example, grass for livestock; onion bulbs and cabbage for humans.
- Allows the exchange of gases with the atmosphere.
- Assists with transport of water through the plant.
- Provides protection. For example, the sap in leaves of aloe vera and the spines of holly leaves discourage herbivores from eating them.

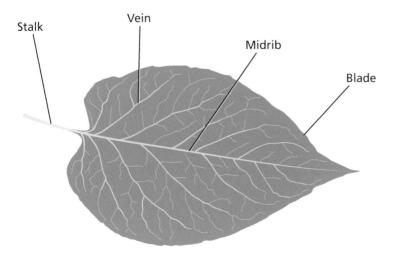

🔁 **Fig. 7.1.6**
The structure of a leaf

The Flower

The role of the **flower** in plants is to allow sexual reproduction to take place.

We will learn more about how flowering plants reproduce later in this chapter.

The Processes of Flowering Plants

Key Words

Xylem
Phloem
Vascular bundles
Transpiration
Stomata
Tropism
Phototropism
Geotropism

Learning Intentions

In this topic we are learning to:

- Outline the role of xylem and phloem tissue in plants.
- Recognise the role played by stomata in the exchange of gases with the atmosphere.
- Investigate the response of plants to changes in their environment.

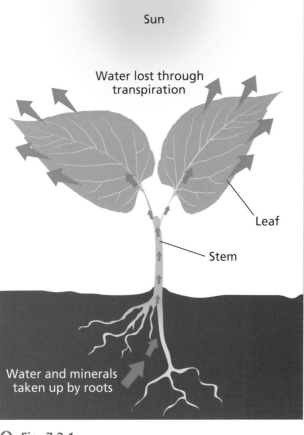

Sun

Water lost through transpiration

Leaf

Stem

Water and minerals taken up by roots

🎧 **Fig. 7.2.1**
Transpiration

Transport in Plants

Plants need water, minerals and food (starch and sugars) to grow and carry out their other processes. These substances are carried around a plant by a transport system.

Transport Tissue

Plants have two types of transport tissue:

1. **Xylem** tissue transports water and minerals.
2. **Phloem** tissue transports food.

Phloem tissue and xylem tissue are found together in **vascular bundles**. These bundles are obvious as the veins on a leaf blade or in a freshly cut celery stem.

Transport of Water and Minerals

1. Water and minerals are taken in from the soil by the roots.
2. The water and minerals travel up the stem in the xylem tissue.
3. Water is delivered to the leaves for use in photosynthesis.
4. Heat energy from the Sun causes the water in the leaves to evaporate. The loss of water vapour from the surface of a plant is called **transpiration**.

Observing the transpiration stream

1. Place a freshly cut stem of celery into a solution of food dye and observe it for 48 hours.
2. Remove the celery stem from the dye solution and rinse. Record your observations.
3. Where has the dye collected? Why?

Water vapour released from leaves

Plan, design, carry out and write up an investigation to show that water is lost through the leaves of a plant by transpiration.

Transport of Food

1. Glucose is sugar made in the leaves during photosynthesis. Some of this glucose is used by the leaves.

2. Some glucose is also stored in the stems and roots as starch. Sugars and starch are types of carbohydrates.

3. The glucose must be converted into sucrose (another carbohydrate) before it can be carried to all the parts of the plant by the phloem tissue.

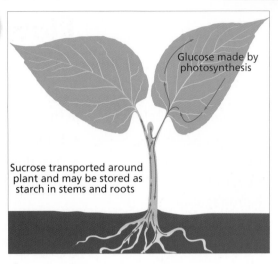
Glucose made by photosynthesis

Sucrose transported around plant and may be stored as starch in stems and roots

⋒ **Fig. 7.2.2**
The transport of food (carbohydrate) around a plant

Exchange of Gases

Stomata are small pores on the underside of leaves through which gases and water pass out of the plant.

- The carbon dioxide needed for photosynthesis is absorbed from the atmosphere through the stomata. The oxygen produced as a waste product exits through the stomata.

- The oxygen needed for respiration enters the leaf through the stomata. The carbon dioxide produced as a waste product exits through the stomata.

Tropisms

Like all organisms, to survive plants must be able to sense and respond to changes in their environment.

The directional growth response of a plant to a stimulus is called a **tropism**.

- **Phototropism** is the growth of a plant toward light. It allows it to get as much light as possible for photosynthesis.

- **Geotropism** is the growth of a plant in response to the force of gravity. The roots grow downwards to access water and mineral nutrients from the soil. The shoots grow away from the force of gravity.

Investigating phototropism and geotropism

Plan, design, carry out and write up an investigation of both the phototropic and geotropic growth response of suitable seeds or seedlings.

⋒ **Fig. 7.2.3**
Phototropism is the growth of a plant toward light

Asexual Reproduction in Flowering Plants

Learning Intentions

In this topic we are learning to:

- Explore various ways that plants may reproduce asexually.
- Describe artificial methods of asexual reproduction in plants practised in agriculture and horticulture.

Reproduction is the ability to produce new individuals of the same species. It ensures that a species will continue into future generations.

There are two forms of reproduction:

- Asexual reproduction
- Sexual reproduction

Most plants can reproduce both ways. For example, strawberries can reproduce asexually by producing runners but can also reproduce sexually using their flowers.

🎧 **Fig. 7.3.1**
Strawberry plants reproduce asexually through their runners

🎧 **Fig. 7.3.2**
Strawberries also reproduce sexually through their flowers

Asexual Reproduction

In **asexual reproduction**:

- Only one parent is involved.
- No gametes are produced and no fertilisation takes place.
- New individuals are clones that are genetically identical to each other and to the parent plant.

Asexual reproduction in plants may happen naturally or artificially.

Natural Asexual Reproduction in Plants

The roots, stems, leaves and buds of plants are sometimes adapted for natural asexual reproduction.

When a plant, such as the strawberry plant, reproduces asexually, it produces a new stem at the base of the parent plant. This new stem, called a **runner**, grows across the surface of the ground. A bud at the tip of the runner produces a new root and shoot system.

This new plant stays connected to the parent plant for a period of time to access water, minerals and food (sugars) from the parent plant. Eventually, the part of the runner stem between the parent plant and the new plant dies away. At this stage, the new plant is entirely independent.

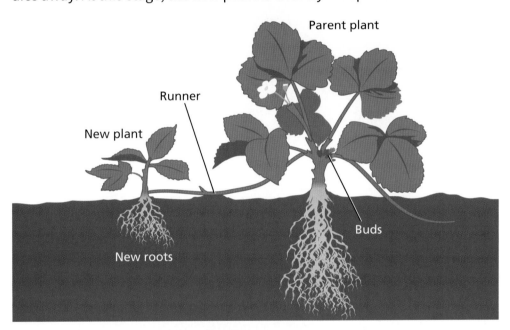

↻ Fig. 7.3.3
A strawberry plant reproducing asexually using runners

Fun Fact

Some plants reproduce asexually by producing small plants along the edge of the leaf. These are called plantlets. If conditions are suitable, plantlets fall from the leaf on to the soil and develop into a new plant.

Bryophyllum is an example of a plant that uses this method of asexual reproduction. One species of *Bryophyllum* is known as 'Mother of Thousands', which also hints at its interesting method of asexual reproduction!

⌒ Fig. 7.3.4
Plantlets on the edges of leaves of *Bryophyllum*

Bulbs

Some plants reproduce asexually using bulbs. A **bulb** is a short stem with fleshy leaves and buds.

At the end of the growing season, leftover food is transported to these buds. Each bud becomes swollen with food and forms a new bulb. Plants that reproduce asexually using bulbs include onions, daffodils, tulips and garlic.

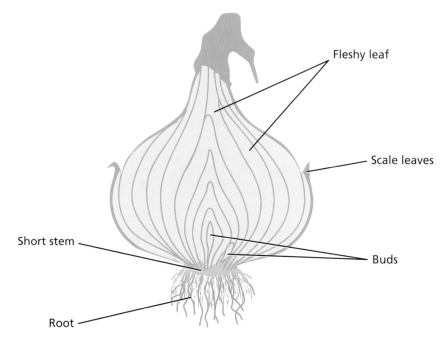

➲ **Fig. 7.3.5**
An onion bulb

➲ **Fig. 7.3.6**
A sprouting daffodil bulb

Artificial Asexual Reproduction in Plants

Farmers and gardeners often make use of a plant's natural ability to reproduce asexually to grow crops faster.

The artificial control of asexual reproduction in plants is called **vegetative propagation**.

Over thousands of years, humans have developed a number of ways to control asexual reproduction in plants, including the following examples:

- Taking **cuttings** is the easiest way to clone a plant. Cuttings can be taken from the stem, root or leaf. If the cutting is placed in suitable conditions, a new plant will grow that is identical to the parent plant.

- **Grafting** involves joining a bud or stem of a valuable plant to a plant that already has a well-developed root system. Grafting is used to grow new fruit trees that produce high-quality fruit.

- **Micropropagation** (also known as tissue culture) is the newest method of vegetative propagation. A small sample of tissue is taken from the root, stem, leaf or bud of the parent plant and cultured in a laboratory. Large numbers of disease-free plants are produced in a short period of time.

Fig. 7.3.7
A plant cutting producing new roots

Fig. 7.3.8
Fruit tree grafting

Fig. 7.3.9
Plant tissue being separated for micropropagation

119

Sexual Reproduction in Flowering Plants

Key Words

Sexual reproduction
Seed
Fruit
Stamen
Carpel
Anther
Filament
Stigma
Style
Ovary
Pollination
Embryo
Plumule
Radicle
Germination

Learning Intentions

In this topic we are learning to:

- Examine the role of the flower in the sexual reproduction of plants.
- Outline the stages involved in the sexual reproduction of plants.

All flowering plants can also reproduce sexually.

In **sexual reproduction**:

- Male and female flower parts are involved.
- Each parent produces gametes.
- The gametes fuse during fertilisation to produce a zygote. The zygote then divides and develops into a **seed**.
- The offspring produced are genetically different to each other and the parents.
- In certain flowering plants, a **fruit** may form around the seed. The seed acts as a food store and the fruit helps to disperse seeds.

Sexual reproduction gives plants a better chance to adapt to the environment. The best adapted offspring will survive and reproduce.

The Flower

The flower is the part of the plant that contains the male and female sex organs.

- The male organs are the **stamens**.
- The female organs are the **carpels**.

➲ Fig. 7.4.1
The structure of a flower

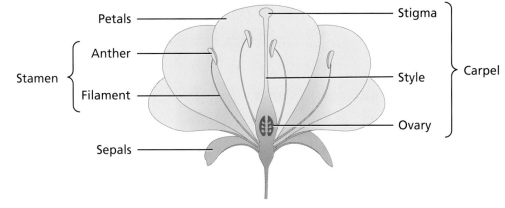

Petals — Stigma
Anther —
Stamen { Style } Carpel
Filament —
Ovary —
Sepals —

Roles of the Parts of a Flower

- The stamens are in a circle around the carpel. They are made up of two parts:
  1. The **anther** produces pollen. The pollen produces the male gamete (sperm). The anther also releases pollen grains.
  2. The **filament** is a stalk that positions the anther so the pollen can be blown away by the wind or picked up by an insect.

- The carpels are in the centre of the flower. They are made up of three parts:
  1. The **stigma** acts as a landing area for pollen.
  2. The **style** is a stalk that positions the stigma for pollen collection.
  3. The **ovary** contains ovules, which produce the female gamete (egg). It is also where fertilisation takes place. After fertilisation, the ovary develops into the fruit.
- The sepals protect the flower as a bud.
- The petals attract insects for pollination.

The Stages of Sexual Reproduction in Flowering Plants

There are five stages in the sexual reproduction of a plant:

1. Pollination
2. Fertilisation
3. Seed (and fruit) formation
4. Seed (and fruit) dispersal
5. Germination

1. Pollination

For fertilisation to take place, the male gamete in the pollen must get to the female gamete in the ovary.

The transfer of pollen from the anther to the stigma is called **pollination**.

Pollination can be carried out by the wind, by insects or by other animals.

Fun Fact

Lots of people suffer from hay fever caused by a reaction to pollen. When do you think hay fever is at its peak? Why?

🎧 Fig. 7.4.2
Hay fever is caused by pollen in the air

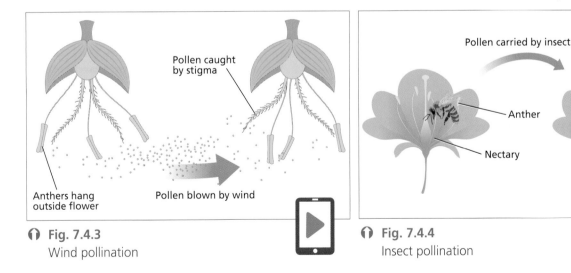

🎧 Fig. 7.4.3
Wind pollination

Pollen caught by stigma

Anthers hang outside flower

Pollen blown by wind

🎧 Fig. 7.4.4
Insect pollination

Pollen carried by insect

Stigma

Anther

Nectary

2. Fertilisation

1. If a pollen grain of the same species lands on the stigma, a pollen tube grows.
2. The pollen tube delivers the male sperm to the female egg in the ovule of the ovary.
3. The sperm and egg fuse to form a zygote.

121

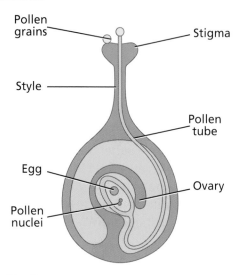

Fig. 7.4.5
Fertilisation in a flowering plant

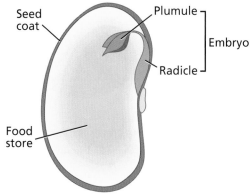

Fig. 7.4.6
A seed

4. The zygote divides and develops into the plant **embryo**. The embryo is made up of two parts:
   - The **plumule** will become the plant shoot.
   - The **radicle** will become the plant root.

3. Seed (and fruit) formation

1. The embryo becomes part of the seed.
2. A seed is made up of the embryo, food store and a seed coat.
3. After the formation of the seed, the ovary may develop into a fruit. The fruit surrounds the seed and attracts animals that are looking for food.

4. Seed (and fruit) dispersal

The seeds and fruits of a plant must be carried (dispersed) as far from the parent plant as possible. This means that the young plant will not have to compete with the parent for light, space, water and minerals.

Seeds and fruits are dispersed in the following ways:

- Animal dispersal: animals eat fleshy fruits and pass the seeds out in their faeces. Some plants produce hooked seeds or fruits that stick to animal fur and are dispersed as the animal moves around. For example, cattle disperse the seeds of the burdock thistle.
- Wind dispersal: seeds that can be carried by the wind are typically small and light. Other plants have special features to help their seeds carry further. For example, dandelions produce a parachute-type fruit and sycamores produce a winged-type fruit.

Fig. 7.4.7
Seeds of burdock thistles being dispersed by a cow

Fig. 7.4.8
Dandelion fruit is dispersed by the wind

- Water dispersal: plants that live in or near water, such as the water lily, produce seeds that float and are carried downstream by the current. Coconuts are fruits that are dispersed by water.
- Self-dispersal: sometimes called explosive seed dispersal. For example, peas are scattered by exploding pea pods after the fruit dries out. Gorse disperses seeds in a similar way.

🎧 **Fig. 7.4.9**
Water lily seeds are dispersed by water

🎧 **Fig. 7.4.10**
Pea pods explode and scatter the peas

5. Germination

Germination is the growth of a seed to form a new plant.

Plumule

Radicle

🔄 **Fig. 7.4.11**
Germinating seeds

After dispersal, seeds will germinate if the conditions are suitable. The conditions needed for germination are:

- Water
- Oxygen
- A suitable temperature

1. The seed coat splits and the radicle grows out and downwards into soil. The radicle will develop into the root.
2. Then the plumule emerges and grows upwards, which will develop into the shoot system.
3. Initially, the seed relies on its food store but once the shoot system breaks ground, the seedling can start to photosynthesise. The seedling is now independent and will continue to grow.

Investigating germination

Plan, design, carry out and write up an investigation to examine the factors that affect seed germination.

Chapter Summary

- Flowering plants are the most successful type of plant on Earth.
- Flowering plants have the following organs: root, stem, leaf and flower. Buds, fruits and seeds are also important plant structures.
- Plants transport water and minerals through xylem tissue and food (sugars) through phloem tissue. Transpiration is the loss of water through stomata on the underside of the leaf.
- Plants exchange gases with the atmosphere through stomata.
- Plants sense and respond to changes in their environment. The directional growth response of a plant to a stimulus is called tropism.
- Plants can reproduce asexually and sexually.
- Asexual reproduction involves a single parent only, no gametes and the offspring are clones of each other and the parent plant.
- Asexual reproduction can happen artificially. This is called vegetative propagation. The techniques include cuttings, grafting and micropropagation.
- Sexual reproduction involves one or two parents but always male and female parts of a flower. Gametes are produced and the offspring are genetically different from each other and the parent plant.
- The male part of the plant is the stamen. It is made up of the anther and filament. The anther produces, and releases, a pollen grain, which contains the male sperm. Plants disperse pollen in the wind or via insects and other animals.
- The female part of the plant is the carpel. It is made up of the stigma, style and ovary. If a suitable pollen grain lands on the stigma, the sperm enters the ovary and fertilises the egg to form a zygote. The zygote develops into an embryo, which then becomes part of the seed. The seed may then be surrounded by a fruit.
- The stages in flowering plant reproduction are: 1. Pollination; 2. Fertilisation; 3. Seed (and fruit) formation; 4. Seed (and fruit) dispersal; 5. Germination.
- Seeds are dispersed by animals, wind, water or self-dispersal.
- If water, oxygen and a suitable temperature are present the following spring, the seed will germinate.

The **BIG** Challenge

Your task is to successfully propagate a cutting of a *Coleus* plant, commonly known as painted nettle.

1. Cut off a stem of the parent plant.
2. Remove the lower leaves.
3. Place the stem in a glass of water.
4. Keep a photographic record of the growth of your cuttings.
5. Once your cutting has grown roots, you can put it in a pot or plant it in the garden.

Go to your Portfolio to check what you have learned in this chapter.

Take the chapter 7 quiz on educateplus.ie.

Questions

1. Copy and fill in the blanks:

    a. The root system of a plant is in the ground. The _____ system of the plant is in the air.

    b. The four plant organs are root, stem, _____ and _____.

    c. Plants photosynthesise and _____. These processes play an important role in controlling the concentration of oxygen and _____ _____ in the atmosphere.

    d. Water exits a leaf through _____.

    e. Plants may reproduce _____ and sexually.

    f. In asexual reproduction all the offspring are genetically _____. In _____ reproduction all the offspring are genetically different.

    g. Cuttings, grafting and micropropagation are all forms of _____ _____.

    h. The _____ is the organ responsible for sexual reproduction in plants.

    i. The male organs are the _____. The female organs are the _____.

    j. The five stages of sexual reproduction in flowering plants are _____, fertilisation, _____ formation, seed _____ and _____.

2. Draw a labelled sketch of a flower. Identify all of the structures that make up both the stamen and carpel.

3. Copy and complete the following table to compare asexual reproduction and sexual reproduction in plants.

4. After fertilisation, the petals on a flower shrivel and die. Why does this happen? Give at least two reasons.

5. Define each of the following terms clearly:

    a. Pollination
    b. Fertilisation
    c. Germination
    d. Transpiration

6. Describe the role of fruit in sexual reproduction in plants.

7. Why do you think many gardeners produce fruit and vegetables by vegetative propagation methods rather than from seeds? Give at least three reasons to explain your answer.

8. Draw a large labelled diagram of a wind pollinated flower and an animal (insect) pollinated flower. List three adaptations of each flower type to their mode of pollination.

Characteristic	Asexual	Sexual
Gametes produced? Yes/No		
Pollination? Yes/No		
Fertilisation? Yes/No		
Seed and fruit formation? Yes/No		
Seed and fruit dispersal? Yes/No		
Germination? Yes/No		
Offspring: genetically identical or non-identical?		

Working as a Scientist

Investigation Design

Hydroponics

Hydroponics is the growth of plants without soil using a nutrient solution. The majority of tomatoes, cucumbers and sweet peppers are grown using hydroponics in large polytunnels and greenhouses. Hydroponics allows plants to grow in areas where soil quality is poor.

It is reasonable to ask the question 'Will the concentration of nitrate in the nutrient solution affect the growth of plants?'

This question may be framed as a testable hypothesis: 'The growth of cress seedlings will be increased with higher concentrations of nitrate in the hydroponics nutrient solution.'

Collect the following equipment:

🎧 **Fig. 7.6.1**
Hydroponics

- Cress seeds
- Cotton wool and filter paper
- Perlite (an inorganic medium for growing cuttings)
- 100 cm³ stock solution of potassium nitrate

- Glassware
- Five 2 l plastic bottles
- Old tea cloth or towel
- Test tubes
- Plastic syringes

> **Task 1: Germinate cress seeds**
> Approximately 4–7 days before you begin your investigation, you must sow cress seeds and allow them to germinate.

> **Task 2: Prepare your hydroponics planter**

1 Using scissors, carefully cut the bottles in half so you can turn the top half upside down and rest it in the bottom half. Carefully drill a 10 mm hole in the bottle top. Cut a thin strip of cloth and pull it through the hole in the bottle top – this will act as a wick to absorb the hydroponic solution from the bottom of the bottle and then deliver it to the cress seedlings.

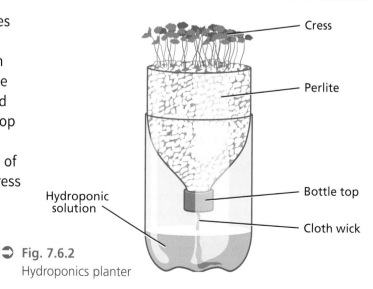

Cress

Perlite

Bottle top

Cloth wick

Hydroponic solution

⮑ **Fig. 7.6.2**
Hydroponics planter

> **Task 3: Prepare your hydroponics solution**
> You may consider the potassium nitrate solution supplied by your teacher as your 100 per cent solution.

2 **Using some of the stock solution, plan how you will make up solutions of the following concentrations: 50 per cent, 25 per cent, 12.5 per cent and 0 per cent. (Hint: serial dilutions.)**

- Add 50 cm^3 of water to the bottom of all five bottles.
- Now, place 50 cm^3 of your 100 per cent solution into Bottle 1, 50 cm^3 of your 50 per cent solution into Bottle 2 and so on for the 12.5 per cent and 0 per cent solution.
- Invert the top of the bottle into the bottom half. Make sure the cloth wick is in the solution.
- Pack the top of the bottle with perlite, making sure that the other end of the wick is left on top of the bed of perlite.
- Finally, select ten seedlings of the same height for each bottle. The seedlings can be placed on a sheet of dry filter paper and then transferred to sit on top of the wick.
- Place the five bottles at the back of the laboratory. Record the initial height of every seedling in each of the five bottles.
- Replace the solution in each bottle every four days and monitor the growth of seedlings for 16 days.

3 **Decide on a suitable data collection sheet for this investigation.**

4 **Write a clear, step-by-step procedure for producing your planter.**

5 **Write a clear, step-by-step procedure for how you produced your hydroponic solutions of different concentrations.**

6 **Why did you need to include a 0 per cent solution in your investigation? What term is used to describe this aspect of a scientific investigation?**

7 **Why was it necessary to select seedlings that were the same height?**

8 **Using all of the data, comment on the trend that you have observed. Does this trend support the original hypothesis?**

9 **Select and produce an appropriate chart or graph to clearly present your data. Once again, comment on any trends. Does this trend support the original hypothesis?**

10 **Comment on likely sources of error? How could you change the design of your investigation to improve accuracy?**

11 **How could you change this investigation to investigate other factors that affect plant growth?**

Chapter 8

Structures and Processes of Life: Humans

What you may already know:

- Humans are animals.
- The human body is very organised and has a number of organ systems.
- Humans reproduce sexually.

What you will learn in this chapter:

- Humans are consumers and have a digestive system for breaking down food.
- Humans have a circulatory system for transporting substances around the body.
- The respiratory system lets humans exchange gases with the atmosphere.
- Sexual reproduction in humans happens when a male sperm fertilises a female egg.

Think BIG

- With the exception of identical twins, why are all humans different?
- Why do humans get sick?

Puzzler

Can you crack this code?

The first letter of each image spells out a key word you will come across in this chapter. Use the hints provided if you need to, or revisit the Puzzler after you finish this chapter.

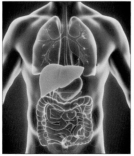 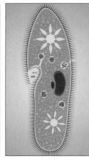   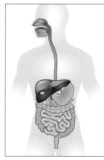

1. Organ that produces bile
2. Organisms with only one cell
3. How organisms get food
4. Short section of DNA
5. Group of organs that work together

1. ___
2. ___
3. ___
4. ___
5. ___

The Organisation of Humans

Learning Intentions

In this topic we are learning to:

- Recognise that humans are multicellular organisms that demonstrate significant levels of organisation.
- Discuss the role of each system within the human body.

Key Words

Specialisation
Division of labour

Humans are the most complex multicellular organism. Over time, our cells, tissues and organs have evolved to carry out specialised and separate roles. For example, red blood cells adapted to transport oxygen around the body and white blood cells adapted to protect us from disease.

- The adaptation of a cell, tissue, organ or system to carry out a special job is called **specialisation**.
- The separate jobs carried out by the different parts of an organism is called **division of labour**.

Together, specialisation and division of labour make an organism very efficient.

Fun Fact

An average adult human is made up of approximately 100 trillion cells!

Human Systems

A system is a group of organs that work together.

There are nine different human systems:

1. Digestive system
2. Circulatory system
3. Respiratory system
4. Reproductive system
5. Musculoskeletal system
6. Nervous system
7. Endocrine system
8. Excretory system
9. Immune system

Each system carries out a special job in the body. For example, the immune system protects us against disease and the musculoskeletal system helps us move around.

All of these systems work together and form an organism.

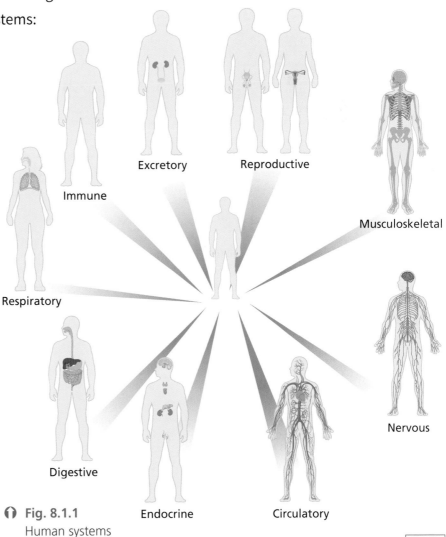

🔊 **Fig. 8.1.1**
Human systems

129

The Digestive System

Learning Intentions

In this topic we are learning to:

- Identify that humans are consumers and must eat and digest food.
- Identify and explain the roles of the organs of the digestive system.
- Explore the health of the human digestive system.

We need food for energy and growth. The food we eat is too big to be delivered directly to the cells of our bodies.

Our digestive system breaks down food into smaller molecules. After the food is digested it can pass into our blood. The blood then carries the food molecules to our cells.

There are two types of digestion:

1. Physical digestion: food is broken down into smaller pieces by the teeth, tongue and churning action of the muscles in the stomach.

2. Chemical digestion: food is broken down into simpler molecules by digestive enzymes and other digestive juices, including acid, in the stomach.

◑ Fig. 8.2.1
The stages of human nutrition

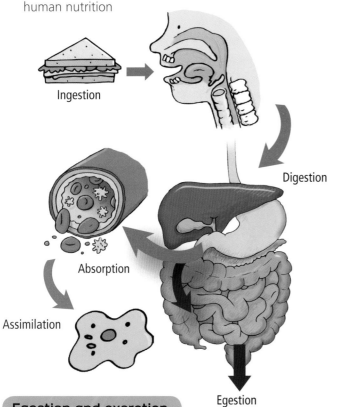

The Stages in Nutrition

There are five stages of human nutrition:

1. **Ingestion**: the food is taken into the mouth.

2. **Digestion**: the food is broken down into simpler, absorbable molecules.

3. **Absorption**: the absorbable molecules are passed into the blood and carried to all of the cells of the body.

4. **Assimilation**: the food is used by the body for energy and to build new cells.

5. **Egestion**: undigested food material is released from the digestive system as faeces.

Egestion and excretion

Egestion is the release of undigested food. Excretion is the removal of the waste products of chemical reactions that were produced within the cells of the body. The excretory organs include the kidneys, lungs and skin. For example, carbon dioxide produced by respiring cells is excreted via the lungs.

The Parts of the Digestive System

There are a number of special organs in the digestive system.

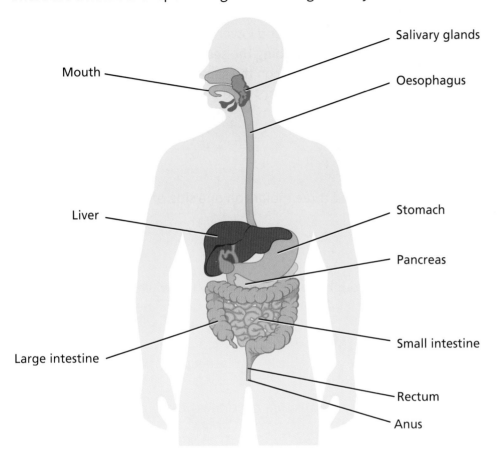

Fig. 8.2.2
The human digestive system

1. Mouth

- Food is ingested through the mouth.
- The teeth physically digest food and the enzymes in saliva chemically digest it.
- There are four types of teeth:
    - Incisors: narrow, sharp teeth at the front of the mouth, similar to chisels. Used for biting, cutting and slicing food.
    - Canines: pointed teeth, often called 'eye teeth'. Used for grasping and tearing food.
    - Premolars: large, rounded teeth. Used for crushing and grinding food.
    - Molars: largest teeth, found at the back of the mouth. Also used for crushing and grinding food.
- Salivary glands secrete saliva onto the food in the mouth. Saliva helps soften the food. Salivary amylase is the enzyme that chemically digests starch to maltose in the mouth.
- Food is swallowed and enters the oesophagus (food pipe).

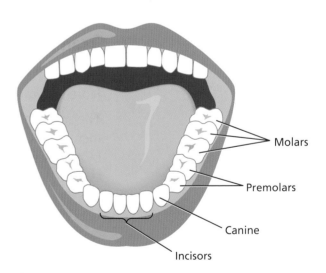

Fig. 8.2.3
The arrangement of human teeth

Investigating salivary amylase

Plan, design, carry out and write up an investigation to examine the factors that influence the activity of salivary amylase.

The human dental formula

A young child has 20 'milk' teeth. A full adult set is made up of 32 teeth. Teeth are arranged in order in the semicircle of each jaw. The teeth in the upper and lower jaws are almost mirror images of one another. The dental formula is a way of describing the sequence and number of different types of teeth in one half of the upper and lower jaw on the same side, from middle front to back. Incisors are noted first, canines second, premolars third and then molars. A full adult set has the following formula:

> **2.1.2.3**
> **2.1.2.3**

That is, two incisors, one canine, two premolars, and three molars on one side of the upper and lower jaw.

2. Oesophagus

- Food is moved through the oesophagus by the wavelike movement of muscles. This continues the physical digestion of food.

3. Stomach

GO Learn more about stomach acid in Chemical World 13.3

- The stomach is an expandable muscular bag that physically churns and temporarily stores food.
- The stomach releases juices that continue the chemical digestion of food.
- Hydrochloric acid in the stomach chemically digests food and kills bacteria.

4. Small intestine

- Food from the stomach enters the small intestine.
- More enzymes complete the breakdown of food.
- The small intestine is densely covered in **villi**. The villi provide an increased surface area to allow food to be absorbed into the bloodstream.

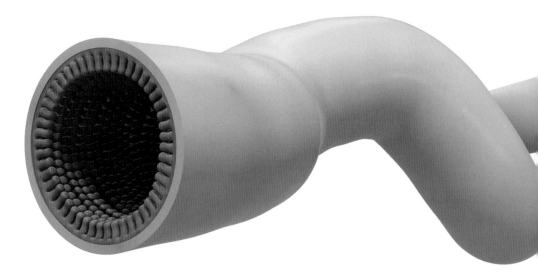

➲ **Fig. 8.2.4**
Villi increase the surface area of the small intestine

5. Pancreas

- Food does not travel through the pancreas. The pancreas produces digestive enzymes. These enzymes pass into the small intestine.

6. Liver

- The liver is the largest internal organ in the body. It has many roles, including detoxifying alcohol and helping to keep body temperature at 37 °C.
- Food does not pass through the liver. The liver produces bile. Bile passes into the small intestine, where it helps to digest fats.

7. Large intestine

- Food from the small intestine enters the large intestine.
- The major role of the large intestine is to reabsorb water into the blood. It also prepares undigested food to be egested in the form of faeces.

8. Rectum and anus

- Faeces are temporarily stored in the rectum before egestion.
- Faeces stimulate the rectum to contract and are passed out via the anus.

Fun Fact

It takes your body around 12 hours to completely digest food after you eat it.

Health of the Digestive System

Like all systems of the body, sometimes the digestive system does not work properly. Problems may arise from:

- Defective genes (genetic disorders and cancers).
- Poor dietary and lifestyle choices.
- Diseases caused by microorganisms (pathogens).

Some common diseases of the digestive system are Crohn's disease, ulcers and gallstones.

⟳ Fig. 8.2.5
Gallstones

Health of the human digestive system

Research a disease of the human digestive system. Source and cite information under the following headings:

1. Cause
2. Signs and symptoms
3. Prevention
4. Treatment

Prepare a short presentation for your classmates.

The Circulatory System

Key Words

Plasma
Haemoglobin
Aorta
Venae cavae
Septum
Atria
Ventricles
Pulmonary artery
Pulse

Learning Intentions

In this topic we are learning to:
- Identify and explain the roles of the organs of the circulatory system.
- Explore the health of the human circulatory system.

The body needs a transport system to supply cells with the molecules they need for energy and growth. This transport system is called the circulatory system.

The circulatory system has three main roles:

1. Transport
2. Defence against disease
3. Homeostasis, including regulating body temperature.

Blood

Blood is a tissue made up of plasma and three types of blood cells – red blood cells, white blood cells and platelets.

⊃ **Fig. 8.3.1**
The composition of blood

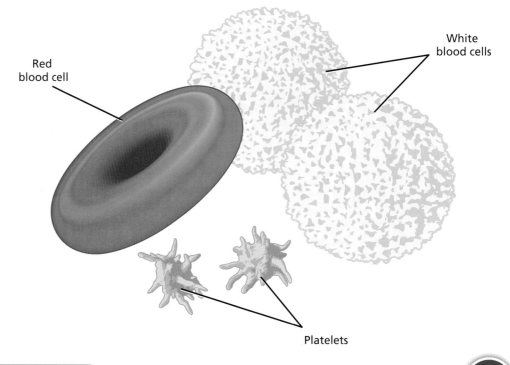

Red blood cell

White blood cells

Platelets

Blood transfusions and blood types

People have different blood types, based on the different chemical markers on the surface of their red blood cells. The most well-known blood type system is the ABO system, which consists of A, B, AB and O blood types.

Do you know your blood type? What would happen if you received a blood transfusion of the wrong type? Would you consider becoming a blood donor?

Plasma

Plasma is the liquid part of blood. It is mostly made of water.

- Plasma transports dissolved substances around the body, including oxygen, glucose, amino acids, hormones and antibodies. It also carries wastes, such as carbon dioxide and urea.
- Plasma carries heat around the body.
- It also carries the blood cells.

Blood cells

- Red blood cells transport oxygen to cells so that respiration can take place. They contain a red pigment called **haemoglobin**. Haemoglobin contains iron and picks up the oxygen for transport.
- White blood cells protect us from disease. White blood cells work by 'eating' harmful microorganisms or by producing antibodies that kill them.
- Platelets are tiny fragments of larger cells. They help the blood to clot. This helps to heal wounds, maintain blood pressure and prevent the entry of pathogens.

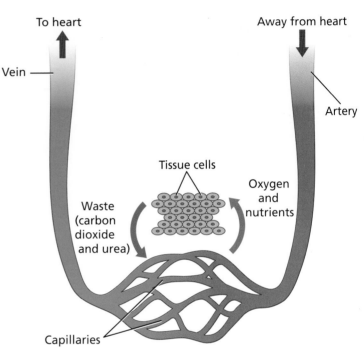

∩ Fig. 8.3.2
Blood vessels

Blood Vessels

Blood flows from and returns to the heart through the blood vessels.

There are three types of blood vessels, as outlined in the following table.

Blood vessel type	Features
Arteries	- Carry blood away from the heart. - Have thick walls to withstand the high pressure of blood pumped out of the heart. - The **aorta** is the major artery in the body. It branches out into a series of smaller arteries that deliver oxygenated blood and dissolved nutrients to all cells of the body.
Veins	- Carry blood to the heart. - Have thinner walls than arteries. The blood pressure in veins is lower than in arteries, so veins also have valves to prevent the backflow of blood. - The **venae cavae** are the major veins. They carry deoxygenated blood, high in carbon dioxide, to the heart.
Capillaries	- Tiny blood vessels that link arteries and veins. There is a huge network of capillaries throughout the body. - The walls of capillaries are very thin so molecules can easily pass in and out of surrounding cells. The molecules exchanged include oxygen, carbon dioxide, glucose, waste and hormones.

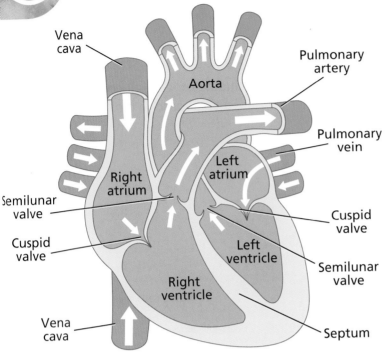

Vena cava
Aorta
Pulmonary artery
Right atrium
Left atrium
Pulmonary vein
Semilunar valve
Cuspid valve
Cuspid valve
Left ventricle
Semilunar valve
Right ventricle
Vena cava
Septum

Fig. 8.3.3
The structure of the heart

The Heart

The heart acts as a pump to drive blood all over the body. It is located in the upper chest between the lungs. It is protected by the ribcage. The heart is made of very strong cardiac muscle that can continuously pump blood.

The heart is a double pump, separated into a left side and a right side by the **septum**.

There are four chambers in the heart. The left and right sides are further divided into upper **atria** (the right atrium and left atrium) and lower **ventricles**, separated by cuspid valves.

How the Heart Pumps Blood

The following are the stages in one complete cycle of blood through the body:

1. Blood with little oxygen and a high concentration of carbon dioxide enters the right atrium through the venae cavae.

2. Blood is then pumped from the right atrium through a cuspid valve and into the right ventricle.

3. The right ventricle contracts and forces blood up and out through a semilunar valve. The blood leaves the heart through the pulmonary artery.

4. The **pulmonary artery** delivers deoxygenated blood to the lungs. At the lungs, carbon dioxide is lost from the blood and oxygen is taken into the blood (gaseous exchange). The blood is now fully oxygenated.

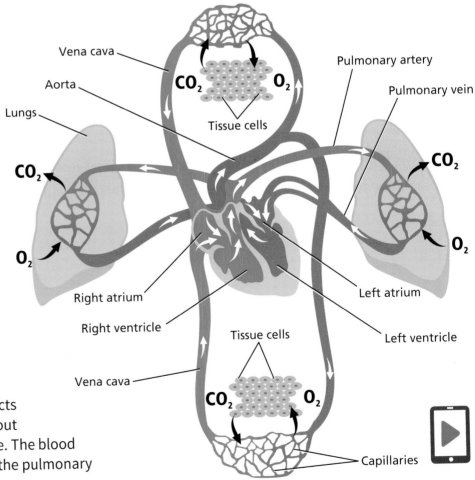

Vena cava
Aorta
Lungs
CO_2
O_2
Tissue cells
CO_2
O_2
Right atrium
Right ventricle
Vena cava
CO_2
O_2
Pulmonary artery
Pulmonary vein
CO_2
O_2
Left atrium
Left ventricle
Tissue cells
Capillaries

Fig. 8.3.4
Blood flow through the heart

5. The pulmonary vein brings oxygenated blood back to the left atrium.

6. Blood is pumped from the left atrium through a cuspid valve and into the left ventricle.

7. The left ventricle contracts and forces blood up and out through a semilunar valve. The blood leaves the heart through the aorta and is distributed to all cells of the body.

8. Exchange of molecules in the blood occurs at the capillaries. Capillaries reunite to form veins, which collect into venae cavae that return to the right atrium. This completes one entire cycle.

Dissecting a heart

1. Source a cow or sheep heart. You may be able to purchase one from your local butcher or your teacher will provide one.

2. Plan and carry out a dissection of the heart. Your teacher will show you how to use a scalpel safely.

3. See if you can identify all of the structures of the heart and trace the pathway of blood through the heart.

4. Record your observations.

Pumping blood

Using the following information, calculate how long it would take to pump all of the blood out of the heart of a typical adult at rest, just once.

- A typical adult has five litres of blood (5,000 cm^3) in their body.
- Each heartbeat typically pumps 70 cm^3 of blood out of the heart and around the body.
- The typical resting heart rate of an adult is 70 beats per minute.

Health of the Circulatory System

Doctors listen for a heartbeat using a stethoscope. The normal heart rate for an adult at rest is approximately 70 beats per minute. A person's age, sex (gender), physical fitness, diet and stress levels affect the heart rate.

The **pulse** is a wave of vibration that passes through an artery in response to blood being forced out of the left ventricle. The pulse can be felt at an artery close to the surface of skin, such as in the wrist. The pulse rate and heart rate are the same. Blood pressure also provides information about the health of the circulatory system. Doctors measure blood pressure using an arm cuff and a stethoscope.

A balanced diet, exercise and rest are very important for a healthy heart.

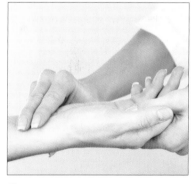

🎧 Fig. 8.3.5
A person's pulse rate being taken

The effect of exercise on pulse rate

Plan, design, carry out and write up an investigation to examine the effect of exercise on pulse rate. You may use the timer on your mobile phone or a stopwatch.

1. Consider how you will measure the pulse.

2. Do you need a control? How will you ensure accuracy?

Health of the human circulatory system

Research a disease of the human circulatory system. Source and cite information under the following headings:

1. Cause
2. Signs and symptoms
3. Prevention
4. Treatment

Prepare a short presentation for your classmates.

The Respiratory System

Learning Intentions

In this topic we are learning to:

- Identify and explain the roles of the organs of the respiratory system.
- Explore the health of the human respiratory system.

Our respiratory system allows us to breathe so gases can be exchanged with the atmosphere.

It is important not to confuse the respiratory system with respiration. So that we can tell the two apart, the respiratory system is often called the breathing system.

⮑ **Fig. 8.4.1**
Breathing allows us to exchange gases with the atmosphere

Oxygen

Carbon dioxide

Water

The respiratory system has three main roles:

1. To take in oxygen from the atmosphere.
2. To give out carbon dioxide and water into the atmosphere.
3. To make sounds, such as speech.

The Parts of the Respiratory System

The respiratory system is made up of a number of special organs:

1. Mouth and nose

- Air enters the respiratory system through either the mouth or nose.
- Air entering through the nose is warmed, moistened, cleaned and spread thinly over a very wide area.
- The hairs and mucus in the nose remove dust and microorganisms that may enter with air.

2. Pharynx

- This is commonly known as the throat.
- It is the common opening for the respiratory and digestive systems.

3. Larynx

- This is more commonly known as the voice box, as it plays a role in speech.

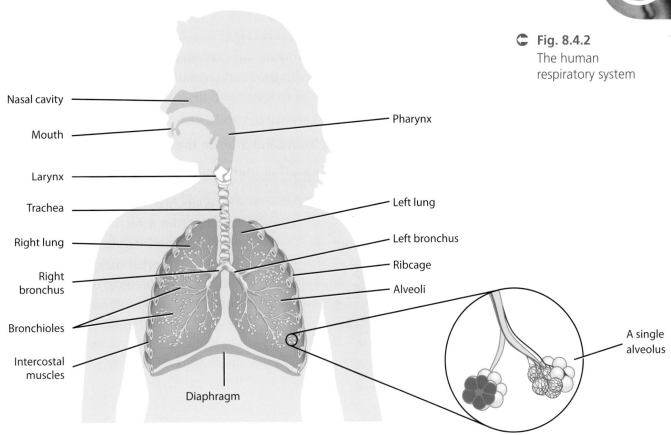

↻ **Fig. 8.4.2**
The human respiratory system

Nasal cavity

Mouth

Pharynx

Larynx

Trachea

Left lung

Right lung

Left bronchus

Right bronchus

Ribcage

Alveoli

Bronchioles

Intercostal muscles

A single alveolus

Diaphragm

4. Trachea

- This is more commonly known as the windpipe.
- The trachea is made from c-shaped rings of cartilage that keep it open.
- It allows air to flow from the pharynx to the bronchus.

5. Bronchus

- The trachea divides into two bronchi, one for each lung. This allows air to flow into and out of the lungs.

6. Lungs

- The **lungs** are two large, spongy, elastic organs located in the chest cavity.
- They can expand easily during inhalation and contract back to normal size during exhalation.

7. Bronchioles

- Each bronchus divides into narrower and narrower tubes in the lung, called bronchioles.

8. Ribcage and intercostal muscles

- The ribcage is made up of 12 pairs of ribs, vertebrae, the sternum (breastbone) and the **diaphragm**.
- The **intercostal muscles** are located between the ribs.
- The role of the ribcage and intercostal muscles is inhalation and exhalation and also to protect the heart and lungs.

9. Diaphragm

- This is a large sheet of muscle involved in inhalation and exhalation.

Heimlich manoeuvre

a b c

The Heimlich manoeuvre is an emergency technique to prevent choking and suffocation when food or some other foreign object obstructs a person's trachea. Why do you think it is called the Heimlich manoeuvre? Research the Heimlich manoeuvre and prepare a short information pamphlet, including text and diagrams, explaining how to correctly carry out this technique.

Alveoli and the Exchange of Gases

The lungs contain millions of tiny air sacs called **alveoli**. The alveoli are in close and extensive contact with blood in capillaries. This is where gases are exchanged between the air in lungs and dissolved gases in the blood.

 Learn more about the diffusion of gases in Chemical World 9.2

- Oxygen moves from the alveoli to capillaries.
- Carbon dioxide moves from capillaries to the alveoli.

Alveoli have many adaptations that make them very efficient at exchanging gases:

- The walls of alveoli and capillaries are very thin, which makes them extremely permeable to gases.
- There are approximately 300,000,000 alveoli in each lung. This provides a large surface area for gaseous exchange.
- Each alveolus is covered in capillaries. This allows for the fast diffusion of gases between the air in alveoli and the dissolved gases in the blood flowing through capillaries.
- Continuous breathing maintains a difference in the concentration of oxygen and carbon dioxide in alveoli and capillaries. This helps diffusion because gases will always move from an area of high concentration to one of low concentration.

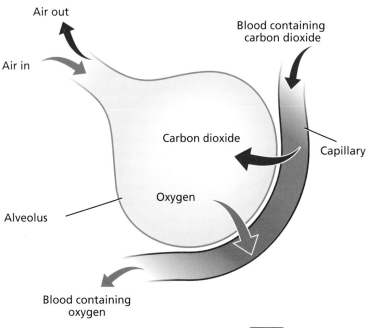

Air out

Air in

Blood containing carbon dioxide

Carbon dioxide

Capillary

Oxygen

Alveolus

Blood containing oxygen

🎧 **Fig. 8.4.3**
The exchange of gases at an alveolus

Comparing the composition of inhaled and exhaled air

Consider the table below, which shows the composition of inhaled and exhaled air.

	Inhaled air (%)	Exhaled air (%)
Oxygen	20.9	16
Carbon dioxide	0.03	4.0
Water vapour	Variable	Variable but more than inhaled air
Nitrogen	78.1	78.1
Noble gases	0.94	0.94

1. Why is there a significant difference in the composition of gases in inhaled and exhaled air? (Hint: consider respiration.)
2. Why does the concentration of nitrogen and noble gases not change?

Now plan and carry out an investigation into the composition of inhaled and exhaled air.

3. Record your observations.

4. Predict any differences in the composition of exhaled air between a smoker and a non-smoker.

Inhalation and Exhalation

- **Inhalation** is the act of breathing in. The diaphragm and intercostal muscles contract and the lungs expand.

  The expansion of the lungs causes a drop in air pressure within the lungs. The air in the lungs is now at a lower pressure than the air outside, so air is drawn in from the atmosphere to the lungs (high pressure to low pressure).

- **Exhalation** is the act of breathing out. The diaphragm and intercostal muscles relax and the lungs return to their original volume.

  Now, the air pressure within the lungs is greater than the air outside, so air is pushed out of the lungs to the atmosphere (high pressure to low pressure).

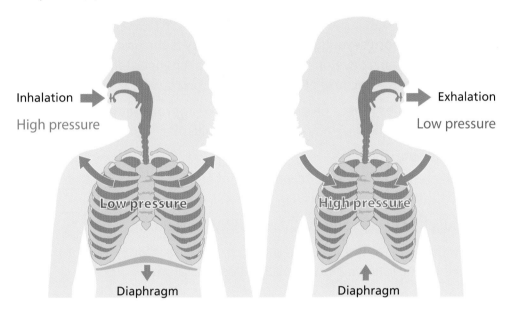

↻ **Fig. 8.4.4**
Inhalation and exhalation

Health of the Respiratory System

Our respiratory system may be negatively affected by a number of factors. Some of these conditions can have a genetic cause or be due to infection by microorganisms. Other diseases may be caused by poor lifestyle choices, such as smoking.

Some common diseases of the respiratory system include lung cancer, asthma and bronchitis.

Health of the human respiratory system

Research a disease of the human respiratory system. Source and cite information under the following headings:

1. Cause
2. Signs and symptoms
3. Prevention
4. Treatment

Prepare a short presentation for your classmates.

Key Words

Puberty
Ovaries
Ovulation
Fallopian tube
Uterus
Cervix
Vagina
Menstrual cycle
Menopause
Testes
Epididymis
Vas deferens
Seminal vesicles
Prostate gland
Cowper's gland
Semen
Penis
Urethra
Embryo
Implantation
Foetus
Placenta
Amniotic fluid
Lactation
Contraception

Learning Intentions

In this topic we are learning to:

- Identify and explain the roles of the organs of the female and male reproductive systems.
- Explore the health of the female and male reproductive systems.
- Research issues surrounding human reproduction.

Like all organisms, humans must reproduce to make sure the species continues into future generations. Like the majority of animals, humans can only reproduce sexually. There are two sexes: female and male.

Puberty

All humans are born sexually immature. **Puberty** is the time when the reproductive organs develop and other physical changes take place. These changes take place because of changing hormone levels.

Puberty in females ranges between the ages of approximately 10 and 16 years, when the following physical changes take place:

- Growth spurts.
- Enlargement of breasts and widening of hips.
- Hair growth under arms and in pubic region.
- Production of eggs and the menstrual cycle begin.

Puberty in males ranges between the ages of approximately 12 and 16 years, when the following physical changes take place:

- Growth spurts.
- Hair growth on face, chest, under arms and in pubic region.
- Broadening of shoulders.
- Enlarged larynx and deepening of voice.
- Production of sperm begins.

The Female Reproductive System

The role of the female reproductive system in human reproduction:

- Producing the egg (female gamete).
- Receiving the sperm (male gamete).
- Providing favourable conditions for the fertilisation, implantation and development of the embryo and foetus.
- Giving birth to the fully developed foetus.

The female reproductive system is made up of a number of special organs:

- **Ovaries** are the primary sexual organs in females. A female has two ovaries. After puberty, one of the ovaries produces an egg every 28 days on average. The release of an egg from the ovary is called **ovulation**. The ovaries also produce important hormones, including oestrogen and progesterone.

- The funnel-shaped opening of the **fallopian tube** captures the egg. Fertilisation of the egg by a sperm usually takes place in the fallopian tube. Following fertilisation, the embryo is carried to the uterus (womb).

- The **uterus** is a hollow organ with a strong muscular wall. After puberty, the wall of the uterus periodically builds up with a dense network of blood capillaries, ready to receive an embryo.

- The **cervix** is the narrow entrance to the uterus. It allows sperm to enter the uterus on its way to the fallopian tube for fertilisation.

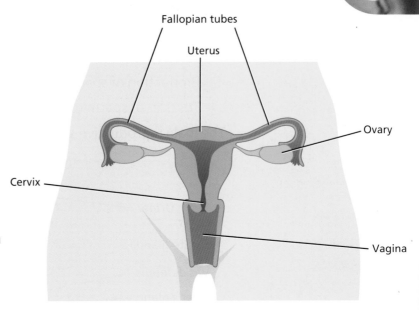

🎧 **Fig. 8.5.1**
The female reproductive system

- The **vagina** is a muscular tube that receives the penis and semen during sexual intercourse. The sperm are deposited in the vagina. The vagina is also the passageway for menstruation and childbirth.

The Menstrual Cycle

A sexually mature male produces sperm continuously and has the potential to impregnate a female at any time. A sexually mature, non-pregnant female normally produces one egg every 28 days and is capable of becoming pregnant only for a short time every month (approximately five days before ovulation and one to two days after ovulation). This is known as the fertile period.

The **menstrual cycle** is the repeating series of changes that take place in the female body to prepare it for pregnancy. The cycle can range from 21 to 40 days. A typical menstrual cycle is 28 days.

Day(s) of cycle	Event
1–5	Menstruation (the period). The lining of the womb detaches and is discharged through the vagina.
6–13	The lining of the womb is built up with blood vessels (capillaries).
14	Ovulation. A mature egg is released from an ovary and enters the fallopian tube.
15–26	The lining of the womb continues to build up. This is the window of opportunity for an embryo to be implanted in the womb.
27–28	If an embryo is not implanted, the lining of the womb starts to break down. The cycle now repeats with menstruation beginning again on Day 1 of the next cycle.

If an egg is fertilised, the menstrual cycle is paused for the duration of pregnancy. The first sign of pregnancy is often that menstruation does not happen.

Menopause signals the end of a female's ability to reproduce and also the end of her menstrual cycle. This typically takes place when a woman is in her late 40s to early 50s.

The Male Reproductive System

The role of the male reproductive system in human reproduction includes:

- Production of sperm (male gamete).
- Transfer of sperm to the vagina of the female.

The male reproductive system is made up of a number of organs:

⊃ **Fig. 8.5.2**
The male reproductive system

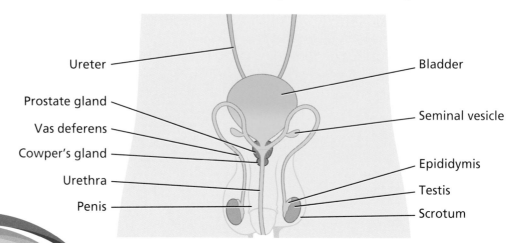

Ureter — Bladder
Prostate gland — Seminal vesicle
Vas deferens — Epididymis
Cowper's gland — Testis
Urethra — Scrotum
Penis

Fun Fact

A fertile male produces millions of sperm each day. The sperm cell is the smallest human cell. It is composed of a head with a nucleus containing 23 chromosomes and a small volume of cytoplasm, a mid-piece and a flagellum (tail). Sperm can survive in the fallopian tube for approximately 6–7 days.

- The **testes** are the primary sexual organs in males. A male has two testes, which produce sperm. The testes lie outside the body, within the scrotum, to ensure the temperature is slightly lower than body temperature. This is important for sperm production and development.

- The **epididymis** is a coiled tube on the outside of each testis that stores sperm and allows them to mature fully. The **vas deferens** (sperm duct) is a tube that transfers sperm, as part of the semen, from the epididymis to the urethra during ejaculation.

- The **seminal vesicles**, **prostate gland** and **Cowper's gland** produce fluids that nourish the sperm and allow them to swim. Together, these fluids and sperm make up **semen**.

- The **penis** transfers semen into the vagina of the female during sexual intercourse. The penis is made up of spongy tissue that fills with blood and becomes erect.

- The **urethra** passes through the penis. During ejaculation, semen is transferred through the urethra to the vagina of the female.

Sexual Intercourse

During sexual intercourse, the erect penis of the male enters the woman's vagina. The movement causes sperm to be released. This is called ejaculation. The sperm are placed in the vagina and then swim through the cervix and uterus to the fallopian tubes.

Fertilisation

Fertilisation is the fusion of the male sperm and the female egg to form a zygote. This takes place in the female's fallopian tube.

Pregnancy

In the fallopian tube, the zygote immediately starts to divide to produce a ball of identical cells called an **embryo**.

The embryo reaches the uterus approximately five days after fertilisation. It is embedded into the capillary-lined wall of the uterus. This process is called **implantation**.

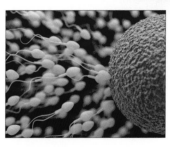

Fig. 8.5.3
Fertilisation

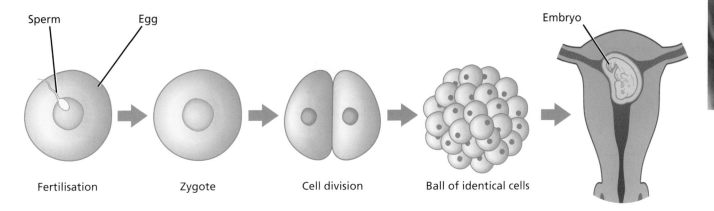

| Sperm | Egg | | | Embryo |

Fertilisation → Zygote → Cell division → Ball of identical cells

The female is considered to be pregnant when fertilisation is followed by the successful implantation of the embryo in the lined wall of the uterus.

A typical human pregnancy lasts for 40 weeks (about nine months). Over this period, the embryo develops into a **foetus**, ready to be born.

Fig. 8.5.4
The zygote divides to form the embryo

The placenta

Immediately after implantation, the **placenta** starts to develop. The placenta is a temporary organ that allows materials to pass between the mother and the foetus. The umbilical cord links the placenta to the foetus.

The embryo receives oxygen and food from the mother's blood. Carbon dioxide and other wastes are also removed from the embryo via the mother's blood.

The placenta is not a perfect barrier. As a result, the mother must avoid toxic chemicals, such as those found in cigarette smoke and alcohol, for the duration of pregnancy. These substances may harm a developing foetus.

Fun Fact

The implanted embryo passes the human chorionic gonadotropin (hCG) hormone into the mother's blood. Pregnancy test kits can detect this hormone in the pregnant female's urine. Test kits often indicate the positive presence of hCG by a colour change.

The embryonic period

Over the next eight weeks, all organ systems continue to develop.

The embryo is surrounded by **amniotic fluid** within an amniotic sac. This sac provides a protective and temperature-stable environment.

The foetal period

By the end of the eighth week, the embryo is approximately 3 cm long, nourished by the placenta. It is becoming recognisably human. From this point, the embryo is called a foetus.

The foetal period usually goes from week 9 to week 40. The foetal period is a time of rapid growth as all tissues and organs mature.

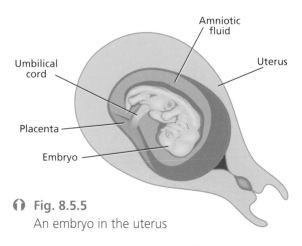

🎧 **Fig. 8.5.5**
An embryo in the uterus

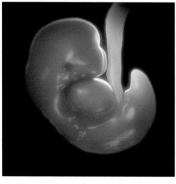

🎧 **Fig. 8.5.6**
An embryo at seven weeks

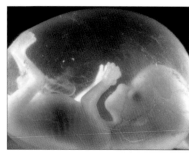

🎧 **Fig. 8.5.7**
A foetus at 14 weeks, surrounded by the amniotic sac

Birth

The infant is born after approximately 40 weeks, just as the placenta begins to break down.

Birth happens in three stages:

1. Labour

- The muscles in the wall of the uterus begin to contract. These contractions become stronger, longer and more frequent. This causes the cervix to widen.
- The amniotic sac bursts due to pressure from the contracting uterus and the amniotic fluid escapes through the vagina. This is commonly referred to as the 'breaking of the waters'.

2. Delivery of the baby

- The baby passes, head first, from the uterus through the cervix and along the vagina and is born.
- The umbilical cord is clamped and cut to close off blood vessels. The stump soon falls off, forming the 'belly button'.

3. Delivery of the placenta

- After delivery, the placenta detaches from the uterus and passes out of the body as the afterbirth.

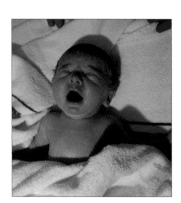

🎧 **Fig. 8.5.8**
A newborn baby

Feeding

The mother may choose to breastfeed the infant. The production of breast milk is called **lactation**. For the first three days after birth, the mammary glands in a mother's breast produce colostrum – a yellowish, nutritious liquid rich in antibodies that protect the infant from infection.

After this period, the breasts produce milk, which is ideally suited to meet the nutritional needs of a human infant for the first four to six months of life.

🎧 **Fig. 8.5.9**
Breastfeeding

Family Planning and Contraception

Family planning is the decision to control the number of children and how close together they are born.

Contraception is the prevention of ovulation, fertilisation or implantation. Contraceptive methods play a role in family planning. There are four different types of contraception, as shown in the following table.

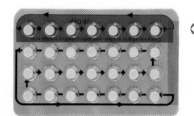

C **Fig. 8.5.10**
A month's cycle of the contraceptive pill

Method	Example
Natural	· Total abstinence from sexual intercourse.
Mechanical	· Condom: a thin, rubber sheath that covers the penis and prevents sperm entering the vagina. · A diaphragm: a dome-shaped rubber cup that fits over the cervix and prevents sperm entering the uterus.
Chemical	· Contraceptive pill: contains oestrogen or progesterone and prevents ovulation.
Surgical	· Tubal ligation: the fallopian tubes are cut and sealed, which prevents fertilisation. · Vasectomy: the cutting or tying-off of the sperm ducts. There will be no sperm in semen.

Apart from total abstinence, no form of contraception is 100 per cent effective at preventing pregnancy or sexually transmitted infections (STIs).

Health of The Human Reproductive System

A number of conditions or diseases can affect the health of the female and male reproductive systems.

- Infertility is the inability to produce children. Males and females are equally likely to be infertile.
- Cancers that affect the reproductive organs include cervical cancer in women and prostate cancer in men.
- Sexually transmitted infections, such as chlamydia and gonorrhoea, can affect men and women.

Health of the human reproductive system

Research a disease of the human reproductive system. Source and cite information under the following headings:

1. Cause
2. Signs and symptoms
3. Prevention
4. Treatment

Prepare a short presentation for your classmates.

The medical, ethical and societal impacts of human reproduction

Reproduction is the ultimate goal of all organisms and humans are no exception. It is unsurprising that society takes a great interest in the issues that surround human reproduction.

In pairs, research, prepare and present a short report (250 words) to your classmates about one of the following topics:

- *In vitro* fertilisation (IVF)
- Genetic screening of unborn embryos
- Future impact of reduced number of children in developed countries
- Age of consent
- A relevant topic of your choice (with agreement of your teacher)

Your report must be unbiased and include scientifically accurate information. You should clearly cite all sources of information.

Chapter Summary

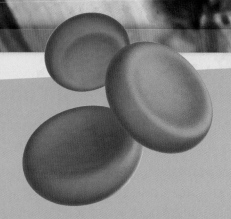

- Human bodies are highly organised. There are nine separate systems that work together to form a body.

- There are five stages of human nutrition: ingestion, digestion, absorption, assimilation and egestion. Digestion is either physical or chemical.

- The major organs of the digestive system are the mouth, oesophagus, stomach, small intestine, pancreas, liver, large intestine and anus.

- The circulatory system transports different materials around the body, including oxygen, glucose, hormones, antibodies and wastes such as carbon dioxide and urea.

- Blood has three major roles: transport, defence against disease and homeostasis (to control body temperature).

- Blood is made up of plasma and three types of blood cells: red blood cells, white blood cells and platelets.

- There are three types of blood vessels: arteries, veins and capillaries.

- The heart is divided into four chambers and acts as a pump to drive blood all over the body.

- The respiratory system exchanges gases with the atmosphere. Oxygen enters the blood from the atmosphere and carbon dioxide and water leave the blood.

- The major organs of the respiratory system include the mouth and nose, pharynx, larynx, trachea, bronchus, lungs, bronchioles, ribcage and intercostal muscles and diaphragm.

- Exchange of gases occurs at alveoli of lungs.

- Humans reproduce sexually. The ovary produces an egg in females and the testes produce sperm in males.

- The menstrual cycle is a repeating series of changes in the lining of the uterus.

- The male's penis transfers semen (with sperm) to the female's vagina during sexual intercourse.

- The sperm travels to the fallopian tube. If an egg is also present, then fertilisation may occur resulting in the formation of a zygote.

- The zygote divides to form an embryo, which implants in the uterus.

- The placenta forms to nourish the baby and remove waste.

- Contraception is the prevention of ovulation, fertilisation and implantation.

The BIG Challenge

Very often, the diseases that affect human health are caused by poor lifestyle choices and can be avoided by making simple changes to our lives. As a class, your task is as follows:

1. To brainstorm and agree on one simple task that each person can perform every day that will improve the average health and fitness of the entire class.

2. Decide on and measure a baseline value of fitness for the class.

3. Follow your strategy for a school term.

4. Measure class fitness again and compare results.

Go to your Portfolio to check what you have learned in this chapter.

Take the chapter 8 quiz on educateplus.ie.

Questions

1. Copy and fill in the blanks:

   a. Humans have evolved a _____ system to break down food.

   b. The five stages of human nutrition are _____, digestion, _____, assimilation and _____.

   c. Humans have evolved a _____ system to transport key molecules around the body.

   d. There are three types of blood cells: _____ blood cell, _____ blood cell and _____.

   e. The _____ is the major artery and the _____ _____ are the major veins in the body.

   f. The respiratory system allows humans to exchange _____ with the _____.

   g. Breathing in is referred to as _____ and breathing out is referred to as _____.

   h. Humans reproduce _____. The male gamete is the _____ and the female gamete is the _____.

   i. Fertilisation occurs in the _____ _____.

   j. Contraception may be of one of four types: natural, _____, chemical or _____.

2. Draw a large labelled diagram of the human digestive system. Using your diagram:

   a. Outline the five stages of human nutrition.

   b. Clearly show the difference between physical and chemical digestion.

   c. Outline the adaptations of the small intestine for absorption.

3. Describe the composition of blood and clearly explain the role of each part of blood.

4. Why do some athletes train at high altitudes?

5. Draw a large labelled diagram of the human heart. Using your diagram:

   a. Outline the flow of blood through the heart and associated blood vessels.

   b. Outline the adaptations of capillaries for exchange of molecules between blood and cells.

6. Draw a large labelled diagram of the human respiratory system. Using your diagram:

   a. Outline the adaptations of alveoli for exchange of gases between the atmosphere and blood.

   b. Clearly trace the movement of blood leaving the right atrium of the heart all the way back to the right atrium. Comment on the oxygen status of blood, the chambers of the heart, named blood vessels and the role of the lungs.

7. Draw a large labelled diagram of the female reproductive system. Using your diagram:

   a. Identify the location of (i) ovulation, (ii) fertilisation and (iii) implantation.

   b. Outline three roles of the placenta.

   c. Describe the three stages of birth.

8. Draw a labelled diagram of the male reproductive system.

9. Copy and complete the following table by identifying appropriate examples of contraception.

Form of contraception	Male	Female
Natural		
Mechanical		
Chemical		
Surgical		

10. Write a short essay outlining the contribution of Sir Robert Geoffrey Edwards to medicine.

Working as a Scientist

Responsible Science

Analysing Ireland's Health

1 The following table of data produced using surveys carried out by the Irish Universities Nutrition Alliance (IUNA) shows the changing weight status of the Irish population in 1990, 2001 and 2011.

Survey	Normal weight (%)	Overweight (%)	Obese (%)
Irish National Nutrition Survey (1988–1989)	49	39	11
North/South Ireland Food Consumption Survey (1997–1999)	42	39	18
National Adult Nutrition Survey (2008–2010)	39	37	24

  a. Select a suitable chart or graph to present this data.

  b. Comment on the trend, if any, evident in the data.

2 The following bar chart illustrates the increasing obesity rates among the adult population in OECD countries over the last 20 years.

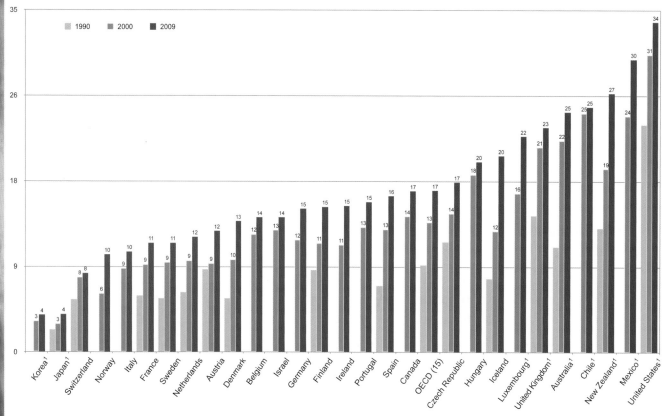

[1] Data are based on measurements rather than self-reported height and weight.

🎧 Fig. 8.7.1

Increasing obesity rates in OECD countries (%)

a. What does the acronym OECD stand for? Identify three roles of this organisation.

b. Of the 28 countries studied, where does Ireland rank in terms of obesity? How does the Irish data compare to the OECD average?

c. Calculate the percentage increase in obesity of the overall Irish population between 2000 and 2009.

3 **Consider the following bar chart, which illustrates the prevalence of diabetes among adults aged between 20 and 79 years in a number of different countries in 2010.**

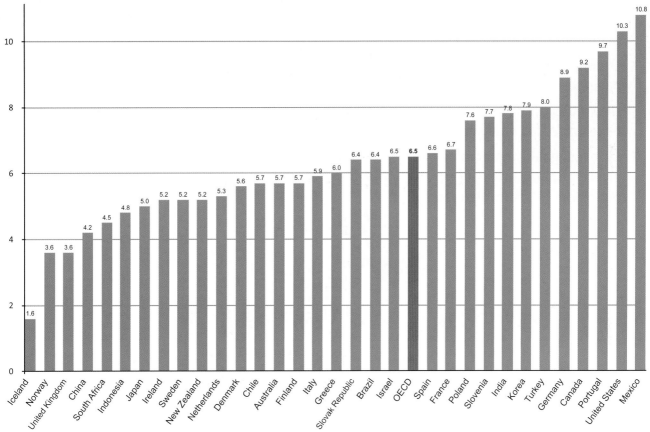

Note: The data cover both type 1 and type 2 diabetes.
Data are age-standardised to the World Standard Population.

🎧 **Fig. 8.7.2**
Prevalence of diabetes in OECD countries (%)

a. What percentage of the Irish population was diabetic in 2010? Where does Ireland rank in terms of diabetes? How does the Irish data compare to the OECD average?

b. Using only the bar chart provided, can we be certain that all of these are cases of type 2 diabetes?

c. Internationally, there is growing evidence of a link between rising levels of obesity and type 2 diabetes. Research relevant Irish data and consider if a similar link is evident in Ireland.

d. Research the medical, economic and social impacts of diabetes. Now complete the following paragraph: 'If I were Minister for Health, I would tackle the growing epidemic of type 2 diabetes by…'

Chemical World

We use a wide range of materials every day. In Chemical World we will explore these materials – how they are formed and how they can change.

Atoms and elements are the building blocks of all materials.

Without materials there would be no clothes, plastics, fuels, cleaning products or pain relief.

Over time, human beings have learned how to make new and better materials. We have learned how to get metal from rocks and how to make glass from sand.

New materials have improved modern life. For example, lighter, stronger materials have made for better sports equipment.

By investigating materials, we can predict and control how things change. These investigations can lead to new technology and help us understand how to protect our planet for future generations.

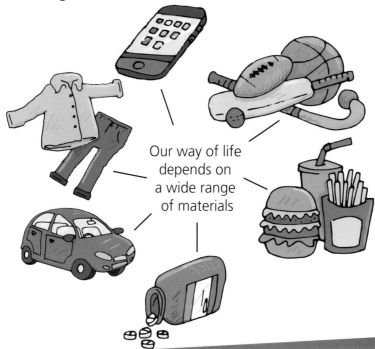

Our way of life depends on a wide range of materials

What you may already know:

- Everything is made up of materials: food, cars, mobile phones and even you.
- Different materials have different properties.
- Materials can exist as solids, liquids and gases.

Think BIG

- What are materials made up of and why do they behave the way they do?
- What are atoms, elements, compounds and mixtures?
- How are new materials made and how does this affect our environment?

Code Breaker

Can you crack this encrypted message?

Use the key below to figure out the quote by famous scientist Marie Curie. Each number represents a letter of the alphabet. 'I', 'G' and 'T' have been filled in to get you started.

A	B	C	D	E	F	G	H	I	J	K	L	M	N	O	P	Q	R	S	T	U	V	W	X	Y	Z
26	25	24	23	22	21	20	19	18	17	16	15	14	13	12	11	10	9	8	7	6	5	4	3	2	1

I [W A S] T[A]UGHT THAT THE WAY
18   4 26 8   7 26 6 20 19 7   7 19 26 7   7 19 22   4 26 2

OF PROGRESS WAS NEITHER
12 21   11 9 12 20 9 22 8 8   4 26 8   13 22 18 7 19 22 9

SWIFT NOR EASY.
8 4 18 21 7   13 12 9   22 26 8 2 .

Marie Curie

In Chemical World you will learn about:

What Matter is Made Of

What you may already know:

- Materials can be grouped as solids, liquids or gases.
- It is possible to change a solid to a liquid by adding heat.
- It is possible to reverse some changes but not others.

What you will learn in this chapter:

- How the particle theory explains the properties of solids, liquids and gases and how it can be used to explain changes of state.
- The differences between physical and chemical changes.
- The law of conservation of mass.

Think BIG

- How is it possible to smell the perfume the person beside you is wearing?
- How do you make a rain jacket waterproof?
- Why is graphene (extracted from graphite, the material used in pencils) a revolutionary material?

Puzzler

Can you solve this puzzle?
What element do all of the following have in common?

(Hint: this element is also the nickname for the valley in California where many of the world's technology companies are based.)

The Particle Theory and States of Matter

Key Words

Matter
Mass
States of matter
Solid
Liquid
Gas
Particles
Particle theory
Viscosity

Learning Intentions

In this topic we are learning to:

- Recognise that matter is made up of particles.
- Describe the properties of solids, liquids and gases.
- Use the particle theory to explain the properties of solids, liquids and gases.

In science, materials are known as **matter.**

Matter is anything that takes up space and has a mass. **Mass** is a measure of the amount of matter in an object.

There are three **states of matter**:

- **Solid:** for example, wood and rock.
- **Liquid:** for example, water and milk.
- **Gas:** for example, air and oxygen.

All matter exists in one of these three forms.

 GO Learn more about mass and how it can be measured in Physical World 15.3

Investigating matter

Part 1

1. Use samples of a solid, liquid and gas to plan, design, carry out and write up an investigation that will confirm the statement 'Solids, liquids and gases all have a mass.'

2. What piece of equipment would you use to measure the mass of each material?

Part 2

3. Using equipment in the school laboratory, set up the following investigation:

   Place a dry tissue in the bottom of a clear container. Turn the container upside down into a basin of water.

⟳ **Fig. 9.1.1**
Investigation set-up

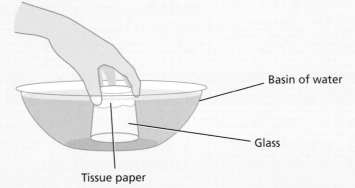

Basin of water

Glass

Tissue paper

a. Predict what will happen to the piece of tissue paper and explain your prediction.

b. Carry out the investigation.

c. Explain what you observed and draw a conclusion.

Particle Theory

The Ancient Greeks were the first to suggest that everything is made up of small **particles**. These particles are too small to be seen.

Scientists still believe that everything is made from very small particles. This idea is called **particle theory**. Particle theory is used to explain the properties of solids, liquids and gases.

Properties of Solids, Liquids and Gases

Particles in solids, liquids and gases are not still. They all have some energy, which causes them to move.

Solids, liquids and gases differ in how much energy the particles that make them up have, and how close these particles are to each other.

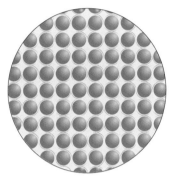

🎧 **Fig. 9.1.2**
Particles in a solid state

The Solid State

- When a substance is in the solid state, the particles that make up the substance touch because they are packed tightly together.
- The particles do not move around but they are not completely still either. They vibrate on the spot.
- This explains why solids cannot flow and have a fixed shape.

The Liquid State

- When a material is in the liquid state, the particles are very close together. The particles touch each other.
- The particles in a liquid have more energy than the particles in a solid. This means that the particles can move around and slide past each other.
- This explains why a liquid can flow and change its shape.

Viscosity is the term that is used to describe the flow rate of a liquid. For example, water is less viscous (more runny) than syrup.

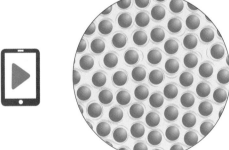

🎧 **Fig. 9.1.3**
Particles in a liquid state

Investigating the speed of liquids at different temperatures

1. Choose a variety of different liquids (for example, water, golden syrup, tomato sauce, vegetable oil, glycerine or cream). Plan, design, carry out and write up an investigation to determine which of these liquids moves (or flows) the fastest.
2. How can you make this a fair test?
3. Predict what changes you would see in your results if you cooled the liquids in the refrigerator before the investigation.
4. Compare the flow of the various liquids at room temperature and after they have been refrigerated.

The Gas State

- When a substance is in the gas state, the particles are spread out far apart from each other. There is a lot of space between particles in a gas.

- As particles in a gas move to fill the container they are in, gases do not have a fixed volume.

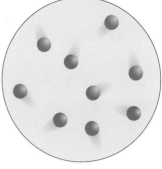

🎧 Fig. 9.1.4
Particles in a gas state

Compressing gases

We know that particles in a gas have lots of space between them.

Compression happens when particles are forced closer together to make them fit into a smaller space.

For example, the gas particles in a spray can of deodorant or hairspray are pressed together to fit into the can. When the contents of the can is sprayed, the particles can spread out again to fill the air.

We will learn more about this spreading out of gas in the next topic.

Compression of matter

Using plastic syringes, plan, design, carry out and write up an investigation to find out if it is possible to compress various solids, liquids and gases from the following list: water, sand, air, milk, flour, sugar and marshmallow. If there are other items you would like to test, include them in your investigation.

The table below gives a summary of the properties of solids, liquids and gases.

	Does the substance have a fixed mass?	Does the substance have a fixed volume?	Does the substance have a fixed shape?	Does the substance flow?	Can you compress the substance easily?
Solid	Yes	Yes	Yes	No	No
Liquid	Yes	Yes	No	Yes	No
Gas	Yes	No	No	Yes	Yes

Similarities and differences

Using four separate sets of Venn diagrams, compare and contrast the following:

a. The properties of a solid and a liquid.

b. The properties of a liquid and a gas.

c. The properties of a solid and a gas.

d. The properties of solids, liquids and gases.

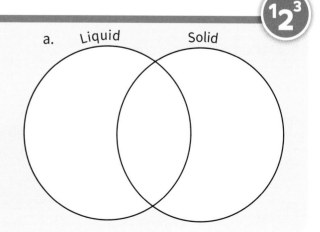

Diffusion

Learning Intentions

In this topic we are learning to:

- Model the diffusion of a gas using the particle theory.

The particle theory can also be used to explain **diffusion**. Diffusion is the spreading out of particles to fill the space they are in.

For example, if somebody spills some perfume in your classroom, your nose will soon pick up the smell. The smell of the perfume quickly spreads through the room. However, you cannot see any perfume in the air.

Perfume is made up of small particles. It has a low boiling point and easily becomes a gas at room temperature.

Diffusion happens by itself. You do not need to mix or stir the substances.

Diffusion in gas

1. Spray some perfume at the top of the classroom.

   a. Predict which students will be the first to smell the perfume.

   b. Predict how long it will take for all the students in the room to smell the perfume.

2. Draw a diagram to explain how the smell of the perfume reached your nose (remember to include the air particles that also fill the room).

➲ Fig. 9.2.1

Diffusion in liquids

In small groups, set up the investigation shown in Fig. 9.2.2. Your aim is to determine if the temperature of the water has any effect on how the food dye moves in the water.

1. Before you start, predict the results of this investigation and explain your prediction.

2. What will you do to make this investigation a fair test?

3. What did you observe when food colouring was placed in each cup?

4. Explain what happened using the particle model.

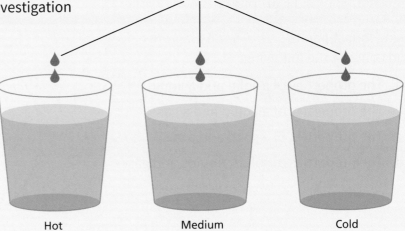

➲ Fig. 9.2.2

Food dye

Hot   Medium   Cold

Diffusion of different substances does not happen at the same speed. Three factors affect the speed of diffusion:

1. Temperature: the higher the temperature of the gas or liquid, the more energy the particles will have and the faster they will diffuse.

2. Size of the particles: smaller particles move quicker than larger particles when the temperature is the same.

3. State of the diffusing substance:
   - In gases, diffusion happens quickly because the particles are far apart.
   - In liquids, diffusion happens slowly because particles are closer together and there is more chance of the particles hitting each other.
   - Diffusion does not happen in solids as the particles do not move.

🎧 **Fig. 9.2.3**
Diffusion in a liquid

Diffusion in air

Air contains particles of argon, nitrogen, carbon dioxide and oxygen.

The relative mass of each particle is:

Argon = 40
Nitrogen = 28
Carbon dioxide = 44
Oxygen = 32

Put the particles in order of how quickly they diffuse, starting with the particle that diffuses the fastest. Give a reason for your answer.

I smell dinner!

At dinnertime, you and your little brother notice that you can smell your dinner cooking in the kitchen, even though you are upstairs in your bedrooms. Your little brother thinks this is magic, but you know it is actually science.

Use diagrams to explain how you can smell dinner cooking in the kitchen if you are upstairs.

⮌ **Fig. 9.2.4**

Changes of State

Key Words

Melting
Boiling
Physical change
Melting point
Freezing
Evaporation
Boiling point
Condensation
Sublimation

Learning Intentions

In this topic we are learning to:

- Use the particle theory to explain changes of state involving solids, liquids and gases.
- Explain the following terms: melting, boiling, evaporation, condensation, freezing and sublimation.
- Interpret data to find out the state of a substance at various temperatures.

When solids are heated, their particles gain energy and move apart. The particles break free from their fixed positions and start to move past each other. The solid changes to a liquid. When a solid changes to a liquid it is called **melting**.

When a liquid is heated, the particles gain even more energy and break free from each other. The liquid turns into a gas. When a liquid turns into a gas it is called **boiling**.

These changes are called physical changes. In a **physical change**, no new substance is formed, there is no change in mass and the reaction can be easily reversed.

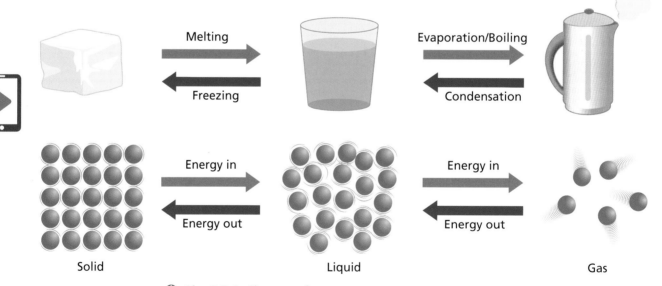

◑ Fig. 9.3.1 Changes of state

Melting and Freezing

What happens when an ice cube melts? The heat causes the water particles that make up the ice to vibrate faster. The solid ice cube changes state to become liquid water. The temperature a substance melts at is called its **melting point**. The melting point of ice is 0 °C.

Cooling a liquid takes energy from its particles so they can only vibrate, not move around. The liquid freezes into a solid. When a liquid changes into a solid it is called **freezing**. The freezing point of water is 0 °C.

Evaporation and Boiling

Both evaporation and boiling will cause a change of state from a liquid to a gas. However, they take place slightly differently.

In a liquid, some particles have more energy than others. The particles with the most energy leave the surface, spread out and form a gas. This is called **evaporation**. The liquid does not bubble and evaporation happens at all temperatures.

For example, on a rainy day puddles form. When the Sun comes out, the puddles dry up. This is due to evaporation. The water particles at the surface of the puddle gain enough energy to escape as gases.

Evaporation

Boiling

 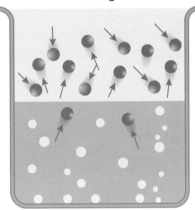

C **Fig. 9.3.2**
The differences between boiling and evaporation

In the case of boiling, all particles in the liquid are involved – they all have enough energy to break free. The temperature at which a liquid changes to a gas is called the **boiling point**. The boiling point of water is 100 °C.

Evaporation is slower than boiling, but the overall result of a liquid changing to a gas is the same.

Hanging out the washing

In good weather, washed clothes can be hung outside to dry. For wet washing to dry, the liquid water particles need to be changed to gas particles and be moved away from the washing.

Use diagrams to explain why washing dries more quickly on a warm and windy day.

C **Fig. 9.3.3**
Washing drying on a line

Investigating evaporation rates

In groups, discuss how you might carry out the following tasks. Choose one investigation to write up. Share your findings with the other groups in your class.

Part 1

Given the following fabrics – cotton, wool, polyester and acrylic – plan, design, carry out and write up an investigation to find out which fabric will dry the fastest.

Part 2

Given the following liquids – water, milk, salty water and syrup – plan, design, carry out and write up an investigation to find out which liquid will evaporate the quickest at room temperature.

Part 3

Given the following containers – a cup, a beaker, a saucer and a plate – plan, design, carry out and write up an investigation to find out how the shape of the object affects the evaporation rate.

Solid, liquid or gas?

If you know the melting point and the boiling point of a substance you can predict the state it will be in at room temperature (room temperature is approximately 20 °C).

Using the table below, list the state of each substance at room temperature.

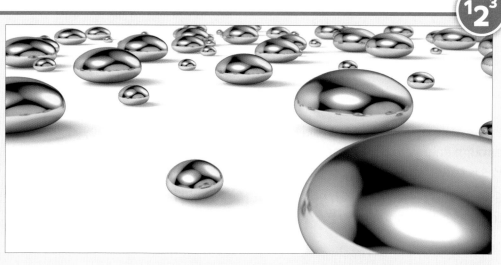

⋒ **Fig. 9.3.4**
Mercury droplets

Substance	Melting point (°C)	Boiling point (°C)	State at room temperature
Water	0	100	
Ethanol	−114	78	
Propanol	−126	97	
Gallium	30	2,205	
Gold	1,063	2,970	
Oxygen	−218	−183	
Mercury	−39	357	

Construct a graph of the ranges of the melting and boiling points for the substances listed in the table above.

Interpreting evaporation data

Miriam is investigating evaporation. She takes a small damp tissue and places it in the garden shed. She hangs a big wet towel beside a heater. The tissue in the shed dries first. Miriam comes to the conclusion that cold conditions speed up evaporation.

1. How could Miriam improve her investigation?
2. Does the evidence support her conclusion? Why?

Condensation

Cooling a gas takes energy from its particles so they slow down and move closer together. The gas condenses to a liquid. This is called **condensation**.

'Foggy' windows

Explain why windows of a car 'fog up' on a cold, wet day.

⮕ Fig. 9.3.5

Sublimation

When some substances are heated, they do not melt but turn straight into a gas. They do not form a liquid. This is called **sublimation**.

For example, carbon dioxide is solid at temperatures below −78.5 °C.

At this temperature and above, solid carbon dioxide changes state to become a gas. It does not normally exist as a liquid.

Solid carbon dioxide is also known as 'dry ice' and is often used for special effects at concerts.

↻ Fig. 9.3.6
Dry ice

Properties of Materials

Key Words

Properties
Product life cycle
Carbon footprint
Recycling

Learning Intentions

In this topic we are learning to:

- Investigate the properties of various materials.
- Conduct research on the recycling habits of your classmates.

The features and behaviour of a material are called its **properties**. Materials have different properties, which make them useful for different jobs.

The following table shows the properties of different materials and explains what they mean.

Property	Meaning	Opposite
Absorbent	The material is able to soak up liquid easily	Waterproof
Elastic	The material can stretch and then return to shape	Rigid
Flexible	The material can bend without breaking	Rigid
Transparent	You can see through the material	Opaque
Strong	The material cannot be broken easily	Weak

Investigating the properties of materials

1. In small groups, gather a variety of materials from home and the classroom, such as a plastic and a wooden ruler, a fork, a cup, a rubber glove, a towel and a ball.

2. Develop and carry out a series of investigations to find out if the material each object is made of is:
   - Absorbent or waterproof
   - Elastic or rigid
   - Flexible or rigid
   - Transparent or opaque
   - Strong or weak

3. Record your results in one table.

Product Life Cycle

All products go through five steps during their production. This is called the **product life cycle**.

1. Extraction (removal) of raw materials
2. Manufacturing
3. Packaging and distribution
4. Product use
5. End-of-life disposal

All the steps in the product life cycle have some type of environmental impact.

1. Extraction of raw materials

2. Manufacturing

3. Packaging and distribution

4. Product use

5. End-of-life disposal

Environmental Impact of Producing Materials

The production of materials can have a negative impact on our world.

During each step of the product life cycle, damage is caused to our environment. For example, the extraction of materials could result in raw material sources being used up for future generations.

All stages of the process could release carbon dioxide into the atmosphere. This adds to global warming (also known as the 'greenhouse effect').

The total greenhouse gas emissions caused by an organisation, event, product or individual is known as its **carbon footprint**.

When companies make plans for a new product, they must think about and try to reduce the impact it will have on the environment.

GO Learn more about global warming in Earth and Space 25.2

'Emission'

Any substance that is released into the air (atmosphere) is called an emission. Emissions can be harmful.

For example, sulfur dioxide is an emission when iron is produced. Sulfur dioxide can cause acid rain.

Recycling

We have taken steps to reduce waste by reusing or **recycling** whatever materials we can.

Recycling reduces the need to extract raw materials.

Recycling means taking an unwanted object and reusing the materials it is made of. Paper, glass, metal and plastic can all be recycled.

As recycling still involves the transportation, sorting, cleaning and remaking of a new object, it also has a small negative impact on the environment.

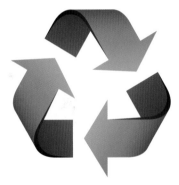

🎧 Fig. 9.4.2
Recycling symbol

Teenagers and recycling

Complete a written report on recycling habits among your classmates. Conduct research to determine their attitudes towards recycling and what and how they recycle.

1. Design a questionnaire that you can use to collect data on recycling.
2. Ask ten classmates to complete the questionnaire.
3. Analyse and present your data. What type of data is it? How will you present this data?

 GO Learn more about waste management in Earth and Space 25.3

Physical Change Versus Chemical Change

Learning Intentions

In this topic we are learning to:

- Distinguish between physical and chemical changes.
- Investigate whether mass is changed or unchanged when chemical and physical changes take place.
- Verify the law of conservation of mass.

Matter can undergo physical and chemical changes.

- In a **physical change**, matter changes shape or state but no new substance is formed. Changing states, such as melting or boiling, are physical changes.
- In a **chemical change**, a new substance is formed. All chemical reactions are examples of a chemical change.

The table below shows the differences between chemical and physical changes.

Physical changes	Chemical changes
No new substance is formed	A new substance is formed
Easy to reverse	Not easy to reverse

The Law of Conservation of Mass

The **law of conservation of mass** states that matter cannot be created or destroyed but can change from one form to another. In both physical and chemical changes, the total mass of matter stays the same.

Physical or chemical change?

With a partner, classify the following as either an example of a physical or a chemical change. Explain the reasons for your conclusion. (Hint: has a new substance been made? Is the reaction reversible?)

Boiling water in a kettle	Burning wood in an open fire
A ball breaking a glass window	Fireworks exploding
Lighting a candle	Tearing up a sheet of paper
Baking a cake	Sugar dissolving in water
Ice cream melting	Photosynthesis
Crushing up a plastic bottle	A snowman melting
An iron nail rusting	Getting a haircut
Dyeing your hair blonde	

Fig. 9.5.1
Fireworks exploding

Observing and distinguishing between physical and chemical changes

Part 1

Carry out the following short tasks and find out if a physical or a chemical change is taking place. Copy and complete this table.

Predict: Will it be a chemical or a physical change?	Activity	Observations	Physical or chemical change?	Explain why it is an example of a physical or a chemical change
	Add drops of water to a teaspoon of salt			
	Add drops of vinegar to a teaspoon of baking soda			
	Heat some candle wax on a metal lid (do not let the wax catch fire)			
	Heat a cracker in a Bunsen burner flame			
	Heat a piece of steel wool in a Bunsen burner flame			

Part 2

1. Place some ice cubes in a sealable plastic bag. Measure the mass of the ice cubes and the bag. Set the bag aside until the ice cubes have melted.
2. Predict whether the total mass of the bag and the ice will have increased, decreased or stayed the same.
3. Find the mass of the plastic bag once all the ice has melted.
4. Explain your result. Is this a physical or a chemical change? Explain your conclusion.

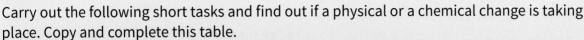

⊃ Fig. 9.5.2 Ice cubes melting

Part 3

1. Pour 20 cm³ of vinegar into a large sealable plastic bag and find the mass of the bag and the vinegar.
2. Measure out 5 g of baking soda and wrap the baking soda in a small sheet of tissue paper. Find the mass of the tissue paper and the baking soda.
3. Calculate the mass of the tissue paper and the baking soda plus the mass of the vinegar and the sealable bag. Record the total mass in your Portfolio.
4. Drop the tissue paper into the bag of vinegar and seal it quickly. Before you do this, predict whether the total mass of the bag, the vinegar, the tissue paper and the baking soda will have increased, decreased or stayed the same.
5. Once the reaction has stopped, find the mass of the bag. Explain your result. Is this a physical or a chemical change? Explain your conclusion.
6. Why is it recommended that you use a larger bag?

Ahhhh, fizz

When you open can of fizzy drink, does the mass of the drink increase, decrease or stay the same? Is there a chemical or a physical change taking place?

⊃ Fig. 9.5.3 A can of fizzy drink being opened

Chapter Summary

- Materials are made up of tiny particles.
- Matter is anything that takes up space and has a mass.
- There are three states of matter: solid, liquid and gas.
- Solids have a fixed mass, a fixed volume and a definite shape. They cannot flow and they cannot be compressed.
- Liquids have a fixed mass, a fixed volume and an indefinite shape. They can flow and they cannot be compressed.
- Gases have a fixed mass, an indefinite volume and an indefinite shape. They can flow and they can be compressed.
- The change of state from a solid to a liquid is called melting. The temperature at which a substance melts is called its melting point.
- A substance changes from a liquid to a gas by either boiling or evaporation. The temperature at which a substance boils is called its boiling point.
- The change of state from a gas to a liquid is called condensation.
- The change of state from a liquid to a solid is called freezing.
- Sublimation is when a solid changes directly into a gas without going through the liquid state.
- Diffusion is the spreading out of particles to fill a space.
- Materials have different properties that make them useful for different jobs.
- A physical change is one in which no new substance is formed. A physical change can be reversed easily.
- A chemical change is one in which a new substance is formed. A chemical change cannot be reversed easily.
- The law of conservation of mass states that matter cannot be created or destroyed but can change from one form to another.
- In both physical and chemical changes, the total mass of the matter involved stays the same.

The BIG Challenge

Using your phone or a digital camera and some modelling clay, put together a short digital animation (approximately 30 seconds long) showing how a change of state from a solid to a liquid to a gas can be explained using the particle theory.

Tips

- Script your animation before you start.
- Keep the camera in the same position each time by using a retort stand.
- Use a maximum of eight pictures to begin with.
- Use a maximum of 12 particles in the model of the solid, liquid and gas.
- Share the animation with the rest of your class. Discuss which animation best helped you to understand the science of particle theory.

Go to your Portfolio to check what you have learned in this chapter.

Take the chapter 9 quiz on educateplus.ie.

Questions

1. Copy and fill in the blanks.
   a. There are three states of matter: _____ , _____ and _____ .
   b. The particles in a solid are packed _____ together. The particles are in a fixed position but they do _____ .
   c. The particles in a liquid can _____ past each other. This allows liquids to _____ .
   d. The particles in a gas are _____ far apart. As a result of this, gases can be _____ .
   e. _____ is the spreading out of particles to fill the space they are in.
   f. A _____ _____ is one in which a new substance is formed. An example of such a change is _____ .
   g. A _____ _____ is one in which no new substance is formed. An example of such a change is _____ .
   h. The law of conservation of mass states that _____ cannot be _____ or _____ .

2. Describe an activity that you carried out in the laboratory to show that a gas takes up space and has a mass.

3. Using the particle theory, explain why it is possible to pour a liquid but not a solid.

4. a. Using the diagram below, name arrows D, E, F, and G with the appropriate phase change (e.g. D = freezing).

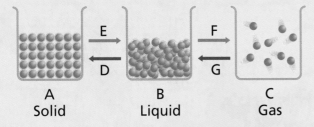

A	B	C
Solid	Liquid	Gas

   b. Which arrows indicate the energy being added?
   c. Which arrows indicate the energy being taken away?

5. Explain, using diagrams, three ways a substance can change from a solid to a gas.

6. Explain why it is quicker to dry your hair with a hairdryer than to let it dry naturally.

7. A student sets up the following investigation to find out if the mass of a substance increases, decreases or stays the same when it goes from a solid to a liquid (i.e. melts).

   a. Before the student started, they put some film over the top of the beaker. Why did they do this?
   b. During the investigation, the student noticed some drops of water on the outside of the beaker. How did these water droplets get there?
   c. The student decided to dry the outside of the beaker before getting the final mass of the beaker after all the ice had melted. Was this the correct thing to do?
   d. Did the mass of the overall set-up (the beaker, the film and the ice) increase, decrease or stay the same after the ice had melted to water? Explain your answer.

8. State which of the changes listed below are examples of a chemical change and which are examples of a physical change.
   a. Burning diesel in the engine of a car.
   b. Dissolving sugar in coffee to make it taste sweet.
   c. Lighting a firework.
   d. Cutting paper.
   e. Adding carbon dioxide to drinks to make them fizzy.
   f. Using bacteria to make yoghurt from milk.

   In examples a–f, explain why it is either a physical or a chemical change.

Working as a Scientist

Presenting and Analysing Data

Investigating Changes of State

Freda and Paul have been learning about changes of state. They are using some of the ideas they learned about in topic 9.3 to investigate the temperature changes that occur over time when a solid is heated to its gaseous form.

Freda and Paul decide to use ice for this investigation. They collect the equipment they need and carry out the investigation as follows:

> **Step 1:** Place the crushed ice straight from the freezer into the beaker.
>
> **Step 2:** Put the thermometer into the ice.
>
> **Step 3:** Start to heat the beaker of ice with a Bunsen burner.
>
> **Step 4:** Record the temperature on the thermometer every minute.
>
> **Step 5:** Continue until the ice has melted into water and the water has boiled for a few minutes.

1 Draw the investigation set-up that Freda and Paul would have used. Remember to label your diagram.

2 Freda and Paul had the option of using an alcohol thermometer or a digital thermometer. What advice would you give them when choosing one over the other?

3 What safety precautions should Freda and Paul have observed during the investigation?

The following is the data set that Freda and Paul collected during this investigation.

Time	0	1	2	3	4	5	6	7	8	9	10	11	12
Temperature	−5	−2	0	0	15	31	45	60	75	90	100	100	100

Freda and Paul's teacher was happy with the investigation they carried out, but had one tip for them on how to improve their results table.

4 Can you see how Freda and Paul might have improved their results table?

After completing their results table, Freda and Paul decided to represent their data on a graph. Before graphing their data, Freda reminded Paul of the hints their teacher had given them for drawing graphs:

- Make sure that the scale on each axis is correct.
- Label the *x*-axis and the *y*-axis and do not forget to include units.
- Plot the points and join the points together.
- Always make sure that the graph has a title.
- Always put the quantity that you control on the *x*-axis.

5 What type of graph would you suggest they use and why?

6 Draw the graph that Freda and Paul would have drawn.

Freda and Paul's teacher then asked them to comment on the shape of the graph they had just drawn.

7 List as many things as possible about the shape of the graph you have just drawn.

Freda and Paul noted that on their graph there were horizontal parts at 0 °C and another at 100 °C.

8 Can you suggest what the heat energy being supplied by the Bunsen burner is being used for at these two temperatures?

After discussion, Freda and Paul spoke to their teacher about their findings. She explained to them that what they observed was a type of heat called latent heat. Latent heat is heat that causes a change of state and not a change in temperature.

When heat is applied by the Bunsen burner, the temperature usually rises. However, when heat causes a change in state (solid to liquid or liquid to gas) and not a change in temperature it is latent heat. It is the heat needed to turn a solid to a liquid and a liquid to a gas.

'Latent'

The word 'latent' comes from Latin *latēns*, meaning 'lying hidden'.

Freda and Paul wanted to carry out the investigation again using another substance in order to see if this hypothesis held true for all substances.

9 How would Freda and Paul make sure that this was a fair comparison with the results they got for water?

Freda and Paul's teacher suggested that they use a substance called lauric acid. This is a solid at room temperature. Here are the results collected by Freda and Paul for the lauric acid:

Time (mins)	0	1	2	3	4	5	6	7	8	9	10
Temperature (°C)	75	64	54	45	45	45	45	45	35	22	12

10 Looking at the results above, did Freda and Paul carry out the two investigations in the same manner? Explain your answer.

11 Is it possible for the data sets for the water and lauric acid to be included on the same graph? Explain your answer.

Chapter 10

The Building Blocks of the Chemical World

What you may already know:

- Atoms are very small particles. They are so small they cannot be seen with the naked eye.
- Elements and compounds have symbols. The chemical symbol for water is H_2O.
- The periodic table is a list of all known elements.
- Examples of metals are iron and copper.

What you will learn in this chapter:

- How to build a model of the atom and use it to explain the structure of an atom.
- What an element is and to recognise the symbols for various elements.
- How to use the periodic table to explain some of the properties of elements.
- How to tell the difference between metals and non-metals and list the properties of each.

Think BIG

- How do chemists use the periodic table?
- Why are some metals more expensive than other metals?

Puzzler

Can you solve this puzzle?

Which two letters of the alphabet do not appear on the modern periodic table on page 462?

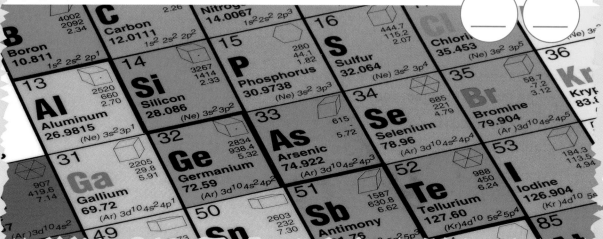

Atoms and Elements

Learning Intentions

In this topic we are learning to:

- Outline how our understanding of matter has evolved over time.
- Explain what an element is.
- Identify the chemical symbols for a number of elements.

An **atom** is a tiny particle.

Atoms are far too small to see with only a light microscope. Scientists have to use very powerful electron microscopes to get a closer look at atoms.

Early Ideas About Atoms

Over time, scientists have gained a greater understanding of the structure of atoms.

More than 2,000 years ago, some Ancient Greeks suggested that everything was made up of four elements: earth, air, fire and water. However, they did not investigate this idea scientifically.

Key Words

Atom
Element
Chemical symbol

GO Learn more about electron microscopes in Biological World 1.3

↪ **Fig. 10.1.1**
Ancient elements

Over 200 years ago, the chemist John Dalton developed a theory about atoms. Unlike the Ancient Greeks, Dalton based his ideas on investigations he carried out.

- Dalton was the first to suggest that everything is made up of tiny particles called atoms.
- Dalton also suggested that some substances are made up of atoms that are the same as each other.
- Dalton was able to use his theory to explain the wide variety of substances on Earth. He stated that atoms could join together in different ways to make new substances.

Thanks to Dalton's theory, we now have a very simple and useful definition of an **element**.

🎧 **Fig. 10.1.2**
John Dalton

173

Elements

An element is a substance made up of only one type of atom.

For example, gold is an element, as it is made up of only gold atoms. Nitrogen is also an element, as it is made up of only nitrogen atoms.

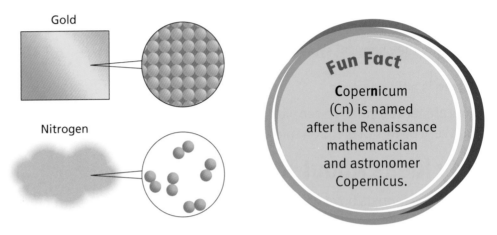

⊃ Fig. 10.1.3
Gold and nitrogen are elements

Fun Fact

Copernicum (Cn) is named after the Renaissance mathematician and astronomer Copernicus.

There are over 100 known elements. They are listed in the periodic table, which we will look at later in the chapter.

All material – everything we use – is made from these elements. Elements exist as solids, liquids or gases.

People and Science

Robert Boyle was a seventeenth-century scientist and inventor. He was born in Lismore, County Waterford.

Boyle was one of the pioneers of the modern scientific method. In 1661, he was the first scientist to suggest the name 'element'.

⊃ Fig. 10.1.4
Robert Boyle

Chemical Symbols

'Au'

The Latin word *aurum* means 'yellow'. This explains why the symbol for the element gold is Au.

Each element has its own name and **chemical symbol**. Scientists all over the world use these symbols for each element.

- Most of the symbols are based on the English name of the element.
- Some symbols are based on their Latin names.
- Other symbols are named after the scientists who discovered them.

When writing the chemical symbol for an element, we use a capital letter. If the symbol has a second letter, it is always a small letter.

Researching elements

Look at the names of elements and their symbols below and answer the following questions:

1. Which elements have symbols based on their Latin names?
2. Why is the symbol for silicon Si and not S?

Element	Symbol	Element	Symbol
Hydrogen	H	Sulfur	S
Helium	He	Iron	Fe
Nitrogen	N	Copper	Cu
Neon	Ne	Lead	Pb
Oxygen	O	Gold	Au
Silicon	Si	Sodium	Na
Chlorine	Cl	Potassium	K

🎧 **Fig. 10.1.5**
The chemical symbol for silicon

3. Research lead (Pb). How did this element get its name? What job got its name from this element and why? Why is this element no longer used in this trade?

An abundance of elements

The following table shows the percentages of the different elements in the rocks of the Earth's crust. Look at this data and discuss it with your class.

1. Construct a graph to represent this data.
2. Why is the type of graph you have chosen appropriate?
3. What other type of graph would be suitable and why?

Element	Percentage
Oxygen	48
Silicon	25
Aluminium	8
Iron	6
Calcium	4
Sodium	3
Potassium	2
Magnesium	2
Other	2

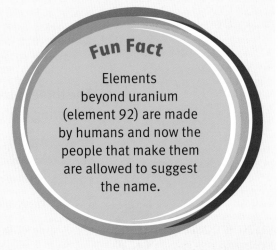

Fun Fact

Elements beyond uranium (element 92) are made by humans and now the people that make them are allowed to suggest the name.

Subatomic Particles

Learning Intentions

In this topic we are learning to:

- Calculate the number of protons, neutrons and electrons in an atom using the atomic number and mass number.
- Classify protons, neutrons and electrons in terms of mass, charge and location in the atom.

Inside the Atom

While Dalton's ideas about atoms are very useful, he was wrong in thinking that atoms could not be broken into smaller pieces.

After many scientific investigations, we now know that an atom is made up of even smaller particles called **subatomic particles**.

The atom is made up of three subatomic particles:

- **Protons**
- **Neutrons**
- **Electrons**

'Atom'

The word 'atom' comes from the Greek for 'cannot be divided'.

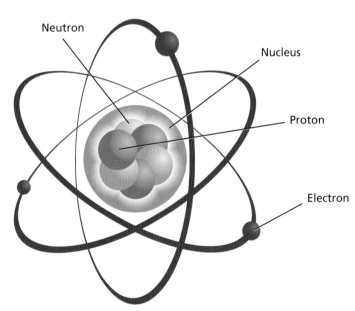

⊃ **Fig. 10.2.1**
Atomic structure

The three subatomic particles are quite different from each other. The following table summarises the properties of the three subatomic particles.

Subatomic particle	Mass	Charge	Location in the atom
Proton	1	Positive (+1)	Nucleus
Neutron	1	Neutral (0)	Nucleus
Electron	1/1,836	Negative (−1)	Orbiting the nucleus

Remembering charge

Protons are *positive* and *neutrons* are *neutral*.

Note that:

- Protons and neutrons have the same mass.
- Electrons have so little mass that scientists treat their mass as zero. It takes almost 2,000 electrons to have the same mass as a proton or a neutron.

How our understanding of atoms evolved

Using the following information, create a timeline for your classroom showing how our understanding of atoms has evolved over time.

1913: Niels Bohr suggests that electrons are found in shells around the nucleus.

1909: Ernest Rutherford discovers the proton.

400 BC: Democritus suggests that all things are made of particles.

1931: Ernest Walton and John Cockcroft discover that the nuclei of atoms can be split to form new elements.

1932: James Chadwick proves that neutrons exist.

1911: Ernest Rutherford discovers the nucleus.

1805: John Dalton suggests that atoms of the same element are alike.

1897: J. J. Thomson discovers the electron.

Today: Research on the structure of the atom is taking place at CERN, the European Organization for Nuclear Research, in Switzerland.

Atomic and Mass Numbers

Atoms of each element have a specific number of protons, neutrons and electrons.

The **atomic number** is the number of protons in the atom of that element.

The number of protons is equal to the number of electrons in neutral atoms. They are neutral because the number of positive charges (protons) and the number of negative charges (electrons) are equal.

The **mass number** is the total number of protons and neutrons in an atom.

For example, Fig. 10.2.2 tells us the following information about an atom of lithium:

- Lithium has 3 protons.
- Lithium has 3 electrons (the positive and the negative charges are equal, so if lithium has 3 protons it must have 3 electrons).
- The total number of protons and neutrons in an atom of lithium is 7.
- Lithium has 4 neutrons (to calculate the number of neutrons in an atom you need to subtract the atomic number (for lithium, this is 3) from the mass number (for lithium, this is 7).

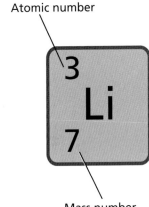

Atomic number

Mass number

🎧 **Fig. 10.2.2**
The atomic number and mass number of lithium. Note that the atomic number is always the smaller number.

Making connections

Use the periodic table to complete the table below.

Atomic number	Mass number	Number of protons	Number of neutrons	Number of electrons	Name of element	Symbol of element
6	13					
	24	12				
	40			20		
13			14			
	56	26				Fe

Atomic Structure

People and Science

Niels Bohr won the Nobel Prize in Physics in 1922 for his 'services in the investigation of the structure of atoms and of the radiation emanating from them'.

🎧 Fig. 10.3.1
Niels Bohr

Learning Intentions

In this topic we are learning to:

- Develop a model to help explain the basic structure of an atom.
- Reflect on the contribution of Niels Bohr to atomic theory.

Electronic Configuration

Danish scientist Niels Bohr came up with the idea of electron shells to explain **atomic structure**.

Electron shells are the spaces where electrons orbit. The shells are also called energy levels.

- The first shell (the one closest to the nucleus) has space for 2 electrons.
- The second shell has space for up to 8 electrons.
- The third shell also has space for up 8 electrons.

The electrons fill up the shells from the inner shells out.

Describing the location of electrons in an atom is called the **electronic configuration**.

Figure 10.3.2 shows the Bohr atomic models for nitrogen and sodium.

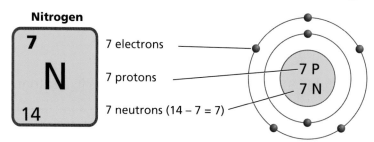

There are 7 electrons in total: 2 in the first shell and 5 in the second shell.

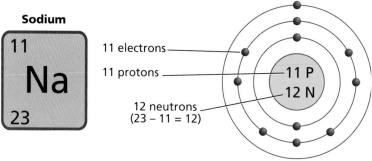

⮐ Fig. 10.3.2
Bohr models of nitrogen and sodium

There are 11 electrons in total: 2 in the first shell, 8 in the second shell and 1 in the third shell.

Scientists do not draw a model of an atom every time. They use a shorthand version of the electronic configuration showing the number of electrons in each shell, working outwards from the nucleus.

For example, the shorthand versions of nitrogen and sodium are:

- Nitrogen: N: 2, 5
- Sodium: Na: 2, 8, 1

Electronic configurations

Part 1

Using materials provided by your teacher, use the information on page 178 to create Bohr atomic models of the elements shown in Fig. 10.3.3.

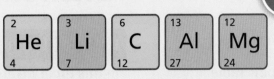

🎧 **Fig. 10.3.3**

Part 2

Write the shorthand version of the electronic configuration for the same elements.

Isotopes

The atoms of some elements can exist with different masses. The number of protons in the atoms of the element is the same, but the number of neutrons differ.

Atoms with the same number of protons but different numbers of neutrons are called **isotopes**. For example, carbon can have three isotopes.

➲ **Fig. 10.3.4**
The three possible isotopes of carbon

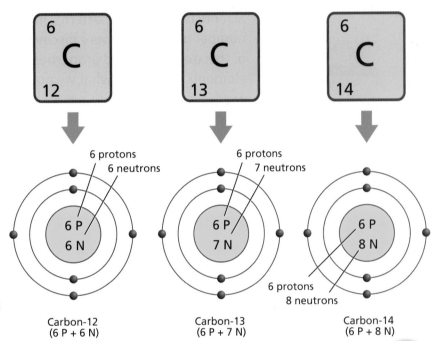

Carbon-12
(6 P + 6 N)

Carbon-13
(6 P + 7 N)

Carbon-14
(6 P + 8 N)

Comparing isotopes

1. In pairs, discuss what the atoms in Fig. 10.3.4 have in common.

2. Make a model of the nuclei of the three isotopes in Fig. 10.3.4. What materials would be most appropriate to use for these models?

3. Discuss how these atoms differ from each other.

4. You may have met one of these forms of carbon in your history class. Which one? Write a paragraph to explain how this isotope of carbon is useful to historians.

Isotopes of chlorine

Two isotopes of chlorine exist: Cl–35 and Cl–37. Using the periodic table, answer the following questions:

1. What is the atomic number of chlorine?

2. How many protons, neutrons and electrons does the isotope Cl–35 have?

3. How many protons, neutrons and electrons does the isotope Cl–37 have?

4. What do the two isotopes have in common?

5. How do the two isotopes differ?

6. Draw the Bohr model of the atom for each isotope.

7. Write out the electronic configuration for each isotope.

The Periodic Table of the Elements

Key Words

Periodic table
Groups
Periods

Learning Intentions

In this topic we are learning to:

- Outline the contribution of John Newlands and Dmitri Mendeleev in developing the periodic table.
- Describe and explain the structure of the periodic table.

Scientists like to find patterns. In the nineteenth century, a large number of elements were discovered. Scientists noticed that some of these elements had properties in common, so they arranged the elements to develop what we now know as the **periodic table**.

The modern periodic table groups elements to show patterns in their properties.

The Alkali Metals (Group 1); The Alkaline Earth Metals (Group 2); The Halogens (Group 7); The Noble Gases (Group 8)

Metals | Non-metals

	Group 1	Group 2											Group 3	Group 4	Group 5	Group 6	Group 7	Group 8
1st Period			1 H hydrogen 1															2 He helium 4
2nd Period	3 Li lithium 7	4 Be beryllium 9											5 B boron 11	6 C carbon 12	7 N nitrogen 14	8 O oxygen 16	9 F fluorine 19	10 Ne neon 20
3rd Period	11 Na sodium 23	12 Mg magnesium 24											13 Al aluminium 27	14 Si silicon 28	15 P phosphorus 31	16 S sulfur 32	17 Cl chlorine 35.5	18 Ar argon 40
4th Period	19 K potassium 39	20 Ca calcium 40	21 Sc scandium 45	22 Ti titanium 48	23 V vanadium 51	24 Cr chromium 52	25 Mn manganese 55	26 Fe iron 56	27 Co cobalt 59	28 Ni nickel 59	29 Cu copper 63.5	30 Zn zinc 65	31 Ga gallium 70	32 Ge germanium 73	33 As arsenic 75	34 Se selenium 79	35 Br bromine 80	36 Kr krypton 84
5th Period	37 Rb rubidium 85	38 Sr strontium 88	39 Y yttrium 89	40 Zr zirconium 91	41 Nb niobium 93	42 Mo molybdenum 96	43 Tc technetium (98)	44 Ru ruthenium 101	45 Rh rhodium 103	46 Pd palladium 106	47 Ag silver 108	48 Cd cadmium 112	49 In indium 115	50 Sn tin 119	51 Sb antimony 122	52 Te tellurium 128	53 I iodine 127	54 Xe xenon 131
6th Period	55 Cs caesium 133	56 Ba barium 137	57 La lanthanum 139	72 Hf hafnium 178.5	73 Ta tantalum 181	74 W tungsten 184	75 Re rhenium 186	76 Os osmium 190	77 Ir iridium 192	78 Pt platinum 195	79 Au gold 197	80 Hg mercury 201	81 Tl thallium 204	82 Pb lead 207	83 Bi bismuth 209	84 Po polonium 209	85 At astatine 210	86 Rn radon 222
7th Period	87 Fr francium 223	88 Ra radium 226	89 Ac actinium 227	104 Rf rutherfordium 261	105 Db dubnium 262	106 Sg seaborgium 266	107 Bh bohrium 264	108 Hs hassium 269	109 Mt meitnerium 268	110 Ds darmstadtium 269	111 Rg roentgenium 272	112 Cn copernicium 277	113 Uut ununtrium unknown	114 Fl flerovium 289	115 Uup ununpentium unknown	116 Lv livermorium 298	117 Uus ununseptium unknown	118 Uuo ununoctium unknown

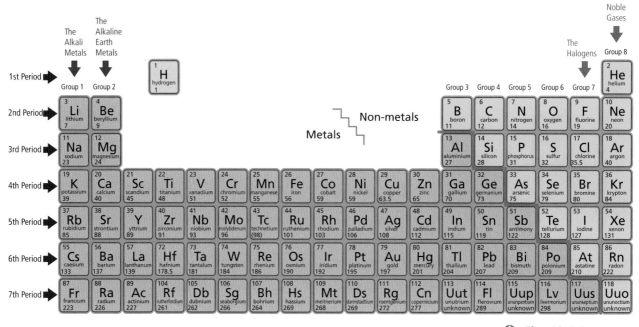

Fig. 10.4.1 The periodic table

Finding the Pattern

In 1829, German scientist Johann Döbereiner started trying to put elements into smaller subgroups. Through investigation, he observed that some elements had similar properties to each other. He put elements in groups of three – these groups were called 'triads'. One of his triads included chlorine, bromine and iodine, as they behaved in similar ways during chemical reactions. As more elements were discovered that did not fit into Döbereiner's groups, his ideas were no longer accepted.

Fig. 10.4.2 John Newlands

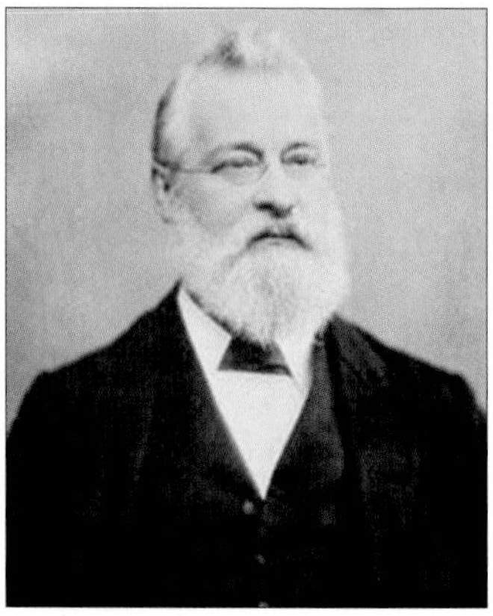

Real progress in organising the elements was made in 1865 by an English scientist called John Newlands. Newlands put the elements in order of the mass of the atoms of each element. He placed the element with the smallest atomic mass first and found that every eighth element had similar properties. Unfortunately, this pattern only worked for the first 15 elements.

When Newlands presented his work on organising the elements, other scientists made fun of his system. Some suggested that he could have done a better job by sorting the elements in alphabetical order.

In 1869, this problem was solved by a Russian chemist called Dmitri Mendeleev. Mendeleev also put the elements in order of the mass of the atoms of each element. He constructed a table of regular (periodic) patterns and lined up elements that had similar properties. He left gaps for elements that had yet to be discovered and was able to use his periodic table to predict the properties of these undiscovered elements.

Scientists were doubtful of Mendeleev's version of the periodic table until 1886, when the element germanium was discovered. Mendeleev had predicted the properties of germanium correctly using his version of the table.

🎧 **Fig. 10.4.3**
Dmitri Mendeleev

The Modern Periodic Table

The modern periodic table has no gaps. There are also more elements in the modern periodic table than in Mendeleev's periodic table.

Elements in the modern periodic table are not arranged by the mass of atoms of the elements. They are arranged in order of increasing atomic number. This means that the element hydrogen, whose atoms have one proton, comes first in the periodic table, and so on.

Groups

Groups are the vertical columns of elements. There are eight groups in the periodic table. All the elements in a group have similar properties. If you look back at Fig. 10.4.1, you can see that some groups have a specific name:

Group 1: The alkali metals **Group 2:** The alkaline earth metals

Group 7: The halogens **Group 8:** The noble gases

Germanium ⓐⓑⓒ

Find out how the element germanium got its name. (Hint: think of a country with a similar-sounding name.)

🎧 **Fig. 10.4.4**
Germanium

Patterns within groups 1 2 3

1. Using what you learned about electronic configurations earlier in 10.3, draw or write the electronic configurations for the following elements:

   Group 1: Lithium, sodium and potassium

   Group 2: Beryllium, magnesium and calcium

   Group 7: Fluorine, chlorine and bromine

   Group 8: Neon and argon

2. Do you notice any pattern that would explain why each element is in the group they are in?

Fun Fact

Four new elements – 113, 115, 117 and 118 – were officially added to the periodic table in early 2016, filling the seventh period.

Periods

Periods are the horizontal rows of elements across the periodic table. There are two elements in the first period, hydrogen and helium. The second period, starting with lithium, has eight elements. The period number also tells us the number of shells an atom has.

Metals and Non-Metals

Key Words

Malleable
Ductile
Conductor
Alloy

Learning Intentions

In this topic we are learning to:

- Classify an element as a metal or a non-metal using the periodic table.
- Investigate the properties of metals and non-metals.
- Describe what an alloy is and give examples of common alloys.

The majority of elements on the periodic table are metals. A stepped line, like a stair, is often used to separate the metal and non-metal elements (see Fig. 10.4.1 on page 180). Any element to the left of the stepped line is a metal. Any element to the right of the stepped line is a non-metal.

The following table summarises the properties of metals and non-metals. Notice that metals and non-metals have opposite properties to each other.

Property	Metals	Non-metals
Appearance	Shiny	Dull, often coloured
Melting point	High (solids at room temperature)	Low (liquids or gases at room temperature)
Density	High (a metal feels heavy for its size)	Low (a non-metal feels light for its size)
Strength	Strong	Weak
Malleable	**Malleable** (can be hammered into various shapes without cracking)	Not malleable, non-metals are brittle and break easily
Ductile	**Ductile** (metals can be drawn out to form a wire)	Not ductile
Conducts heat	Good **conductors** of heat	Poor conductors of heat
Conducts electricity	Good conductors of electricity	Poor conductors of electricity

 Learn more about conductors and insulators in Physical World 18.2

Researching metals and non-metals

Not all metals and non-metals have the properties listed in the table above. Discover the exceptions to the usual characteristics of metals and non-metals by researching the following questions:

1. Which metal is liquid at room temperature?
2. Which metals are soft at room temperature?
3. Which non-metal is liquid at room temperature?
4. Which non-metal (in the form of graphite) can conduct electricity?
5. Which form of carbon is extremely hard and has a very high boiling point?

Metals versus non-metals

Jim and his class were asked by their teacher to investigate the properties of metals and non-metals. Jim felt that the easiest way to show the difference between metals and non-metals was to use a magnet. His hypothesis was that all metals would be attracted to the magnet and all non-metals would not.

contd ⮕

1. Using diagrams and a set of instructions, explain how Jim may have carried out his investigation.
2. Once you have written out your method and agreed it with your teacher, carry out this investigation. Do you think Jim's hypothesis was correct?
3. There is one major problem with using this method to show the difference between metals and non-metals. Explain what this problem is.

Metal or non-metal?

You and your partner will be given various elements. Plan, design and carry out tests to determine if an element is a non-metal or metal. You will determine if the material is a metal or a non-metal based on the results of a test to find out whether or not the sample is a good conductor of heat.

How will you go about this investigation? Record your procedure and findings.

Alloys

Some metals are most useful when they are in their pure state. For example, pure copper is used in electrical wires as it is an excellent conductor of electricity. Copper is often described as a soft metal.

Some metals are more useful when they are mixed with other metals. For example, if tin is mixed with copper, the resulting substance is much stronger than copper alone. The mixture of copper and tin is called bronze.

Bronze is an example of an **alloy**. An alloy is a mixture of metals. When a metal is mixed with other elements, usually other metals, the properties of the metal change. We will learn more about mixtures in the next chapter.

Alloy presentation

In small groups, research one of the following alloys and put together a presentation for the rest of the class.

Brass	Bronze	Solder	Stainless steel	Alnico

Your presentation should include information on:

1. The composition of the alloy.
2. What the alloy is used for.
3. A brief history of this alloy.
4. Why the properties of this alloy are better than the individual substances that make it up.

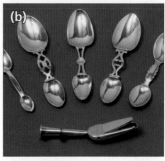

Fig. 10.5.1
Metals: (a) gold, (b) silver and (c) copper

Fig. 10.5.2
Alloys: (a) bronze and (b) steel

Chapter Summary

- All substances are made up of tiny particles called atoms.
- Some substances contain only one type of atom. These are called elements.
- Elements cannot be broken down into simpler substances.
- Every element has its own chemical symbol, which appears in the periodic table of the elements.
- The three subatomic particles that make up an atom are the proton, neutron and electron.
- Protons are positive and are found in the nucleus.
- Neutrons are neutral and are found in the nucleus.
- Electrons are negative and are found orbiting the nucleus.
- The atomic number of an element is the number of protons in an atom of that element.
- The mass number of an element is the total number of protons plus neutrons in an atom of that element.
- Isotopes are atoms of the same element that have the same number of protons but a different number of neutrons.

- The electronic configuration of an atom shows which shells the electrons are located in.
- The periodic table is an arrangement of elements in order of increasing atomic number.
- Vertical columns of elements in the periodic table are called groups.
- Horizontal rows of elements in the periodic table are called periods.
- Elements in the same group in the periodic table have similar properties to each other. They also have the same number of electrons in their outermost shell.
- Metals are materials that are usually hard, dense, shiny and have high melting points. They are good conductors of heat and electricity.
- Metals can be hammered into shape (malleable) and can be stretched into wire (ductile).
- Non-metals are materials that are usually soft, dull and have low melting points. They are poor conductors of heat and electricity.
- An alloy is a mixture of metals.

The BIG Challenge

We use many different elements every day. Your body is made up of 26 elements. You are composed of oxygen, carbon, hydrogen, nitrogen, calcium, potassium, phosphorus, sulfur, sodium and magnesium, to name but a few.

In pairs, research the elements present in an object that you use in your everyday life. It could be something you eat or drink, a piece of sports equipment or even your mobile phone.

Put together a poster containing the information you find out. For each element that is present in your object, include the reason why that element is needed. Compare your poster with your classmates' posters.

Go to your Portfolio to check what you have learned in this chapter.

Take the chapter 10 quiz on **educateplus.ie**.

Questions

1. Copy and fill in the blanks.

a. All substances are made up of very small particles called _____ .

b. Substances that contain only one type of _____ are called _____ .

c. The number of protons in a carbon atom is _____ .

d. The three subatomic particles are _____ , _____ and _____ .

e. The _____ and _____ are found in the nucleus of the atoms.

f. The atomic number is the number of _____ in the nucleus of the atom.

g. The mass number is the number of _____ and _____ in the nucleus of the atom.

h. An isotope is an atom of the same element that has the same _____ number but a different _____ number. Isotopes have the same number of _____ but different numbers of _____ .

i. In the periodic table vertical columns of elements are called _____ and horizontal rows of elements are known as _____ .

j. Metals are substances that have a high _____ _____ and can conduct _____ and _____ .

2. Why are water (H_2O) and carbon dioxide (CO_2) not considered to be elements?

3. Write down the names of two elements that, at room temperature, are:

a. Solids

b. Liquids

c. Gases

4. Use the table below to answer the following questions.

Element	Atomic number	Mass number
Oxygen	8	16
Chlorine	17	35
Zinc	30	65
Tungsten	74	187

a. Which element has the highest number of protons?

b. How many protons are in an atom of oxygen?

c. Where are protons found in the atom?

d. How many neutrons are in an atom of zinc?

e. Which element contains the same number of protons and neutrons?

f. Draw and write the electronic configuration for oxygen and chlorine.

5. The table below shows the data for six elements. Turn to page 462 to see where these elements are found on the periodic table.

Element (symbol)	Melting point (°C)
Lithium (Li)	180
Sodium (Na)	98
Potassium (K)	64
Neon (Ne)	−249
Argon (Ar)	−189
Krypton (Kr)	−157

Compare the melting point patterns for group 1 and group 8. What happens to the melting point as you go down group 1 and group 0?

6. List two ways the modern periodic table is different to the periodic table developed by Dmitri Mendeleev.

7. Suggest a reason for each of the following:

a. Copper is used in electrical wires.

b. 'Silver' coins are not made out of pure silver.

c. Aircrafts are made out of aluminium.

d. Pots and pans are made out of stainless steel.

Working as a Scientist

Responsible Science

Copper

Copper is a metal. It is soft, easily bent and a good conductor of electricity. This makes copper useful for electrical wiring. Copper does not react with water, which makes it useful for plumbing. The table below shows the uses of copper:

Use	Percentage (%)
Building and construction	45
Electric and electronic products	23
Transportation equipment	12
Consumer and general products	12
Industrial machinery and equipment	8

1 **What is the chemical symbol for copper?**

2 **Represent on a chart the main uses of copper as outlined above.**

3 **Investigate three items in your everyday life that would not exist without copper.**

Copper has a number of properties that allow it to be used in many ways. The table below lists the properties of copper:

Good electrical conductor	Tough
Good thermal conductor	Non-magnetic
Corrosion resistant	Attractive colour
Antibacterial	Easy to alloy
Easily joined	Recyclable
Ductile	Malleable
	Catalytic

4 **Using the information above, identify the properties of copper that make it suitable for use in the following items:**

Pipes	Electrical cables	Jewellery	Food preparation	Coins	Door knobs

The History of Copper

Copper and gold are the oldest metals known to man and were found in ancient times in their native form. Their bright colour made them easily visible. Copper was one of the first metals ever extracted and used by humans, and it has made vital contributions to sustaining and improving society since its discovery. The Copper Age was a time period between the Neolithic and the Bronze Age.

🎧 **Fig. 10.7.1**
Native copper

During this period copper was used for edged weapons such as knives, swords, spearheads, and axes were made of copper, as were brooches, pins, belt boxes and vessels for food and drink.

Bruce G. Trigger, *A History of Archaeological Thought*

5 Investigate what the term 'native form' means and explain why copper is found in this form.

6 Based on what you have learned in this chapter and in history lessons, suggest a reason why the Copper Age only existed for a short time before the Bronze Age began.

Copper Mining

About 200 years ago, the United Kingdom and Ireland were important sources of copper for the world. In Ireland, there were a large number of copper mines in places such as Avoca, County Wicklow; Allihies, County Cork, and Bunmahon, County Waterford. The Copper Coast in County Waterford is named after this historic metal-mining industry. Today the biggest copper mines are in Chile and North America. The mines in these countries produce many millions of tonnes of copper ore per year.

Metals are often found as compounds in ores. An ore is a rock or mineral that has enough metal in it to make it worth extracting. In the case of copper, it is worth extracting when there is about 2 kg of copper per 1,000 kg of ore.

The main ores of copper are chalcopyrite, bornite and malachite. Copper can be extracted from its ore in a number of ways:

- Underground mining
- Open pit
- Leaching

Finding the correct information online can be very difficult. It is not always easy to know which sources contain the correct facts. Being able to work out what information is trustworthy is an important skill for school, work and day-to-day life.

The most reliable information is:

- found on official websites or academic journals
- written by an expert in the field
- up to date
- peer-reviewed (reviewed by other scientists in the same field)
- balanced and unbiased.

🎧 Fig. 10.7.2
A copper mine

7 Research the impact that the different methods of extracting copper from its ore have on the environment. In your report, give a brief description of the method of extraction and develop a list of pros and cons for each method.

8 How will you make sure that you have found the most reliable, accurate, unbiased and up-to-date information available?

Medicinal Copper

Copper is needed for our bodies to work properly. It is one of several micronutrients. These are minerals that are found in very small, but vital, quantities in our bodies.

9 Investigate why copper is needed in our diet.

10 List foods that are the best sources of copper.

Compounds, Mixtures and Solutions

What you may already know:

- All matter is made up of small particles.
- Elements are the basic materials that all other materials are made from.
- Some substances dissolve in water while others do not.

What you will learn in this chapter:

- To describe the three classes of matter: elements, compounds and mixtures.
- To define pure and impure substances.
- To investigate the difference between elements, compounds and mixtures.
- That elements combine in many ways to produce compounds that make up all living and non-living things.
- To define solutions and give examples of solutions.
- To describe various methods of separating mixtures.

Think BIG

- How does nail varnish remover work?
- If chlorine is a poisonous gas, why can we put sodium chloride (table salt) on our food?
- Where does sugar go in a hot cup of tea?

Puzzler

Can you crack this code?

The first letter of each image spells out a key word that you will come across in this chapter. Use the hints provided if you need to, or revisit the Puzzler after you finish this chapter.

1.

Metal used to make aircraft

2.
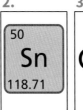
Metal with the chemical symbol Sn

3.
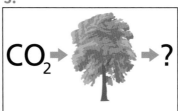
Gas produced by trees

4.
Solid Liquid Gas
Anything that takes up space and has a mass

Compounds and Mixtures

Key Words

Pure substance
Impure substance
Compound
Bond
Mixture
Molecules

We can divide all substances into two groups: **pure substances** (elements and compounds) or **impure substances** (mixtures).

Compounds

We know that elements are substances that have only one type of atom. Substances made by joining together two or more elements are called **compounds**.

The elements in a compound are chemically joined together by strong forces called **bonds**. You can only separate the elements in a compound by using energy.

We encounter many compounds in everyday life. For example:

- Water is a compound made up of two elements bonded together: hydrogen and oxygen.
- Sugar is a compound made up of three elements bonded together: carbon, hydrogen and oxygen.

A compound may be a solid, a liquid or a gas at room temperature.

Mixtures

A **mixture** is a material containing two or more elements or compounds that are in close contact and are mixed. For example, seawater is a mixture of water and salts.

The substances in a mixture can be separated from each other without a chemical reaction, in the same way that different coloured sweets can be picked out from a mixed packet and put into separate piles.

The table below shows the main differences between compounds and mixtures.

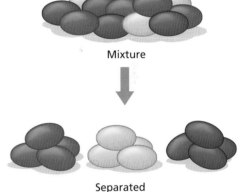

Mixture

Separated

🎧 Fig. 11.1.1
A mixture of sweets

	Compound	Mixture
Composition	Made up of a single substance. You cannot change the amount of each element in a compound; it stays the same	Made up of two or more substances physically combined. You can change the amount of each substance in a mixture
Bonded/not bonded	Elements are joined together by a chemical bond	Substances are not chemically joined together
Properties	The properties of the compound are different from the properties of the elements it contains	Each substance in a mixture keeps its own properties
Separation	Compounds can only be separated into the elements that make it up by using a chemical reaction	Each substance in a mixture is easily separated from each other

Properties of Compounds

The properties of compounds are often very different from the properties of the elements that make them up.

The following table compares the properties of two elements and the compound they make up when they are chemically combined.

Element	Element	Compound
Sodium: very reactive with water. Stored in oil	Chlorine: a poisonous green gas	Sodium chloride: a white crystal used to flavour food
Hydrogen: explosive gas, burns with a pop	Oxygen: a gas needed to support combustion (burning)	Dihydrogen monoxide (water): a very important liquid needed to support life

Using models

Using building blocks, create models to represent the following:

- An element containing five atoms.
- A mixture of three different elements.
- A compound made of two different elements.
- A compound made of three different elements.
- A mixture of two different compounds.
- A mixture of an element and a compound.
- A mixture of two elements and a compound.
- The following substances: water (H_2O) and carbon dioxide (CO_2).

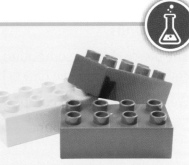

ᴖ **Fig. 11.1.3**
Building blocks

> **Hints**
> - Each block represents an atom.
> - An element contains just one type of atom.
> - A compound contains two or more types of atoms joined together.
> - A mixture is two or more substances not joined together.

Water molecule

Carbon dioxide molecule

Oxygen molecule

Molecules

Atoms are nature's building blocks. When atoms are joined together by bonds they make molecules.

Molecules are groups of two or more atoms bonded together. They are the smallest part of an element or compound that has the chemical properties of that element or compound.

Familiar molecules include:

- Water: two hydrogen atoms bonded to one oxygen atom.
- Carbon dioxide: one carbon atom bonded to two oxygen atoms.
- Oxygen: two oxygen atoms bonded together.

We will look at how and why molecules bond later.

ᴖ **Fig. 11.1.4**
Examples of molecules

Purity

Pure substances contain only atoms or molecules of that substance. For example, oxygen and sulfur.

It is important to be able to test the purity of a substance. This is done by measuring the physical properties of the substance:

- Melting point
- Boiling point
- Density.

For example, pure water will freeze at 0 °C and boil at 100 °C. If there are any impurities in the water, these values will change.

Impurities can be added to water in order to influence its physical properties. For example, adding salt to water lowers its freezing point, causing ice to melt.

In winter, grit is spread on roads. Grit is made up of crushed rock and salt. The salt is used to stop ice forming. It does this by reducing the freezing point of any water on the road surface. This means that temperatures would have to drop lower than 0 °C before the water on the road would form ice.

Measuring the effect of impurities

It takes 58 g of salt to raise the boiling point of a litre of water by just one half of a degree Celsius. How much salt would have to be added to raise the boiling point of water to 103 °C?

How do impurities affect the physical properties of substances?

1. Plan, design, carry out and write up an investigation to find out the effect that different salts have on the rate at which an ice cube melts.

2. Grit is also called 'rock salt'.

   What is the purpose of the crushed rock in grit? Discuss in groups and use diagrams to explain your answer.

🎧 **Fig. 11.1.5**
A gritter truck

11.2 Chemical World

Solutions

Key Words

Solution
Solute
Solvent
Soluble
Insoluble
Suspension
Solubility
Solubility curve

Learning Intentions

In this topic we are learning to:

- Explain the terms solute, solvent and solution and how they relate to each other.
- Measure the solubility of different solids at different temperatures.

When a solid dissolves in a liquid, the solid breaks up and its particles move and fill the spaces between the particles of the liquid. This means that the two different types of particles are completely mixed up.

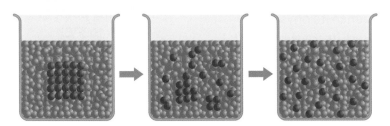

🎧 **Fig. 11.2.1**
How sugar dissolves in water

Figure 11.2.1 shows how sugar dissolves in water. At the beginning you can still see the sugar, but if it is left for a period of time, or if it is stirred, the particles will mix with the water to produce a colourless **solution**.

- The substance that dissolves is called the **solute**.
- The substance the solute dissolves into is called the **solvent**.
- A solution is formed when a solute dissolves in a solvent.

We encounter many solutions in everyday life. For example:

- Seawater is a solution of salt and water.
- Sparkling water is a solution of carbon dioxide gas and water.
- A cup of instant coffee is a solution of coffee powder and water.

Solids that dissolve are called **soluble**. Solids that do not dissolve are called **insoluble**.

If a solid does not dissolve, it may either settle to the bottom of the liquid or end up floating throughout the liquid, making it cloudy. This is called a **suspension**.

Soluble or insoluble?

You are given the following substances: sand, sugar, salt, chalk, oil, tea leaves, candle wax, instant coffee and coffee beans. Plan, design, carry out and write up an investigation to find out if these substances are soluble or insoluble in water.

1. Make a prediction before you carry out this task about which substances will dissolve and which substances will not.
2. What factors will you need to keep constant to make sure this is a fair test?
3. What unit would you use to measure solubility?
4. Is dissolving a physical or a chemical change?
5. How would you reverse dissolving? Use a diagram to explain your suggestion.

Solubility

The amount of a substance that can dissolve in a solvent depends on three things:

1. The nature of the substance. Is the substance soluble, partially soluble or insoluble?
2. The volume of the solvent.
3. The temperature of the solvent.

Solubility is a measure of how much solute can dissolve in a fixed volume of solvent to make a saturated solution.

In a solution where the solute is a solid, usually more of the solute will dissolve as the temperature of the solvent increases. Figure 11.2.2 shows the solubility of sodium chloride in water at increasing temperatures.

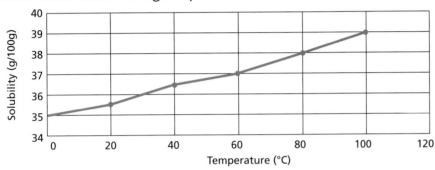

↻ **Fig. 11.2.2**
Solubility of sodium chloride in water at varying temperatures

Gases dissolve in water but show an opposite trend to solids. As the temperature increases, gases become less soluble in the solvent. Figure 11.2.3 shows what happens to the volume of oxygen gas in water as the temperature is increased.

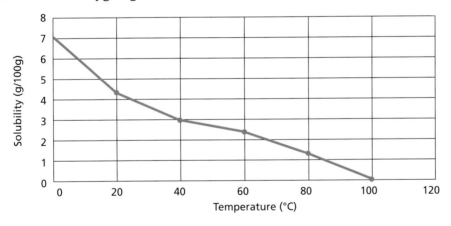

↻ **Fig. 11.2.3**
Solubility of oxygen in water at varying temperatures

How temperature affects solubility

Plan, design, carry out and write up an investigation to compare how the temperature of pure water affects the solubility of two of the following: sodium chloride, sugar, copper sulfate.

Before you start this investigation, think about the following:

1. What variable will you change?
2. What variable will you measure?
3. What variables need to be kept the same each time?

To reach a conclusion in this investigation, you should construct a graph of temperature versus solubility. As temperature is the factor you are changing, this should be placed on the *x*-axis. This type of graph is called a **solubility curve**.

Crystallisation

Key Words

Concentration
Dilute solution
Concentrated solution
Saturated solution
Crystallisation

Learning Intentions

In this topic we are learning to:

- Compare concentrated and saturated solutions.
- Investigate and demonstrate crystallisation.

Types of Solutions

The term **concentration** is used to describe how much solute is dissolved in the solvent. It is measured in g/l (grams per litre).

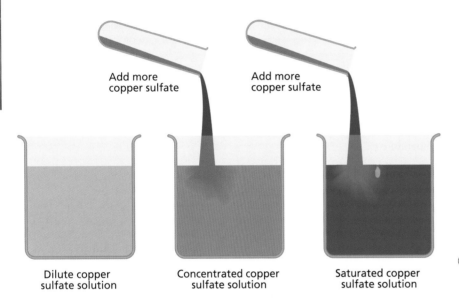

Add more copper sulfate

Add more copper sulfate

Dilute copper sulfate solution

Concentrated copper sulfate solution

Saturated copper sulfate solution

- A **dilute solution** contains a small quantity of solute in a large quantity of solvent.
- A **concentrated solution** contains a large quantity of solute in a small quantity of solvent.
- A **saturated solution** is a solution that contains as much solute as possible at a given temperature.

↻ **Fig. 11.3.1**
Dilute, concentrated and saturated solutions

Concentration of solutions

Using the diagram below, answer the questions that follow. Each circle represents a particle of the solute.

Choose A, B, C, D, E or F as the answer to each question:

500 cm³
Solution A

500 cm³
Solution B

500 cm³
Solution C

500 cm³
Solution D

250 cm³
Solution E

250 cm³
Solution F

⌒ Fig. 11.3.2

1. Which solution is most concentrated?

2. Which solution is least concentrated?

3. Which two solutions have the same concentration?

4. When solutions E and F are combined, the resulting solution has the same concentration as which solution?

5. If you evaporate half of the water in solution B, the resulting solution has the same concentration as which solution?

Crystallisation

Crystals are tiny, solid particles that often form regular shapes. Salt, snowflakes and diamonds are all examples of crystals.

Crystals are formed by cooling a saturated solution. The formation of crystals is called **crystallisation**.

🎧 Fig. 11.3.3
A diamond crystal

Investigating crystals

Observe the following crystals under a light microscope: sugar, salt and copper sulfate. Sketch what they look like under the microscope. How do they feel?

GO Learn how to use a light microscope in Biological World 1.2

Forming crystals

A saturated solution of copper sulfate contains 76 g of dissolved solute at 100 °C. At 20 °C, only 20 g of copper sulfate will remain dissolved. What mass of crystals will form if a saturated solution of copper sulfate is cooled from 100 °C to 20 °C?

🎧 Fig. 11.3.4
Sugar crystals on sticks

Crystal growing challenge

In small groups, plan, design, carry out and write up an investigation to grow the largest crystal possible in the school laboratory.

Here are a few useful points to remember:

- Crystals are formed when a saturated solution is cooled.
- Cooling a saturated solution quickly will result in small crystals. Cooling it more slowly will result in larger crystals.
- Some substances that you can grow crystals of are table salt, granulated sugar, Epsom salts, copper sulfate and alum. However, after carrying out your research, you may prefer to use another substance.
- How will you measure the size of the biggest crystal that you form?
- You may need to carry out this investigation more than once so you can accurately adjust your procedure to give a greater size crystal.

Fun Fact

The water in the Dead Sea is almost six times as salty as most ocean water. As a result, its density is much greater than fresh water. This is why people float in the Dead Sea.

GO Learn more about density in Physical World 17.7

🎧 Fig. 11.3.5
Kathleen Lonsdale

People and Science

Dame **Kathleen Lonsdale** was a crystallographer who was born in 1903 in Newbridge, County Kildare. In 1924, she joined a crystallography research team. She pioneered the use of X-rays to study crystals. Lonsdale was involved in work on the synthesis of diamonds and discovered the structure of benzene. She was one of the first women in the Royal Institution and the first female professor in chemistry at University College London.

Separating Mixtures

Filtration
Chromatography
Evaporation
Distillation
Magnetism
By-product
Fractional distillation
Polymerisation
Biodegradable
Fracking

Learning Intentions

In this topic we are learning to:

- Separate various mixtures using appropriate techniques.
- Examine the various by-products of separation.
- Investigate the advantages and disadvantages of fracking as a means of extracting natural gas.

We know that a mixture is formed when two or more substances are physically mixed together.

One of the characteristics of mixtures is that they can often be easily separated. Separation can be done in a number of ways:

---

1. **Filtration** is used to separate insoluble solids from liquids. Filtration involves using a material that allows only the liquid to pass through but not the solid.

An example of filtration is separating sand (the insoluble solid) from water (the liquid) using filter paper.

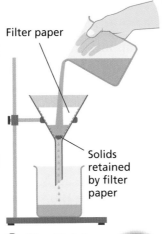

Filter paper

Solids retained by filter paper

🎧 **Fig. 11.4.1**
Filtration

Filtration test

Plan, design, carry out and write up an investigation to determine which material is the most effective at filtering: a paper towel, a cleaning cloth, photocopying paper, nylon, cotton or a coffee filter.

1. What precautions would you need to take to ensure this is a fair test?
2. Present your findings as a results table and a suitable graph.

---

2. **Chromatography** is used to separate mixtures of substances that are in solution.

The different substances are carried up a piece of chromatography paper by the solvent at different rates.

An example of a mixture that can be separated by chromatography is inks in a marker.

⊃ **Fig. 11.4.2**
Chromatography

---

3. **Evaporation** is used to separate a liquid and a soluble solid.

The solvent is evaporated and the solute is left behind in the evaporating dish.

An example of a mixture that can be separated by evaporation is salt and water.

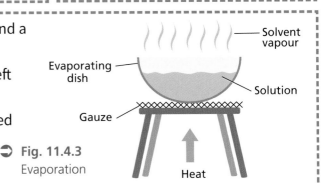

Solvent vapour

Evaporating dish

Solution

Gauze

Heat

⊃ **Fig. 11.4.3**
Evaporation

4. Distillation is used to separate a liquid and a soluble solid when you want to keep the solvent (liquid) or when separating two miscible liquids (liquids that mix).

Distillation separates miscible liquids based on their boiling point. The liquid with the lowest boiling point will evaporate first. A Liebig condenser is used during distillation.

Examples of mixtures that can be separated by distillation are salt and water or water and alcohol.

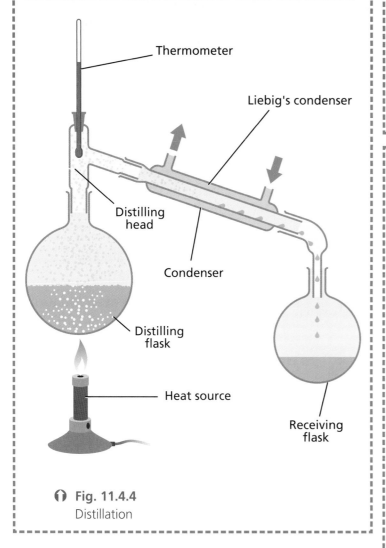

🎧 **Fig. 11.4.4**
Distillation

5. Magnetism can be used if one of the substances in the mixture is magnetic. This substance will be attracted to a magnet. The rest of the mixture will not.

An example of a mixture that can be separated by magnetism is sand and iron filings.

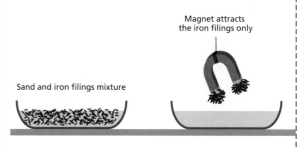

🎧 **Fig. 11.4.5**
Magnetism

6. Separating immiscible liquids:
Immiscible liquids are liquids that do not mix. The less dense liquid will float on top of the other liquid. A separating funnel can be used to separate immiscible liquids.

An example of a mixture of immiscible liquids is oil and water.

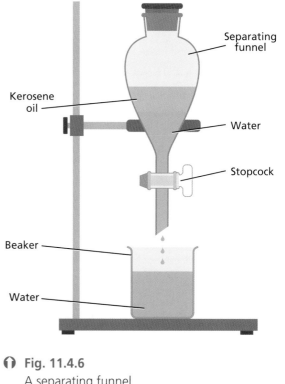

🎧 **Fig. 11.4.6**
A separating funnel

When separating mixtures, you are left with two types of products: the primary product, which you wanted from the mixture, and the **by-product**.

The by-product is a secondary product from the process.

Sometimes the primary product and by-products are wanted. Scientists always try to find a use for by-products so they can reduce waste and increase profits.

Separating mixtures

Using your knowledge of separation techniques, plan, design, carry out and write up an investigation for some of the following scenarios. Identify the by-products of your investigation. For the tasks that you do not carry out, suggest how you might separate that mixture.

Part 1 You are stranded on a desert island. How would you get pure water from the sea water?

Part 2 In the school laboratory, a number of substances accidentally get put back into the same container. How would you separate iron filings, salt and sulfur powder?

Part 3 How would you investigate the variety of colours used to coat a sweet of your choice?

Part 4 You are working as an environmental scientist and sampling river water. During an oil spillage, you collect a sample of water from a river. How would you remove the mud and oil from a sample of the river water?

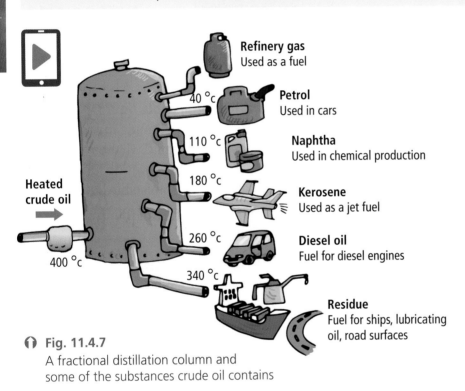

Fig. 11.4.7
A fractional distillation column and some of the substances crude oil contains

Fractional Distillation

Crude oil is a thick, black liquid found beneath the Earth's surface. It is a mixture of many different products that are only useful when they are separated.

Crude oil is separated by **fractional distillation**.

The crude oil is heated and turns into a gas. The gas is put into a large tower and cools as it rises up the tower. Substances with high boiling points turn to liquid at the bottom of the tower and substances with low boiling points turn to liquid at the top.

Plastics

Some of the most useful products of fractional distillation are plastics.

Plastics are good insulators of heat and electricity and are easy to manipulate and work with. We use plastics in many aspects of our lives.

The table below lists a number of types of plastics and their uses.

Plastic	Properties	Examples of products
Polythene	Flexible, strong and inexpensive	Plastic bags and lunch boxes
PVC	Weather resistant and strong	Gutters and window frames
Polystyrene	Rigid or foam	Food containers
Nylon	Can be spun into fabrics	Carpets, tights and ropes

Plastics are manufactured as follows:

Step 1: Raw materials are separated from crude oil by fractional distillation (as described above). These are called monomers.

Step 2: Monomers are reacted together to create long chains called polymers.

Polymerisation is when small repeating units called monomers bond together to form larger chains called polymers.

Word cues a b c

Mono means 'one' and *poly* means 'many'.

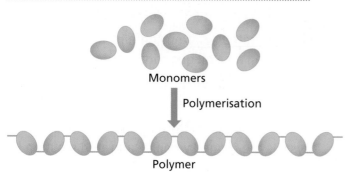

↻ **Fig. 11.4.8**
Polymerisation

Monomers

Polymerisation

Polymer

Environmental Impact of Plastics

Plastics are **non-biodegradable**. This means that bacteria cannot break them down. Plastics are also harmful when burned as they release poisonous fumes.

Many plastics are now recycled and scientists are developing ways to manufacture plastics that can be broken down into water and carbon dioxide.

Fracking

Natural gas is usually extracted by drilling through rock to get to the underground well of gas. The gas comes to the surface very easily using this method because it is at high pressure.

Scientists have discovered that there is a huge amount of natural gas trapped in the rock shale. Collecting the natural gas in shale is not as easy as collecting gas from the underground wells. A method called **fracking** (from the term 'hydraulic fracturing') has been developed to help extract this gas.

Fracking involves drilling down into the earth and injecting a mixture of water, sand and chemicals into the rock at high pressure, which releases the gas trapped inside the rock.

The table below highlights the advantages and disadvantages of fracking.

↻ **Fig. 11.4.9**
Fracking

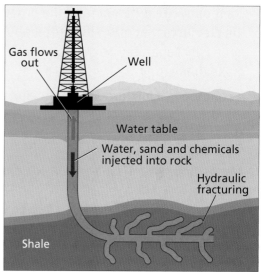

The fracking debate 🔍

Prepare a class debate to argue the following statement: 'Ireland should consider hydraulic fracturing to meet growing energy needs.'

Advantages	Disadvantages
Provides access to difficult-to-reach stores of oil and natural gas	Large amounts of water are needed for the process
Releases the natural gas methane, which is the least polluting of all the fossil fuels	Fracking may result in small earthquakes
Provides a fuel source as alternative renewable sources of energy are investigated	Natural gas is a non-renewable form of energy

Chapter Summary

- An element is a substance that is made up of one type of atom.

- Compounds are formed when two or more elements are joined chemically.

- Mixtures are formed when two or more substances are mixed together physically.

- A pure substance is a substance that contains only atoms or molecules of that substance.

- Molecules are groups of two or more atoms joined together.

- The properties of the substances that make up a mixture remain the same. Mixtures are easily separated back into the substances that make them up.

- When compounds form, the properties of the compound are different from the properties of the elements that make it up. Compounds are not easily separated back into the elements that make them up.

- A solution is a mixture of a solute and a solvent.

- A solute is the substance that is dissolved.

- A solvent is the liquid that the solute dissolves in.

- A substance that dissolves in a solvent is soluble.

- Solubility is a measure of how much solute will dissolve in a solvent.

- A dilute solution contains a small quantity of solute in a large quantity of solvent.

- A concentrated solution contains a large quantity of solute in a small quantity of solvent.

- A saturated solution is a solution that contains as much solute as possible at that temperature.

- Crystallisation is the formation of crystals. Crystals are formed when a saturated solution is cooled.

- There are a number of different methods used to separate mixtures, such as filtration, chromatography, evaporation, distillation and magnetism.

- Filtration is used when separating a liquid and an insoluble solid.

- Evaporation is used when separating a liquid and a soluble solid.

- Distillation is used to separate substances with different boiling points.

- When two liquids mix they are described as miscible. The opposite of miscible is immiscible.

- Fractional distillation is used to separate crude oil into the useful components that make it up.

The BIG Challenge

Using the particle theory, develop models to explain the following:

- Sand can be separated from water by filtration but salt cannot.

- Evaporation is a useful method to separate sugar from a solution.

- Evaporation in an open container is an unsuitable method to reclaim fresh water from sea water.

Go to your Portfolio to check what you have learned in this chapter.

Take the chapter 11 quiz on educateplus.ie.

Questions

1. Copy and fill in the blanks.

a. A _____ is made up of two or more substances physically joined.

b. A compound is made up of two or more elements _____ joined.

c. When a compound forms, its properties are _____ to the properties of the _____ from which it is made.

d. A _____ is a mixture of a solute and a _____.

e. A dilute solution is one that contains a _____ quantity of solute in a _____ quantity of solvent.

f. Substances that dissolve are said to be _____.

g. Crystals form when a _____ is cooled.

h. Filtration is used to separate a _____ and an _____ _____.

i. Crude oil is a _____ of many useful products. It is separated up into these products by _____ _____.

j. Distillation is used to separate liquids that have different _____ _____.

2. For models 1–3 below, answer questions a–c.

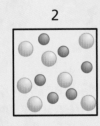
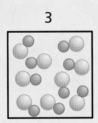

a. How many atoms are present in the model?

b. How many different types of atoms are present in the model?

c. Is this model representative of an element, compound or mixture? Explain your answer.

d. Which diagram shows an example of molecules?

3. Table salt (sodium chloride) is made up of the elements sodium and chlorine. Sodium is a very reactive metal and chlorine is a poisonous gas with a distinctive odour. Why does salt not smell, poison you or fizz in your mouth?

4. Using your knowledge of elements, compounds and mixtures, classify the following substances into the different categories in the table below: magnesium, air, hydrogen, water, salty water, iron oxide, chlorine, sulfur, diet cola.

Element	Compound	Mixture

Explain your reason for placing each substance above in the category you chose.

5. Using your own colours for atoms, draw four diagrams to show:

a. A mixture of three elements.

b. A pure compound.

c. A pure element.

d. A mixture of two compounds.

6. Answer the questions that follow this diagram showing air in a balloon.

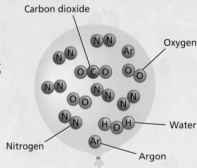

a. How many molecules are there in the balloon?

b. How many different types of molecules are there?

c. How many atoms are there?

d. How many different types of atoms are there?

e. Does this balloon contain an element, compound or mixture?

f. Name the elements present in air.

g. Name the compounds present in air.

7. Match the example with the description:
Examples: concentrated orange juice in water, a fizzy drink, a marshmallow, sugar in tea.
Descriptions:

a. A gas dissolved in a solid.

b. A solid dissolved in a liquid.

c. A liquid dissolved in a liquid.

d. A gas dissolved in a liquid.

8. Rock salt is salt found in the ground. It contains particles of salt mixed with sand and other rocks. Develop a method for how you might get a pure sample of dry salt from the rock salt. Draw diagrams of the investigation set-up you would use.

Working as a Scientist

Asking Questions and Making Predictions

Disposable Nappies

Andy has an 18-month-old baby brother, Jack. Andy notices that Jack uses three to six nappies a day, depending on the brand his mother buys. Andy's mother buys three types of disposable nappies, depending on which is available at the supermarket: brand X, brand Y and brand Z. Andy notices that Jack uses three brand X nappies, five brand Y nappies and six brand Z nappies in a day.

The following table shows the price of the nappies.

Brand of nappy	Cost	Price of one nappy
X	20 nappies for €10.00	
Y	20 nappies for €9.00	
Z	40 nappies for €10.00	

1 Calculate the price of one nappy from each brand to complete the table.

> **Step 1: Prior knowledge and experience**
> Before starting any investigation, it is useful to make a note of all the relevant information you already know. This will help you to make decisions and predictions about what you will test.

2 Make notes about anything you know about disposable nappies. Why are they needed? What materials are they made from? What brands could Andy's mother have bought at the supermarket? Are nappy age or size related? Do you know anything else about nappies?

> **Step 2: Asking questions**
> Andy's mother has asked him to investigate which nappy brand is giving her the best value for money.

3 What properties should Andy test in order to determine which nappy brand is the best value for money?

4 What predictions could Andy make based on his observations?

5 How conclusive would these observations be? Is there anything else that Andy would need to consider?

Step 3: Developing a line of inquiry

Think about how Andy should carry out his investigation. First he sets out to determine how much water each brand of nappy can absorb. Remember that a scientist changes only one variable at a time.

6 Describe, using a diagram and a set of instructions, how Andy could find out which nappy is the most absorbent.

7 How would Andy make sure that this is a fair test?

From his investigations, Andy found that brand X absorbed 250 cm^3 of water, brand Y absorbed 150 cm^3 of water and brand Z absorbed 145 cm^3 of water.

8 Draw a results table that could be used to record the results of this investigation.

9 What additional tests (other than testing which nappy is the most absorbent) could Andy carry out to find differences between each of the brands?

Step 4: Observations in the real world

Andy realises that urine is not just water. It is a solution of urea, salt and water.

10 Predict how a salt solution will affect the results that Andy obtained in his original investigation.

11 How will Andy need to adjust his investigation to take this into account?

12 How can Andy investigate how to make a salt solution with a concentration that imitates the effect of urine on the nappy's absorbency?

Step 5: Presenting and interpreting data

Once Andy has gathered all of his results, he will need to present them in a way that will explain his findings to his mother.

13 Would a table of results alone demonstrate Andy's findings clearly?

14 Draw a graph that Andy might use to represent the data he collected.

Think about...

If you were the materials scientist in a nappy manufacturing company, what key questions would you ask before deciding which material to use in the manufacturing of nappies?

Chemical Reactions: Fast and Slow

What you may already know:

- A new substance is formed in a chemical change.
- Certain chemical reactions take place quite quickly, while others take a very long time.
- It is possible to speed up or slow down a chemical reaction.

What you will learn in this chapter:

- What a chemical reaction is.
- What factors influence how quickly or slowly a reaction happens.
- What a catalyst is and how it works.

Think BIG

- How do explosions happen?
- How are fireworks made?
- What is the slowest chemical reaction?

Puzzler

Can you crack this code?
The first letter of each image spells out a key word that you will come across in this chapter. Use the hints provided if you need to, or revisit the Puzzler after you finish this chapter.

1.

Hazard symbol

2.

**BRONZE
BRASS
STEEL
SOLDER**

Mixture of metals

3.

74
W
Tungsten
183.84

Element with the chemical symbol W

4.

Hazard symbol

1. ___ ___

2. ___ ___

3. ___ ___

4. ___ ___

Chemical Reactions

Learning Intentions

In this topic we are learning to:
- Describe a chemical reaction.
- Observe and record changes that occur during chemical reactions.

Key Words

Reactants
Products
Effervescence

Chemicals are constantly coming together and forming new substances. For example, when a fuel burns in a fire, when a nail rusts and when an egg is boiled. These processes are called chemical reactions.

The chemicals that react together during a chemical reaction are called **reactants**. The new substance or substances that are formed are called **products**.

We know that the elements in a compound are held together by chemical bonds. When chemical reactions take place, chemical bonds are broken in the reactants and new chemical bonds are formed in the products. For example, in a water molecule (H_2O) bonds are formed between the hydrogen and oxygen atoms.

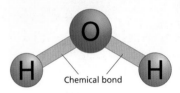

🎧 **Fig. 12.1.1**
A water molecule

Hydrogen + oxygen	→	water
Reactants		Product

When bonds are broken in reactants, energy is taken in from the surroundings. When bonds are made to form a new product, energy is released. This energy can take many forms, such as light, sound or heat.

GO Learn more about chemical energy in Biological World 3.2 and Physical World 16.1

There are a number of signs that a chemical reaction has taken place. You might observe:
- A change in colour.
- A change in temperature.
- The production of light.
- The emission of sound.
- A distinctive smell.
- Bubbles of gas being produced (called **effervescence**).

Observing chemical reactions

From the list of the signs that a chemical reaction is taking place, identify those that are caused by a new product being formed and those that are caused by energy changes.

Observing chemical change

1. Investigate the following examples to find out if a chemical reaction is taking place. Prepare a results table and then fill in the evidence that a chemical reaction has taken place.
   - Strike a match and allow it to burn for a short time.
   - Add 5 g of salt to water in a beaker.
   - Place a strip of fresh magnesium ribbon in 10 cm^3 of dilute copper sulfate solution.
   - Add 5 g of citric acid to 10 cm^3 of dilute sodium hydrogencarbonate solution.

2. How would you safely investigate if there is a change in temperature in each of the above examples?

Endothermic and Exothermic Reactions

Key Words

Exothermic
Endothermic
Energy profile
diagram

Learning Intentions

In this topic we are learning to:

- Distinguish between endothermic and exothermic chemical reactions.
- Produce an energy profile diagram for endothermic and exothermic reactions.

🎧 **Fig. 12.2.1**
Coal burning is an exothermic reaction

Some chemical reactions give out heat. These are **exothermic** reactions. In exothermic reactions, heat energy is given out by the reacting chemicals to the surroundings so that the temperature increases.

Examples of exothermic reactions include:

- Coal burning to heat a room.
- Fireworks exploding.

Other chemical reactions take in heat energy from the surroundings, causing a decrease in temperature. These are called **endothermic** reactions.

Examples of endothermic reactions include:

- Sherbet on your tongue.
- Using an instant cold pack to reduce swelling.

🎧 **Fig. 12.2.2**
The endothermic reaction that takes place in an instant cold pack quickly lowers its temperature

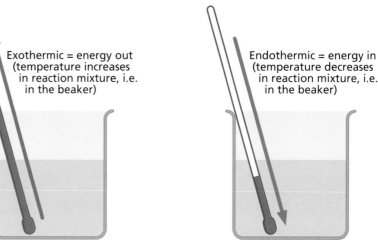

Exothermic = energy out (temperature increases in reaction mixture, i.e. in the beaker)

Endothermic = energy in (temperature decreases in reaction mixture, i.e. in the beaker)

🎧 **Fig. 12.2.3**
Endothermic and exothermic reactions

Remembering chemical reactions

Here is an easy way to remember the difference between exothermic and endothermic reactions:

- **En**dothermic reactions: energy **en**ters the reaction.
- **Ex**othermic reactions: energy **ex**its the reaction.

Interpreting data

The table below shows the temperature changes that take place when substances are dissolved in water. Copy the table and fill in if the reaction is endothermic or exothermic.

Name of substance to be dissolved in water	Starting temperature (°C)	Temperature after dissolving (°C)	Endothermic or exothermic reaction?
Potassium chloride	25	12	
Calcium chloride	25	33	
Sodium hydrogencarbonate	25	15	
Sodium carbonate	25	29	

Energy Profile Diagrams

Energy transfers in chemical reactions are shown in **energy profile diagrams**. These diagrams show the energy stored in the reactants compared to the energy stored in the products.

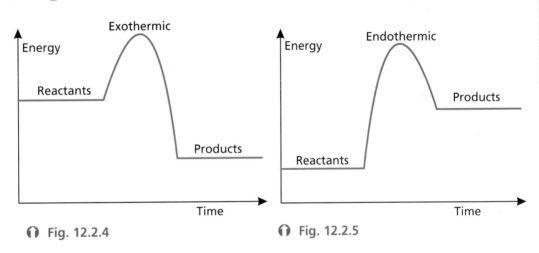

⚪ Fig. 12.2.4   ⚪ Fig. 12.2.5

Figure 12.2.4 shows the energy profile diagram for an exothermic reaction. Notice that the products have less energy than the reactants. This is because energy has been given out.

Figure 12.2.5 shows the energy profile diagram for an endothermic reaction. Notice that the products have more energy than the reactants. This is because the extra energy needed to form the products has been taken in from the surroundings.

Endothermic or exothermic?

Carry out an investigation to find out if the following reactions are exothermic or endothermic:

- Sodium hydroxide and dilute hydrochloric acid
- Calcium chloride and baking soda and water
- Sodium hydrogencarbonate and citric acid
- Vinegar and sodium carbonate
- Calcium chloride and water
- Water and Epsom salts

1. Some students suggest that a polystyrene cup should be used when the reactants have been mixed together, rather than a beaker. Why would a polystyrene cup allow for more accurate results?

2. Should you consider putting a lid on the polystyrene cup? Why?

3. As you are unsure of how each of these substances will react with each other, how can this investigation be carried out safely?

4. Draw the results table you will use to collect information during this investigation.

How Do Chemical Reactions Happen?

Key Words

Collision theory
Activation energy
Rate of reaction

Learning Intentions

In this topic we are learning to:
- Explain activation energy.
- Consider how the rate of a chemical reaction can be monitored over time.
- Interpret a rate of reaction graph.

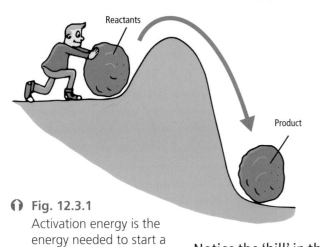
Reactants

Product

⋔ **Fig. 12.3.1**
Activation energy is the energy needed to start a reaction

All substances are made up of particles. Before a chemical reaction happens, the particles in the reactants must collide with each other. This is called the **collision theory**.

The more collisions between particles in a given time, the faster the reaction will take place.

Not every collision will result in a new product being formed. The colliding particles must have a minimum amount of energy.

The minimum energy needed to start a reaction is called **activation energy**.

Notice the 'hill' in the energy profile diagrams for both exothermic and endothermic reactions (Figs. 12.2.4 and 12.2.5, page 207). This hill represents the minimum energy needed to start the reaction. The higher the barrier, the slower the reaction.

Rate of Reaction

Some reactions are slow and some reactions are fast. The **rate of reaction** describes how quickly a chemical reaction happens.

It is very important that scientists can control or change the rate of chemical reactions. For example, in the pharmaceutical industry scientists have to know exactly how much of their product they can make each hour, day or week.

Fast or slow?

12.3

Research the rates of the reactions below and place them in order from fastest to slowest:
- Wine fermenting.
- Baking a cake.
- Dynamite exploding.
- Milk going sour.
- Limestone rock being weathered.
- Iron nail rusting.
- Antacid tablet relieving symptoms of heartburn.

⋔ **Fig. 12.3.2**

The rate of a reaction can be measured by carrying out investigations. During a chemical reaction, it is possible to measure how much reactant is used up or how much product is formed in a certain time.

A chemical change can be measured in three ways:

1. Monitor the production of gas. This can be done in two ways:

   a. By collecting the gas in a gas syringe or graduated cylinder.

   b. By allowing the gas to escape from the flask and recording the loss of mass.

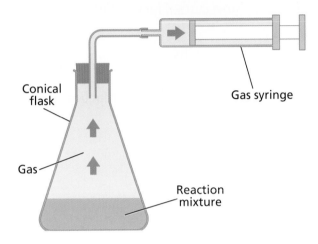

Fig. 12.3.3
Using a gas syringe to monitor volume of gas production in a chemical reaction

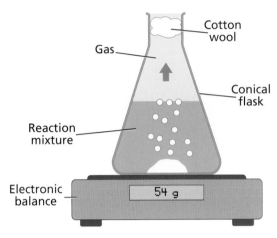

Fig. 12.3.4
Recording loss of mass to monitor gas production in a chemical reaction

2. Monitor the temperature changes during a reaction.

3. Monitor the appearance of the reactants and the products during the reaction. In some cases, the products of a reaction are insoluble. As the product is insoluble, it will become visible and be deposited at the bottom of the flask. In these kinds of reactions, you can measure the time taken for the reaction mixture to go cloudy.

Rate of Reaction Graphs

The slope of a graph can be used to show the rate of change in a reaction.

A fast reaction will produce lots of the product quickly. This will give a steeper slope on the curve when plotted on a line graph, as shown in Fig. 12.3.5.

As the reactants are used up, no more product is formed. This can be seen on a graph when the line levels off.

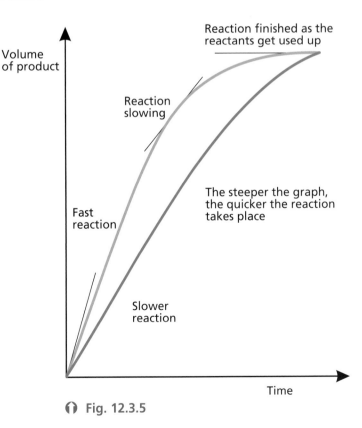

Fig. 12.3.5

Factors Affecting the Rate of a Reaction

Learning Intentions

In this topic we are learning to:

• Identify a number of factors that affect the rate of chemical reactions.

• Use the collision theory to explain how certain factors influence the rate of a chemical reaction.

• Produce and interpret rate of reaction graphs.

A number of factors can influence the rate of a chemical reaction:

• Temperature.

• Concentration of the reactants.

• Surface area of the reactants.

• Adding a catalyst.

Temperature and Rate of Reaction

Temperature has a large effect on the rate of reaction. As heat is added to a reaction, the particles that make up the reactants gain more kinetic energy and move faster.

Particles have more energy at higher temperatures. When these particles collide, they will be more likely to have enough energy to react with each other (activation energy).

Raising the temperature by 10 °C doubles the rate of many reactions.

GO Learn more about kinetic energy in Physical World 16.1

⤵ **Fig. 12.4.1**
The effect of temperature on reaction rate

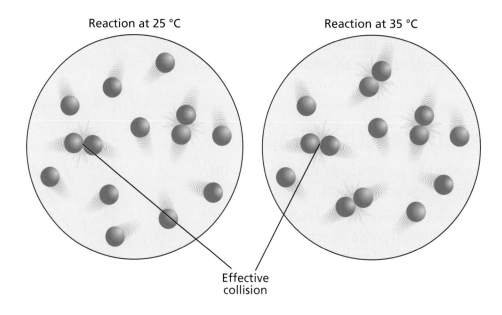

Reaction at 25 °C   Reaction at 35 °C

Effective collision

Investigating how temperature affects the rate of a reaction

A glow stick contains two chemicals in separate tubes. When you crack a glow stick the inner glass tube (which is made of very thin glass) breaks. This allows the two substances in the glow stick to react.

Fig. 12.4.2
Glow sticks

Using glow sticks, plan, design, carry out and write up an investigation about how temperature affects the rate of a reaction.

1. What energy transfers are happening in the glow stick?
2. How can you tell whether the chemical reaction is happening faster or slower in each glow stick?
3. Some people place glow sticks in the freezer to make them last longer. Why do you think this works?

Fun Fact

Glow worms glow because of a chemical reaction that takes place in their tails. This is called bioluminescence. Glow worms glow brighter at warmer temperatures.

Rate of reaction

Niamh was investigating the reaction between magnesium and hydrochloric acid, which produces magnesium chloride and hydrogen gas. The data that she collected can be seen in the table below.

Investigation	A	B	C	D	E
Time needed to collect 10 cm³ of the hydrogen gas (s)	15	4	46	15	30

Use the information in the table to answer the following questions:

1. Which investigation had the slowest rate?
2. Which investigation had the fastest rate?
3. In which investigation is it likely that the testing conditions were the same?
4. The only variable that Niamh changed was the temperature. Which investigation took place at the highest temperature?

Concentration and Rate of Reaction

As you increase the concentration of reactants, you increase the number of particles in a given volume.

As there are more particles in concentrated solutions, there are more collisions. These collisions increase the rate of the reaction.

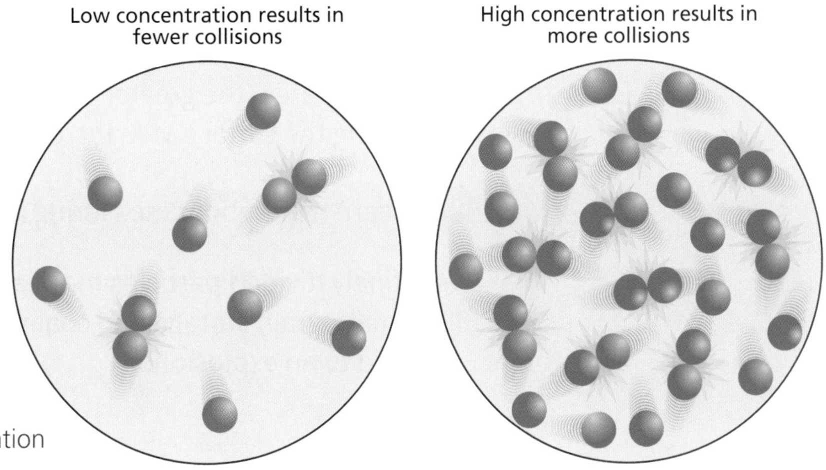

Low concentration results in fewer collisions

High concentration results in more collisions

Fig. 12.4.3
The effect of concentration on reaction rate

Investigating how concentration affects the rate of a reaction

Using a plastic canister or a bottle with a lid that pops off, vinegar and baking powder, make a rocket that launches after 60 seconds.

While designing this investigation, consider the following:

1. What variables will you keep the same?
2. What variables will you change?
3. What safety precautions do you need to take?
4. What energy transfers are happening in this investigation?
5. What changes would you make to get the rocket to launch after 30 seconds?

○ Fig. 12.4.4
The materials needed to make a bottle rocket

Surface Area and Rate of Reaction

Particle size is used to compare the dimensions of the particles in solids. As a particle size gets smaller, the **surface area** increases.

Surface area is a measure of how much of a substance is exposed.

Predict which of the pots of potatoes in Fig 12.4.5 will cook first. Explain your prediction.

⮑ Fig. 12.4.5

Cutting the potato into smaller parts increases its surface area. The larger the surface area, the greater the area available for collisions to take place. Increasing the surface area increases the rate of a reaction.

 Learn more about measuring in Physical World 15.2

Very finely divided particles may cause a 'dust explosion'. This is a danger in flour mills, grain storage and coalmines, where a build-up of dust in the air can lead to an explosion.

Investigating how surface area affects the rate of a reaction

Rhubarb contains a number of acids that give it a sour taste – this is why sugar is added to the vegetable when making a rhubarb tart. One of the acids found in the stalks of rhubarb is called oxalic acid. Oxalic acid reacts with a dilute solution of potassium permanganate and causes the pale pink of the potassium permanganate to become colourless. Oxalic acid is also found in Brussels sprouts, carrots and parsley.

1. Using this information, plan, design, carry out and write up an investigation to find out how increasing the surface area of rhubarb affects the rate at which potassium permanganate loses its colour. While designing this investigation, consider the following:

   a. What variables will you keep the same?

   b. What variable will you change?

   c. What safety precautions do you need to take?

   d. What will your results table look like?

   e. What type of graph will you draw?

2. How could this investigation be changed to show that concentration affects the rate of a reaction?

🎧 **Fig. 12.4.6**
Rhubarb

Catalysts and Rate of Reaction

A **catalyst** is a substance that speeds up the rate of a chemical reaction.

At the end of the reaction, a catalyst is chemically unchanged, meaning it can be used over and over again.

A catalyst works by lowering the amount of energy needed for a reaction to happen (activation energy). Catalysts make it easier for particles to react, as they will need less energy to get over the barrier.

The energy profile diagram in Fig. 12.4.8 shows how a catalyst lowers the activation energy needed for a reaction. Can you tell if it is an endothermic or an exothermic reaction? Explain your answer.

🎧 **Fig. 12.4.7**
Catalysts make it easier for particles to react

GO Learn more about catalysts in Biological World 3.1

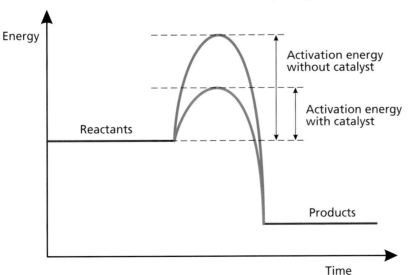

Energy

Activation energy without catalyst

Activation energy with catalyst

Reactants

Products

Time

🔁 **Fig. 12.4.8**
Energy profile diagram showing how a catalyst lowers the activation energy of a reaction

Production of Gases

Key Words

Hydrogen peroxide
Decomposition
Manganese dioxide
Hydrochloric acid
Marble chips

Learning Intentions

In this topic we are learning to:

- Produce and test for the presence of oxygen and carbon dioxide gases.
- Design an investigation to verify that surface area and particle size affect the rate of a reaction.
- Investigate how the presence of a catalyst affects the rate of reaction.

'Displacement'

The word 'displacement' as it is used here means that the gas produced pushes air out of the jar and takes its place.

Be careful though, 'displacement' has a different meaning elsewhere in the science world. See Physical World 17.1 for another use of the word.

When producing a gas, there are three ways the gas can be collected:

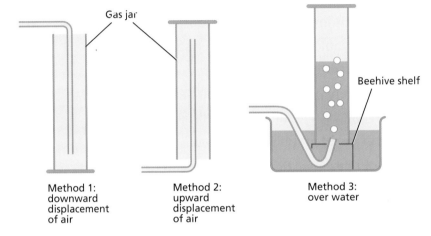

Gas jar

Beehive shelf

Method 1:
downward
displacement
of air

Method 2:
upward
displacement
of air

Method 3:
over water

🎧 **Fig. 12.5.1**
Methods for collecting gas

- **Method 1** can be used for a gas that is heavier (more dense) than air. The gas produced sinks to the bottom of the flask and air is pushed out the top as the flask is filled with the gas.
- **Method 2** can be used for a gas that is lighter (less dense) than air. The gas produced moves to the top of the flask and air is pushed out of the flask as the flask fills with the gas.
- **Method 3** can be used to collect gases that do not dissolve in water. You will easily see when the jar is full of the new gas as there will be no water left in the jar.

Collecting gases

The density of oxygen is roughly the same as the density of air. The density of carbon dioxide is greater than the density of air. Which methods outlined above would be suitable for collecting oxygen and carbon dioxide gases? Explain your answers.

Production of Oxygen Gas

Oxygen is prepared in the laboratory by breaking the chemical bonds in **hydrogen peroxide** molecules. Hydrogen peroxide will break up into water and oxygen gas. The word equation for this reaction is:

> Hydrogen peroxide → water + oxygen gas

The breakdown of hydrogen peroxide into water and oxygen gas is a **decomposition** reaction. In a decomposition reaction, a substance breaks down into simpler substances.

Heat is often used to bring about decomposition. As this is a very slow process, a catalyst is added. Catalysts that can be used include:

- **Manganese dioxide** (a black powder).
- Catalase (found in liver, celery and almost every living cell).

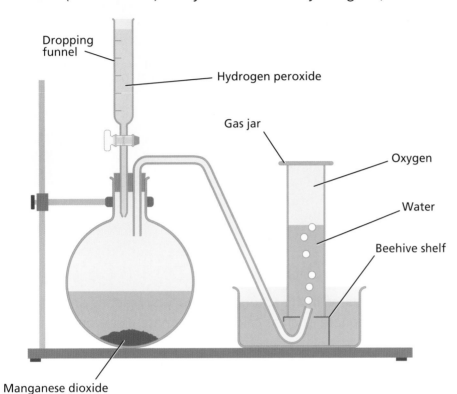

Fig. 12.5.2
A common set-up for the production of oxygen gas

Oxygen gas supports burning (combustion). A fire will not burn unless it has a supply of oxygen. A test for oxygen is that it will relight a glowing splint.

Fig. 12.5.3
A test for oxygen is that it will relight a glowing splint

Comparing catalysts

Plan, design, carry out and write up an investigation to find out if manganese dioxide or catalase is a more effective catalyst for breaking down hydrogen peroxide into water and oxygen.

1. What factors will you change and what factors will you keep constant in this investigation?
2. How will you ensure this is a fair test?
3. How will you ensure that the gas you collect is oxygen?
4. What safety precautions will you need to take?
5. What will your results table look like?
6. What type of graph will you use to display your results?
7. How will you measure the effectiveness of the catalyst?

People and Science

Oxygen was discovered in the eighteenth century by the English scientist **Joseph Priestley**.

Priestley carried out investigations using a bell jar. He discovered that a plant can survive in a sealed jar. He then investigated how this would apply to animals and found that a mouse placed inside a sealed jar will eventually collapse. However, he discovered that a mouse in a sealed jar with a plant will survive as the plant restores oxygen in the air.

Priestley was the first to show that oxygen is needed for animals to survive but that, given time, plants create oxygen, allowing animals to breathe.

⊃ **Fig. 12.5.4**
Joseph Priestley

Production of Carbon Dioxide Gas

Carbon dioxide gas can be prepared in the school laboratory by reacting an acid, such as **hydrochloric acid**, with a carbonate, such as calcium carbonate. The word equation for this reaction is:

Hydrochloric acid + calcium carbonate → calcium chloride + water + carbon dioxide

 Calcium carbonate, also known as...

The common name for calcium carbonate is **marble chips**.

The sedimentary rock limestone is made up of calcium carbonate.

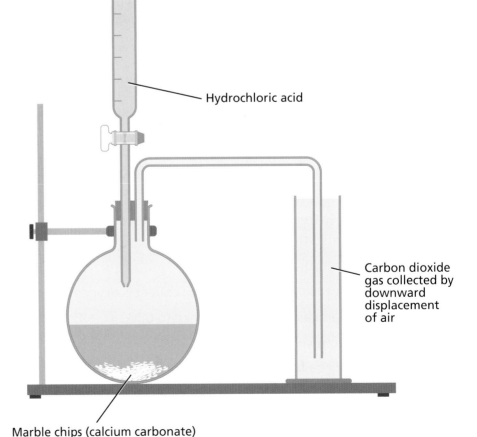

Hydrochloric acid

Carbon dioxide gas collected by downward displacement of air

⊃ **Fig. 12.5.5**
A common set-up for the production of carbon dioxide

Marble chips (calcium carbonate)

Carbon dioxide does not support combustion. In fact, it is very good at putting out fires. For this reason, it is often used in fire extinguishers.

➲ **Fig. 12.5.6**
A carbon dioxide fire extinguisher being used to fight an electrical fire

Pouring gases

Carry out an investigation to show that carbon dioxide gas can be poured from a gas jar and oxygen gas cannot.

Fun Fact

Carbon dioxide is the gas that is used to make drinks fizzy and slightly sour. The first fizzy drink produced was soda water, which was developed by none other than Joseph Priestley.

↪ **Fig. 12.5.7**
A carbonated drink

Marble chips and hydrochloric acid

Plan, design, carry out and write up an investigation to show the link between surface area and the volume of carbon dioxide gas produced in the reaction between hydrochloric acid and different-sized marble chips (calcium carbonate).

1. What factors will you change and what factors will you keep the same in this investigation?
2. How will you make sure that this is a fair test?
3. What will your results table look like?
4. What type of graph will you use to display your results?
5. What safety precautions will you need to take?

Chapter Summary

- A chemical reaction involves the formation of a new substance.
- Exothermic reactions give out heat energy. In exothermic reactions, the temperature goes up.
- Endothermic reactions take in heat energy. In endothermic reactions, the temperature goes down.
- Energy profile diagrams show the energy stored in the reactants compared to the energy stored in the products.
- For a chemical reaction to take place, particles that make up the reactants must collide. This is called the collision theory.
- The more collisions between particles in a given time, the faster the reaction will take place.
- Activation energy is the minimum energy needed to start a reaction.
- The rate of a reaction tells us how quickly a chemical reaction happens.
- Factors that affect the rate of a chemical reaction are: change in temperature, change in concentration, surface area of particles and the presence of a catalyst.
- Increasing temperature increases the kinetic energy of the particles that make up the reactants. It speeds up a reaction because there are more collisions with enough energy to be effective.

- Increasing concentration increases the number of particles in a given volume. This will increase the number of collisions as there are now more particles present to collide with each other.
- Smaller particles have a larger surface area.
- Surface area is a measure of how much surface of a substance is exposed.
- Increasing surface area increases the rate of a reaction.
- A catalyst is a substance that speeds up a chemical reaction. At the end of the reaction, a catalyst is chemically unchanged and can be reused.
- A catalyst works by lowering the activation energy of a reaction.
- Oxygen gas can be produced by reacting hydrogen peroxide and manganese dioxide. Manganese dioxide acts as a catalyst in this reaction.
- Oxygen gas supports combustion. A test for oxygen is that it will relight a glowing splint.
- Carbon dioxide can be produced in the laboratory by reacting an acid and a carbonate, such as hydrochloric acid and calcium carbonate (marble chips).
- Carbon dioxide does not support combustion and is often used in fire extinguishers. It is heavier than air.

The BIG Challenge

1. In groups, design an instant cold pack. Make a poster to present your design and include:
   - The name and logo of your product.
   - Information on when cold packs should be used.
   - Safety advice that users of your product should follow.
   - The reactants used in the manufacturing of the cold pack.
   - A diagram explaining how your cold pack works.
   - Information about the energy changes that are taking place when a cold pack is used.

2. Discuss how you could test how well the cold pack works.

Go to your Portfolio to check what you have learned in this chapter.

Take the chapter 12 quiz on educateplus.ie.

Questions

1. Copy and fill in the blanks:

   a. A _____ reaction involves the formation of a new substance.

   b. Reactions in which there is an increase in temperature are called _____ reactions.

   c. _____ that take in energy from their surroundings and are cold to touch are called _____ reactions.

   d. _____ _____ is the minimum energy required for a chemical reaction to take place.

   e. The more _____ between particles in a given time, the faster the reaction will take place.

   f. A _____ is a substance that speeds up the rate of a reaction without being used up.

   g. Other factors that affect the rate of a chemical reaction are _____, _____ and _____.

   h. _____ is a measure of how much surface of a substance is exposed.

   i. Increasing the concentration of the reactants _____ the rate of a reaction.

   j. _____ is an example of a catalyst used to break up _____ _____ to produce oxygen gas.

2. What signs of a chemical reaction would you observe when:

   a. You fry an egg?

   b. Fireworks go off?

   c. An indigestion tablet is added to water?

3. Plot the data from the table below on a line graph. Put time on the x-axis. Describe the pattern shown and explain why the rates varied.

Time (s)	Volume of O_2 produced at 20 °C (cm³)	Volume of O_2 produced at 30 °C (cm³)
0	0	0
30	6	8
60	12	18
90	17	22
120	21	24
180	24	25
240	25	25

4. List the factors that affect the rate of a reaction. Explain how the factors you have named affect the rate of a reaction.

5. Explain why sliced bread goes stale quicker than unsliced bread.

6. When hydrogen peroxide is left in a clear container at room temperature, it slowly decomposes to produce oxygen and water. Manganese dioxide acts as a catalyst and speeds up this reaction without being chemically changed. Students carried out a number of trials to find the best conditions to make oxygen. The set-up for their investigation is shown below:

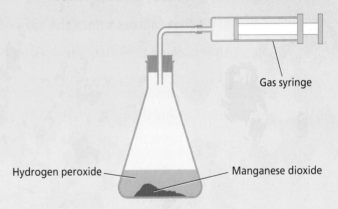

Gas syringe

Hydrogen peroxide — Manganese dioxide

The same volumes and concentrations of hydrogen peroxide were used in each trial. The following table shows the data collected by the students.

Time (s)	Volume of oxygen produced with no manganese dioxide (cm³)	Volume of oxygen produced with 0.65 g of manganese dioxide (lumps) (cm³)	Volume of oxygen produced with 0.65 g of manganese dioxide (powder) (cm³)
0	0	0	0
30	0	8	15
60	0	14	30
90	1	19	45
120	1	23	47
150	2	26	50

   a. Plot the results in the table above using an appropriate graph.

   b. Compare and describe the shape of the graphs produced by the three sets of data.

   c. Explain the difference between the lumps and powdered versions of manganese dioxide.

   d. When the reaction has finished, will the volume of gas produced be the same or different for the two versions of the catalyst?

Working as a Scientist

Investigation Design

Temperature and the Rate of Reaction

A teacher gave the following hypothesis to her class to investigate: 'An increase in temperature of 10 °C will double the rate of a chemical reaction.'

Two students, Sandra and Breda, started to design an investigation to test this hypothesis.

The first thing that Sandra and Breda did was make a list of the factors they knew affected the rate of a reaction. This would help them to find out what factors they would change in their investigation and what factors they would need to keep the same to carry out a fair test.

1 **What factors affect the rate of a chemical reaction?**

After making their list, Sandra and Breda needed to select a reaction for this investigation. They chose the reaction between sodium thiosulfate and hydrochloric acid because the reaction produces an insoluble solid (sulfur). They decided to time how quickly the solution went cloudy at different temperatures.

Sandra drew the following diagram of the investigation set-up in her laboratory copy:

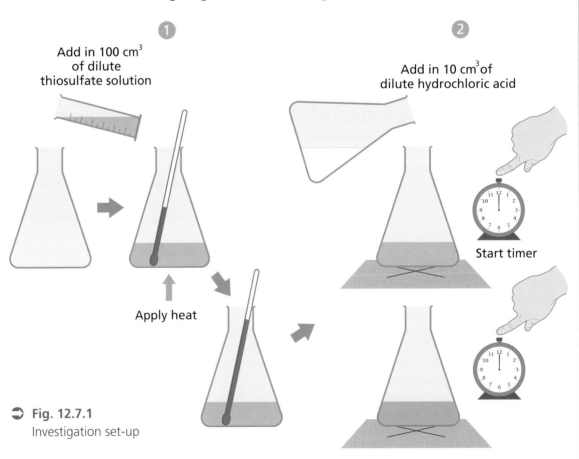

⮫ **Fig. 12.7.1**
Investigation set-up

2 Using Sandra's diagram, write up a list of equipment that the students would need to carry out the investigation.

3 Using Sandra's diagram, write up a step-by-step method that the students would follow during this investigation.

4 What safety precautions should the students take during this investigation?

5 What did the students do to make sure that this was a fair investigation?

Sandra and Breda discussed the range of temperatures they would use. Breda felt that cold acid and warm and hot solutions of the sodium thiosulfate would be enough to test the hypothesis. Sandra did not agree – she felt that Breda's suggestion would only allow them to draw a bar graph of their results.

6 Why would Breda's suggestion have to be drawn on a bar graph?

7 Why would the choices given by Breda not allow the students to test the hypothesis?

After discussing their options, Breda and Sandra decided to use the following temperatures: 20 °C, 40 °C, 60 °C, 80 °C and 100 °C. However, their teacher had safety concerns about the range of temperature values they were going to use.

8 What safety concerns do you think their teacher had?

Before starting their measurements, Sandra and Breda drew up a results table.

9 Draw a blank results table for this investigation.

10 Gather the equipment needed for this investigation and use the steps you developed in question 3 to carry out this investigation in your own school laboratory. Use your results table from question 9 to record your results.

11 Present the results of your investigation in a graph. What type of graph will you use? Why did you choose this type of graph?

12 Write up a conclusion for your investigation. Link the conclusion to the hypothesis at the start of this investigation.

Acids and Bases

What you may already know:

- Acids are substances that can sometimes 'burn' or sting you.
- Vinegar is an acid.
- There is acid in our stomachs that helps with the digestion of food.

What you will learn in this chapter:

- How to distinguish between acids and bases.
- Examples of laboratory and everyday acids and bases.
- What an indicator is and how it is used.
- What happens in a neutralisation reaction.
- How to prepare salt by reacting an acid and a base.

Think BIG

- Why do nettles 'sting'?
- What causes heartburn and how is it treated?

Puzzler

Can you crack this code?
The first letter of each of these images spells out a key word that you will come across in this section. Use the hints provided if you need to, or revisit the Puzzler after you finish this chapter.

1.

Common laboratory acid found in car batteries

2.

Name for a base that is soluble in water

3.

Acid–base indicator

4.

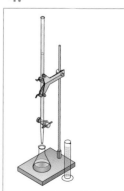

Method to find out how much acid is needed to neutralise an alkali

1. ___ 2. ___ 3. ___ 4. ___

Acids and Bases

Learning Intentions

In this topic we are learning to:

- List examples of everyday acids and bases.
- Discuss how concentrated acids and bases should be handled safely.
- Distinguish between dilute and concentrated solutions of an acid.

Acids

A common belief is that every **acid** is dangerous to touch. However, we come into contact with many harmless acids in our everyday lives.

Common everyday acids include:

- Ethanoic acid: found in the vinegar we use to flavour our food.
- Citric acid: found in citrus fruits, such as lemons and limes.
- Ascorbic acid: found in oranges and kiwi fruits.
- Tannic acid: found in tea.
- Carbonic acid: found in fizzy drinks.

Common laboratory acids include:

- Hydrochloric acid (HCl): also found in our stomachs to aid food digestion.
- Sulfuric acid (H_2SO_4): found in car batteries.

The acids you use in the laboratory are dangerous. So you must be careful when handling them.

⮑ Fig. 13.1.1
Citrus fruits contain citric acid

Key Words

Acid
Base
Alkali
Neutral
Concentrated
Dilute

'Acid'

The word 'acid' comes from the Latin word *acidus*, meaning 'sour'. Our taste buds are designed to detect sour tastes.

Fun Fact

Aqua regia (Latin for 'royal water') is a mixture of concentrated hydrochloric acid and nitric acid. It is so strong that it can dissolve gold!

When Germany invaded Denmark during World War II, the chemist George de Hevesy used aqua regia to dissolve the gold Nobel Prize medals of physicists Max von Laue and James Franck, so that the Nazis could not steal them. The gold/acid solution was ignored by the Nazis, who thought it was just another chemical. When the war ended, the gold was made back into medals and they were given back to von Laue and Franck.

Bases

A **base** is the chemical opposite of an acid.

Common everyday bases include:

- Sodium carbonate: found in washing soda, which is often used to soften water and clean drains.
- Sodium hydroxide: found in caustic soda, which is used to clean drains.
- Magnesium hydroxide: found in Milk of Magnesia, which is used to treat heartburn.

↻ Fig. 13.1.2 Household bases

Common laboratory bases include:

- Sodium hydroxide (NaOH)
- Calcium carbonate ($CaCO_3$)
- Limewater ($Ca(OH)_2$)

An **alkali** is a base that is soluble in water. Washing powder, sodium hydroxide and limewater are all examples of alkalis.

Copper oxide is a base because it will react with acids and neutralise them, but it is not an alkali because it does not dissolve in water.

Substances that do not behave like acids or bases are called **neutral** substances.

'Alkali'

Where else have you come across the word 'alkali' in the Chemical World? Find the link between these two uses of the word.

Using Acids and Alkalis Safely

It is safe to eat the acid in lemons and oranges and to wash our skin with alkaline soap. However, we do have to take safety precautions when handling some acids and bases.

Many acids and bases have a hazard symbol on their container, warning users that they are corrosive. A corrosive substance will destroy or damage other substances that it comes into contact with.

It is important to note that many bases are as corrosive and as dangerous as acids. Caustic soda, an ingredient found in many cleaning fluids, is a corrosive base and must be handled with care.

Working safely with corrosives

If you saw the corrosive hazard symbol on a substance you were about to use, what safety precautions would you take?

The hazards of using acids and alkalis depend on two factors:

- The type of acid or alkali you are using.
- Whether the acid or alkali is dilute or concentrated.

Concentration of Acids and Bases

The acid found in vinegar is dilute ethanoic acid. Adding vinegar to food for flavour does not cause us any harm, yet concentrated ethanoic acid causes severe burns and catches fire easily.

So, what is the difference between vinegar and concentrated ethanoic acid? Pure ethanoic acid does not contain water, whereas vinegar does. The acid in vinegar has been diluted, which makes it safe to eat.

Acidic and alkaline solutions are not all the same:

- Some solutions contain a large amount of acid or alkali particles. These solutions are described as **concentrated**.
- Other solutions contain very few particles of acid or alkali. These are described as **dilute**.

Acids and alkalis are made less concentrated by diluting them carefully with water.

- Concentrated acids and alkalis are corrosive.
- Dilute acids and alkalis are not corrosive but may hurt if they get into cuts on the skin.

◑ Fig. 13.1.3
The hazard symbol for corrosives

◑ Fig. 13.1.5
The acid in vinegar is diluted, making it safe to eat

Dilute versus concentrated

Bottle A contains 350 g of acid in one litre of the solution. Bottle B contains 3.7 g of the same acid in half a litre.

1. Which acid is more dilute?
2. Which acid is more concentrated?
3. What hazard symbol would you expect to see on the bottle for the concentrated acid?
4. If water was added to container B to bring it to the same volume as container A, how would the concentration of the solution in container B change?

⟳ Fig. 13.1.5

pH and Indicators

Key Words

pH scale
Indicator
Litmus indicator
Universal indicator
pH meter

Learning Intentions

In this topic we are learning to:

- Investigate the concentrations of dilute and concentrated acids and alkalis using the pH scale.
- Produce an acid–base indicator from plant material.

It is important to know how concentrated an acid or alkali is to use it safely. Concentrated acid or alkali are nearly always corrosive. To record how concentrated an acid or alkaline solution is, scientists use the **pH scale**.

⊃ **Fig. 13.2.1**
The pH scale

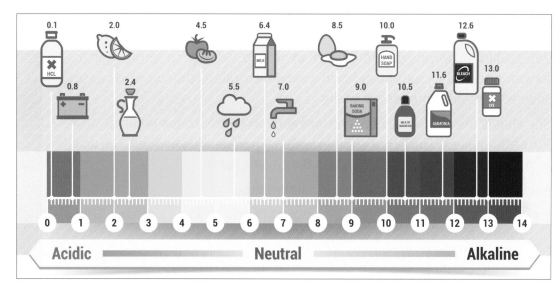

The pH scale goes from 0 to 14.

- A substance that has a pH of 7 on the pH scale is neutral.
- A substance that has a pH below 7 is acidic.
- A substance that has a pH above 7 is alkaline.

Indicators

An **indicator** is a substance that shows whether the solution being tested is an acid or a base. Indicators contain a dye that turns a different colour in acidic or alkaline solutions.

Two commonly used indicators in the laboratory are **litmus indicator** and **universal indicator**.

- Litmus indicator will change colour from blue to red in acids and from red to blue in alkalis. A limitation of litmus is that it does not indicate how concentrated the acid or alkali is.

  – An acid is a substance that turns blue litmus red.

  – A base is a substance that turns red litmus blue.

- Universal indicator is a mixture of dyes that changes colour according to how concentrated an acid or alkali is. The advantage of universal indicator is that it shows the pH of the acid or alkali being tested, whereas litmus only indicates if the substance is an acid, alkali or neutral.

⊙ **Fig. 13.2.2**
Litmus indicator in acid

Another way of measuring pH is to use a digital **pH meter**. A probe is placed in the solution and the pH is displayed on the meter. The advantage of using a pH meter is that it indicates very small differences in pH. pH meters are used in hospitals to measure the pH of a patient's bodily fluids.

 Fig. 13.2.3
A pH meter showing the pH to two decimal places

Investigating the pH of a variety of substances

Plan, design, carry out and write up an investigation to examine the pH of a variety of substances.

Making Indicators

Many plants contain substances that can be used as pH indicators because they change colour in acidic or alkaline solutions. These dyes must first of all be removed from the plant cells.

Extracting dyes from red cabbage

The following steps for extracting dyes from red cabbage to produce an acid–base indicator have been mixed up. Rewrite the steps in the correct order.

1. Collect the cabbage indicator in a beaker.
2. Filter the red cabbage and dye mixture.
3. Leave it to stand for 5–10 minutes.
4. Cut the red cabbage into small pieces.
5. Dip some strips of filter paper into the dye and allow them to dry.
6. Add warm water.
7. Grind up the red cabbage using a mortar and pestle.
8. Test the indicator using a variety of acids and bases.

> **Fun Fact**
>
> Litmus indicator is a solution of dyes taken from lichens. Lichens are organisms that are found growing on leaves and branches, on bare rock (including walls) and on exposed soil surfaces. The roofs of many buildings have lichens growing on them.

Fig. 13.2.4
Lichens growing on stone

Testing the effectiveness of a variety of plant indicators

Plan, design, carry out and write up an investigation to find out if some of the following substances produce an effective acid–base indicator: beetroot, curry powder and carrots. You will need to carry out some research online to help with planning this investigation.

1. What precautions will you take to ensure the research you carry out is reliable?
2. How will you make sure this a fair test?
3. How will you know if the indicator is effective?
4. Draw a diagram of the set-up for this investigation.

Neutralisation

Key Words

Salt
Neutralisation
Titration
Burette
Pipette
Conical flask

Learning Intentions

In this topic we are learning to:

- Plan and carry out a titration between hydrochloric acid and sodium hydroxide.
- Measure pH changes in neutralisation reactions.
- List everyday examples of neutralisation reactions.

Salt

A salt is a chemical compound, formed when the hydrogen part of an acid is replaced by a metal. Examples of salts include sodium chloride, magnesium chloride and calcium chloride.

One way of changing the pH of an acidic solution is to add a base. Acids and bases react together to form a neutral substance (pH 7).

An acid and a base react to produce a **salt** and water. This is known as a **neutralisation** reaction.

$$\text{Acid + base} \rightarrow \text{salt + water}$$

It is important to mix the correct volume of the acid and base to get a neutral solution.

An acid can also be neutralised by reacting it with a carbonate. A carbonate is a base. When a carbonate and an acid react, the products are a salt, water and carbon dioxide gas.

$$\text{Acid + carbonate} \rightarrow \text{salt + water + carbon dioxide}$$

Investigating neutralisation

1. Place 20 cm³ of dilute sodium hydroxide into a conical flask.
2. Record the pH of the base using either universal indicator or a pH meter.
3. Predict what will happen to the pH when you add dilute hydrochloric acid solution to the base.
4. Using a plastic pipette, add dilute hydrochloric acid to the sodium hydroxide.
5. Record the pH changes after every three drops. How much acid was needed to reach a neutral pH in the conical flask?

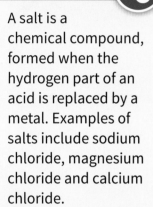

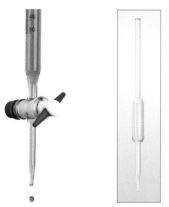

🎧 **Fig. 13.3.1**
A burette

🎧 **Fig. 13.3.2**
A pipette

Titration

A **titration** is a laboratory technique that is used to find out the exact volume of acid needed to neutralise a base.

Before carrying out a titration, it is important to be familiar with the equipment needed:

- A **burette** is a long narrow tube that is closed at the bottom with a tap. The acid is placed in the burette during a titration.
- A **pipette** is designed to deliver an exact volume of solution. A pipette filler is used to draw the solution into the pipette.
- A **conical flask** is designed so that the liquid can be swirled during the titration. In an acid–base titration the base is placed in the conical flask. A white tile is placed under the flask so that the colour change can be seen easily.

To carry out a titration:

1. Transfer 25 cm³ of dilute sodium hydroxide solution into the conical flask using the pipette.
2. Add three drops of litmus indicator to the conical flask and place on a white tile.
3. Using a funnel, fill the burette up to 0 cm³ with dilute hydrochloric acid.
4. Open the tap of the burette and slowly add the acid to the base.

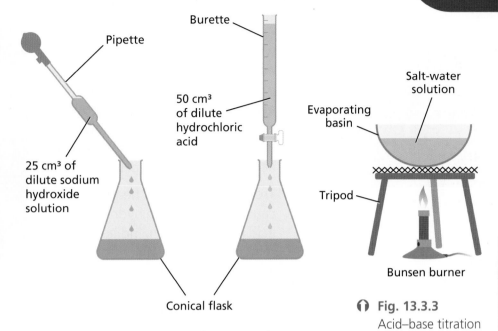

Pipette

Burette

50 cm³ of dilute hydrochloric acid

25 cm³ of dilute sodium hydroxide solution

Conical flask

Salt-water solution

Evaporating basin

Tripod

Bunsen burner

⌒ **Fig. 13.3.3**
Acid–base titration

5. Swirl the conical flask continuously until the indicator changes colour.
6. Repeat twice to get an accurate value of the acid needed to neutralise the base.
7. Calculate the volume of acid needed by getting the average of the acid from the two titrations.
8. Repeat the titration without the indicator.
9. As you are reacting an acid and a base, the products in the conical flask will be salt and water. The salt and water can now be separated using an evaporating basin and a Bunsen burner.

Hydrochloric acid + sodium hydroxide → sodium chloride + water
$$HCl + NaOH \rightarrow NaCl + H_2O$$

Everyday Neutralisation Reactions

Neutralisation reactions take place in a number of everyday circumstances:

- Baking: baking powder helps a cake mixture to rise. It is made up of sodium hydrogencarbonate and a weak acid. When water is added, the two react to produce carbon dioxide gas. The carbon dioxide gas gets trapped in the cake mix and expands when heated. Self-raising flour already has baking powder added to it.

⊃ **Fig. 13.3.4**
Mixing baking powder and water

Titration investigation

Part 1

1. Using a pipette, a beaker and a mass balance, accurately measure out 25 g of water. This should be equal to 25 cm³ of water as the density of water is 1 g/cm³.
2. Repeat this activity but this time use a burette.

Part 2

1. Carry out the titration procedure outlined on this page. Your goal is to neutralise sodium hydroxide with hydrochloric acid and to extract a sample of salt (sodium chloride).
2. If you have access to a pH meter, use it to record the pH changes that occur after every 3 cm³ of acid has been added, up until neutralisation happens. Plot the pH changes on a graph. Put volume of acid on the x-axis and pH on the y-axis.

229

🔊 **Fig. 13.3.5**
Testing the pH of soil

GO Learn more about soil pH in Biological World 6.2

- Agriculture: the pH of soil affects which crops can be grown. Farmers and gardeners always check the pH of their soil. If the soil is too acidic, most crops will not grow well. Farmers can spread powdered limestone (calcium carbonate) on acidic soil to raise its pH.

- Treating indigestion: heartburn is caused by too much hydrochloric acid in the stomach. Indigestion remedies, such as Milk of Magnesia, are made up of a base that will neutralise this acid. The acid in the stomach and the base in the tablet react to give salt and water.

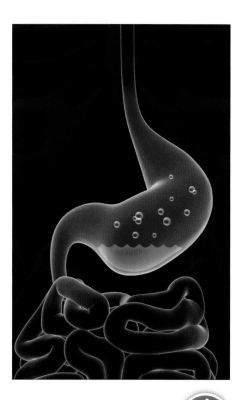

➲ **Fig. 13.3.6**
Indigestion

Which indigestion remedy is best?

Plan, design, carry out and write up an investigation to determine the most effective indigestion remedy.

1. What prior knowledge will you use to help you design this activity?
2. How will you ensure you carry out a fair test?
3. What factors will you measure to find out how effective an indigestion tablet is?
4. What will your results table look like?
5. What graph will you use to best represent the data you have collected?

🔊 **Fig. 13.3.7**
Personal hygiene products balance the body's natural pH

- Personal hygiene products: toothpaste is slightly basic to neutralise the plaque acid in your mouth. Shampoo is also slightly basic to balance the slight acidity of hair. Conditioner is slightly acidic to neutralise the effect of shampoo on the hair and make hair more manageable and shiny.

- Treating stings and bites: bee stings and ant bites are acidic. This is why the skin around the sting becomes inflamed and irritated. Rubbing bicarbonate of soda (sodium hydrogencarbonate) on the area can neutralise the acidity of the sting.

🔊 **Fig. 13.3.8**
Bee stings are acidic

Suggesting a cure

Wasp stings are alkaline. As a class, discuss possible remedies to relieve the symptoms of a wasp sting.

Energy changes in a neutralisation reaction

Plan, design, carry out and write up an investigation into the temperature changes that take place when the following acid–base reactions are carried out:

- Sodium hydroxide reacting with hydrochloric acid.
- Sodium hydroxide reacting with sulfuric acid.
- Sodium hydroxide reacting with ethanoic acid.

1. How will you make sure this is a fair test?
2. What precautions will you take when measuring the temperature change?
3. What will your results table look like?
4. What graph will you use to best represent the data you have collected?
5. Draw an energy profile diagram for the reaction between an acid and a base.
6. A neutralisation reaction releases energy. What term is used to describe this type of reaction?

Reactions of Acids

We have already looked at the reactions between an acid and a base and an acid and a carbonate. Many metals also react with acids.

When a metal and an acid react, they produce a salt and hydrogen gas. Hydrogen gas is very reactive and burns with a pop.

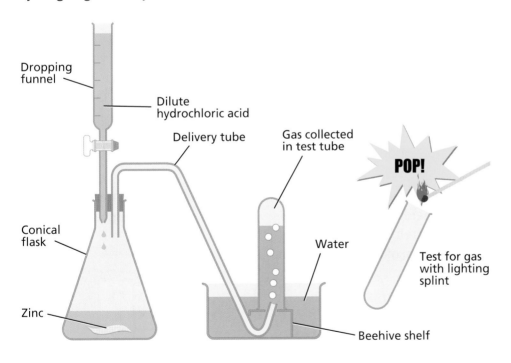

↻ **Fig. 13.3.9**
The set-up to investigate the reaction between a metal and an acid to produce hydrogen gas

Remember:

Acid + base	Salt + water
Acid + carbonate	Salt + water + carbon dioxide
Acid + metal	Salt + hydrogen gas

Chapter Summary

- An acid is a substance that turns blue litmus paper red and has a pH less than 7. Acids have a sour taste.

- A base is a substance that turns red litmus paper blue and has a pH greater than 7. Bases have a soapy feel.

- An alkali is a basic substance which is soluble in water.

- Neutral substances are neither acidic nor basic. Their pH is exactly 7.

- The pH scale shows how acidic or alkaline a substance is and runs from 0 to 14.

- An indicator is a substance that shows whether a solution being tested is an acid or a base.

- Indicators contain a dye that turns a different colour in acidic or alkaline solutions. Commonly used indicators are litmus indicator and universal indicator.

- A neutralisation reaction is a reaction between an acid and a base to form a neutral substance.

- An acid and a base react to produce a salt and water.

- An acid and a carbonate react to produce a salt, water and carbon dioxide.

- An acid and a metal react to produce a salt and hydrogen gas.

- A salt is a chemical compound, formed when the hydrogen part of an acid is replaced by a metal.

- Hydrogen gas is explosive and burns with a pop.

The BIG Challenge

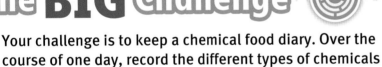

Your challenge is to keep a chemical food diary. Over the course of one day, record the different types of chemicals you eat. You will find these in the ingredients list on food labels or online.

Once you have completed your diary, identify the acids and bases present in your diet. The acids should be easy to identify as they will have 'acid' in their names, but you may need to carry out research on some of the less obvious ingredients.

Complete a table with the following headings:

- Chemical
- Food present in
- Acid or base?

Identify the most common acid and base you consume and research other uses of these substances.

Go to your Portfolio to check what you have learned in this chapter.

?

Take the chapter 13 quiz on **educateplus.ie.**

Questions

1. Copy and fill in the blanks:

   a. _____ taste sour and turn _____ litmus paper _____.

   b. An _____ is used to show whether a substance is an acid or a base.

   c. _____ and _____ _____ are examples of indicators.

   d. The _____ _____ is used to measure how acidic or basic a substance is. It goes from _____ to _____.

   e. A substance with a pH of 7 is described as a _____ substance.

   f. A _____ is a method used to find out how much acid is needed to neutralise a base.

   g. A neutralisation reaction is an _____ _____. This means it is a reaction that gives out energy.

   h. An acid and a base react to give _____ and _____.

   i. A _____ is a chemical compound, formed when the hydrogen part of an acid is replaced by a _____.

   j. The acid in our stomach is called _____ _____. It is needed to help with _____. Excess stomach acid can cause _____.

2. Name two acidic, two basic and two neutral substances.

3. Some foods, such as beetroot, are preserved in vinegar. Explain why the vinegar makes the vegetable last longer.

4. Explain what an indicator is. What are the limitations of testing a substance with litmus indicator?

5. Draw the pH scale and add as many examples as you can for each pH. You may need to research additional examples online.

6. Calculate which solution is more concentrated:

   • Solution A, which has 22 g of alkali dissolved in 250 cm³ of water.
   • Solution B, which has 10 g of the same alkali in 500 cm³ of water.

   Show your calculations.

7. Give an explanation for each of the following:
   a. A mixture of baking soda and vinegar fizz when combined.
   b. Rubbing vinegar on a wasp sting reduces the irritation.
   c. Taking an indigestion remedy relieves the symptoms of heartburn.

8. The soil in Claire's garden has a pH 4.5. Claire really wants to grow an apple tree, which needs a pH of approximately 5.0–6.8 to grow. How can Claire adjust the pH of the soil to ensure that the tree grows? Research other plants she can grow in her garden.

9. Draw the hazard symbol you would see on concentrated acids and bases. Explain what this symbol means.

10. Acid rain can cause the pH of lakes to drop to dangerous levels. How could you deal with this problem?

Working as a Scientist

Making and Recording Observations

Enzymes and pH

Biochemistry is the study of chemical processes within living things (organisms). An enzyme is a biological catalyst. The body has thousands of different enzymes that regulate the chemical reactions in our bodies.

Enzymes are affected by a number of factors, including temperature and pH. Enzymes can be destroyed if pH or temperature become too extreme. If enzymes do not work at their best, it could result in serious illness or even death.

Certain reactions in the liver produce hydrogen peroxide, which is extremely poisonous. Catalase is an enzyme in the human body that breaks down the hydrogen peroxide into water and oxygen.

Two students, David and Ben, decided to plan an investigation to determine which pH is the most effective pH for the enzyme catalase to work. The hypothesis that the students proposed was: 'In very acidic (pH 3) and very basic (pH 11) conditions catalase will not work at its best.'

Before designing their investigation, David and Ben made a list of what they knew already and what they found out while researching the task:

- Hydrogen peroxide breaks down into oxygen and water.
- The better the enzyme is working, the greater the amount of oxygen that will be produced.
- A buffer is a substance that can be used to keep the pH constant.

Based on this knowledge, David and Ben decided to use washing-up liquid to trap the oxygen gas. The higher the level of the washing-up liquid foam, the more oxygen being produced. They decided to use five pH buffers: pH 3, pH 5, pH 7, pH 9 and pH 11.

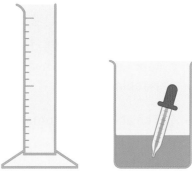

🎧 **Fig. 13.5.1**
Equipment needed for the investigation

1 Suggest why David and Ben chose these five buffers.

David and Ben carried out their investigation by following these steps:

1. Pour 20 cm^3 of buffer pH 3 into a 100 cm^3 graduated cylinder.
2. Using a dropper, add one drop of washing-up liquid to the cylinder.
3. Add 5 g of finely chopped liver to the cylinder.
4. Add 2 cm^3 of hydrogen peroxide to the cylinder.
5. Note the volume of foam in the cylinder after 10 seconds and record it in the results table.
6. Repeat steps 1–5 for the other buffer solutions (pH 5, 7, 9 and 11).

2 Draw a labelled diagram to show how this investigation was carried out.

3 How would David and Ben make sure that they carried out a fair test?

pH	Trial 1 (volume of foam cm³)	Trial 2 (volume of foam cm³)	Trial 3 (volume of foam cm³)	Average volume of foam (cm³)
3	4	6	5	5
5	16	17	18	17
7	20	29	17	22
9	19	20	21	20
11	4	4	4	4

4 Why do you think they repeated each investigation three times?

It is important to analyse data to see if any repeated measurements do not match. These are called outliers. To make sure that results are reliable, the investigation should be repeated until at least two points are close in value.

5 Which data set do you think needed to be repeated again? Explain your choice.

David and Ben constructed the following graphs of their findings.

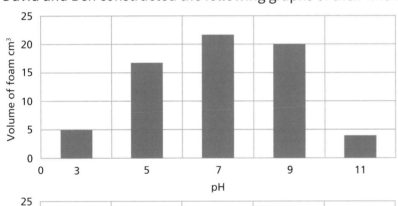

↺ **Fig. 13.5.2**
Effect of pH on the enzyme catalase

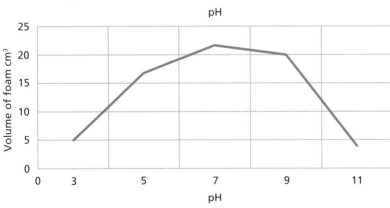

↺ **Fig. 13.5.3**
Effect of pH on the enzyme catalase

6 Discuss the advantages and disadvantages of each graph.

7 David and Ben drew conclusions from their observations about what the pH of blood must be for enzymes to work at their best. What conclusions do you think they came up with?

8 Do some research to find out if these conclusions agree with what is known about the pH of blood. Write a short paragraph to explain why the pH of blood is important for normal body functions.

Chemical Reactions: Bonding

What you may already know:

- A new substance is formed in a chemical reaction.
- Reactions can be endothermic or exothermic.
- The rate of a reaction can be changed by a number of factors, such as temperature.

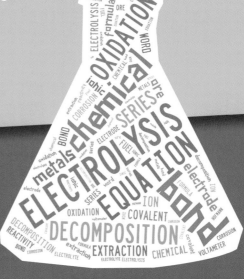

What you will learn in this chapter:

- Different types of chemical reactions.
- How metals react.
- How to use the periodic table to predict the chemical formula of various compounds.
- How to investigate the properties of different materials.

Think BIG

- Why is the chemical formula for water H_2O?
- Where does paper go when it is burned?

Puzzler

Can you crack this code?
The first letter of each of these images spells out a key word that you will come across in this section. Use the hints provided if you need to, or revisit the Puzzler after you finish this chapter.

1.

Chemical name for rust

2.

Essential element for combustion

3.

Group of odourless, colourless gases with low reactivity

1.

2.

3.

Types of Chemical Reactions

Oxidation
Neutralisation
Electrolysis
Law of conservation
  of mass
Fuel
Hydrocarbon
Fire triangle

Learning Intentions

In this topic we are learning to:

- Outline and explain different types of chemical reactions.
- Apply the law of conservation of mass to chemical reactions.
- Investigate combustion reactions.

We already know that chemicals come together in a chemical reaction to form a new substance. The following table gives an overview of the different types of chemical reactions.

Type of reaction	What the reaction involves
Oxidation	Reactions that happen when a substance reacts with oxygen. For example, combustion reactions and corrosion reactions
Neutralisation	Reactions between an acid and a base to form a salt and water
Electrolysis	A reaction that is produced by electricity or produces electricity
Decomposition	A reaction that involves breaking down a substance into simpler compounds or elements. For example, hydrogen peroxide can be decomposed into water and oxygen

In a chemical reaction, the total mass of all the reactants always equals the total mass of the products. This is known as the **law of conservation of mass**.

GO Learn more about electrolysis in Earth and Space 22.3

For example, Fig. 14.1.1 shows that when silver nitrate and sodium chloride are reacted together to produce a silver chloride and sodium nitrate solution, the mass (as shown on the mass balance) stays exactly the same.

Combustion Reactions

Chemical reactions happen at different rates. Combustion (burning) is a fast oxidation reaction.

When a substance burns, it mixes with oxygen in the air and gives out energy in the form of heat and light. You will remember that reactions that give out energy are exothermic reactions.

Fuel is a substance that burns in oxygen to produce heat.

In the school laboratory, a Bunsen burner uses methane or propane as a fuel. The valve controls the amount of air that mixes with the methane. When the air hole is open, more oxygen reaches the fuel, and the flame burns at its hottest.

Fuels, such as turf, coal, natural gas and candle wax, are made up of two elements: hydrogen and carbon. A compound that contains hydrogen and carbon is called a **hydrocarbon**.

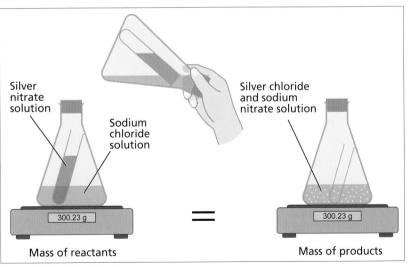

Silver nitrate solution

Sodium chloride solution

Silver chloride and sodium nitrate solution

300.23 g

300.23 g

Mass of reactants = Mass of products

Fig. 14.1.1
The law of conservation of mass

Observing combustion

A candle is made of wax. Candle wax is a fuel. It contains the elements carbon and hydrogen.

Part 1: A candle is placed on a heatproof mat. The candle is then lit. A beaker is placed over the candle.

Part 2: Three candles of different lengths are placed on a heatproof mat. The candles are lit. A beaker is placed over the candles.

Part 3: A floating candle is placed in a basin of water. The candle is lit. A beaker is placed over the candle and on top of the water.

For each investigation:

   a. Predict what will happen.

   b. Set up and carry out the investigation.

   c. Explain your observations.

➲ **Fig. 14.1.2**

| Investigation 1 | Investigation 2 | Investigation 3 |

Investigating the products of combustion

When hydrocarbons are burned, carbon dioxide and water vapour are produced. The word equation for the combustion of hydrocarbons is as follows:

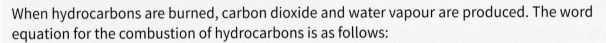

Fuel (hydrocarbon) + oxygen → carbon dioxide + water

1. Name the reactants and the products in the above reaction.

2. Plan, design, carry out and write up an investigation to show that the products of combustion are carbon dioxide and water.

3. What safety precautions did you take during this investigation?

Oxygen in Air

Air is made up of around 21 per cent oxygen gas. The investigation shown in Fig. 14.1.3 is used to show this. Copper turnings are heated using a Bunsen burner. As the copper is heated, air is passed over it by pressing on syringes. This causes a reaction between the copper and the oxygen in the air to form copper oxide.

 Learn more about the composition of air in Earth and Space 22.4

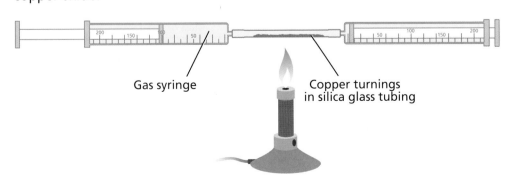

Gas syringe   Copper turnings in silica glass tubing

➲ **Fig. 14.1.3**
Measuring the percentage of oxygen in air

During the investigation, the volume of the air will decrease steadily as the oxygen in it is used up.

Copper + oxygen → copper oxide

Eventually, all the oxygen in the air will be used up to form copper oxide. The apparatus is allowed to cool (as gases expand when they are heated) and it is observed that approximately 20 cm³ of the air has been used up. The conclusion of the investigation is that 20 per cent of the air is made up of oxygen.

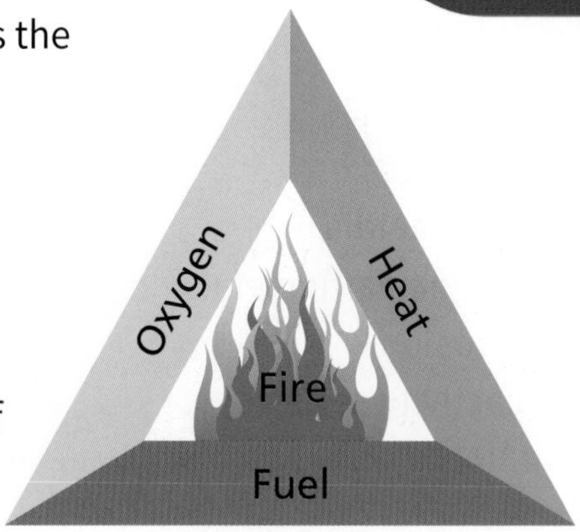

The Fire Triangle

You need three conditions to make a fire happen:

- Fuel
- Heat
- Oxygen

If you remove any part of the **fire triangle**, the fire will go out.

Fig. 14.1.4
Fire triangle

Fire safety

Fires can be put out in a number of ways. Which part of the fire triangle is being taken away in the following situations?

1. Using a carbon dioxide fire extinguisher.
2. Using a fire blanket.
3. A fire engine spraying a fire with water.
4. Creating a fire line during a forest fire.

Fig. 14.1.5
A fire line in a forest

'Silent killer'

In groups, discuss why carbon monoxide is referred to as the 'silent killer'.

Incomplete Combustion of a Fuel

If there is not enough air (oxygen) for complete combustion of a fuel, the reaction is not completely finished.

The word equation for the incomplete combustion of fuel is as follows:

Fuel (hydrocarbon) + oxygen → water + carbon monoxide

Carbon monoxide (CO) forms instead of carbon dioxide. Carbon monoxide is a colourless, odourless, toxic gas that, even in low concentrations, may lead to death.

To prevent poisoning by carbon monoxide:

- Boilers should be serviced regularly.
- Rooms should be well ventilated.
- Carbon monoxide detectors should be installed.

Fig. 14.1.6
Carbon monoxide detector

Reactions of Metals

Alkali metals

Alkaline earth metals

Corrosion

Reactivity series of metals

Learning Intentions

In this topic we are learning to:

• Describe the reactions of the alkali metals and alkaline earth metals.

• Identify the conditions needed for corrosion of metals.

• Organise metals according to how reactive they are with water and dilute acid.

Reaction of Metals with Water

When metals react with water, the products formed are a metal oxide or metal hydroxide and hydrogen gas.

When alkali metals (such as sodium) react with water, the metal floats on the surface of the water. Hydrogen gas is released and a sodium hydroxide solution is formed. This is an alkaline solution (it will turn red litmus indicator blue and has a pH greater than 7).

The word equation for this reaction is:

🎧 **Fig. 14.2.1**
Sodium catching fire when reacted with water

Sodium + water → sodium hydroxide + hydrogen

Sodium reacts faster with water than lithium. Sodium may even catch fire during the reaction. Potassium is even more reactive with water than sodium is.

Similar to the alkali metals, alkaline earth metals become more reactive as you go down group 2 on the periodic table.

Reaction of Metals with Oxygen

Sodium and potassium are shiny when freshly cut but dull almost immediately when they react with oxygen in the air.

When metals react with oxygen, the product formed is a metal oxide. For example:

Alkaline earth metals

Group 2 metals are known as the alkaline earth metals because an old name for oxide was 'earth' and their oxides are alkaline.

Magnesium + oxygen → magnesium oxide

The oxides of sodium and potassium are dull in colour. The oxide of magnesium is white. The oxide of iron is red.

Magnesium oxide is formed in the laboratory using the method shown in Fig. 14.2.3:

🎧 **Fig. 14.2.2**
Freshly cut sodium

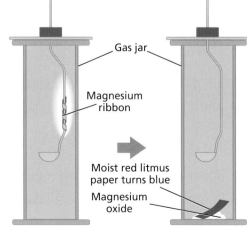

⮑ **Fig. 14.2.3**
Reaction between magnesium and oxygen to produce magnesium oxide

Gas jar

Magnesium ribbon

Moist red litmus paper turns blue

Magnesium oxide

Word equations

1. Write word equations for the reactions between the following metals and water:
   a. Lithium
   b. Potassium
2. Write word equations for the reactions between the same metals and oxygen.
3. Explain why group 1 of the periodic table are known as the alkali metals.

The table below summarises the properties and uses of the **alkali metals** and **alkaline earth metals**.

Alkali metals (group 1 metals)	Alkaline earth metals (group 2 metals)
• Have low meting points • Dull quickly in air but are shiny when freshly cut (they are soft metals stored in oil) • Are more reactive as you go down the group • Lithium is used in batteries. Sodium is used in street lamps and potassium is used in making fertilisers	• Have higher melting points than the alkali metals • Get more reactive as you go down the group • Magnesium is used in fireworks as it burns brightly, and calcium in our diet makes teeth and bones stronger

Corrosion of Metals

Corrosion is the gradual reaction of metals with water and oxygen in their environment.

A metal oxide is formed when a metal reacts with water and oxygen.

A metal oxide you will be familiar with is iron oxide (rust). Iron oxide forms on the surface of iron but it is soft and flakes off allowing the iron underneath to corrode further.

Oxygen and water are both needed for the corrosion of iron to take place. If one factor is missing, the iron will not rust.

The green colour of copper roofs is due to corrosion.

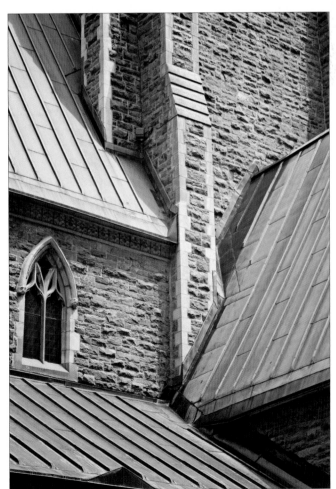

⮑ **Fig. 14.2.4**
A corroded copper roof

Investigating the conditions needed for rusting

Plan, design, carry out and write up an investigation to show that both oxygen and water are necessary for iron to rust.

Hints:

- Calcium chloride is a compound that can be used to remove moisture from air.
- Remove dissolved oxygen from water by boiling the water.
- Placing a layer of oil on top will keep the oxygen out of the water.

1. What variables will stay the same in this investigation? What variable will change?
2. What is a suitable controlled variable in this investigation?

⊃ **Fig. 14.2.5**
Rust on a metal door

Corroded metals are weaker and can be expensive to replace.

Ways to prevent corrosion include:

- Painting the metal will protect cars and large structures such as bridges.
- Covering the metal with a plastic coating prevents exposure of the metal to oxygen and water.
- Greasing the moving parts of the metal with oil.
- Plating (covering) the metal with a thin coating of another metal that does not rust. Chromium plating gives an attractive, shiny effect. Zinc is also used in plating. If the metal coating on the iron is zinc, then the iron is said to be galvanised. Zinc will protect iron even when it gets scratched.

⌒ **Fig. 14.2.6**
Galvanising a metal roof will prevent corrosion

Preventing corrosion

Plan, design, carry out and write up an investigation to examine the effectiveness of three ways of preventing the corrosion of an object containing iron.

Steel is a form of iron that corrodes easily. However, the oxides formed by some metals protect them from corrosion.

- The oxide of aluminium acts as a barrier and protects the aluminium from reacting further with water and oxygen.
- Gold, silver and platinum are unreactive and will never corrode. They remain shiny and this is one of the reasons why they are so valuable.

Changing masses

The investigation shown in Fig. 14.2.7 was set up and monitored over a period of time.

Explain why:

1. The mass of the steel wool increased.
2. Water moved up the boiling tube.

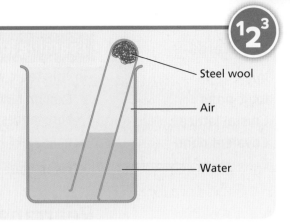

Steel wool

Air

Water

⮌ **Fig. 14.2.7**

Reactivity Series of Metals

As we have seen, some metals are very unreactive (they do not take part in chemical reactions easily) and other metals are very reactive (they combine with other substances easily to make new substances).

Scientists have put the metals in order of their reactivity, from most reactive to the least reactive. This is called the **reactivity series of metals**.

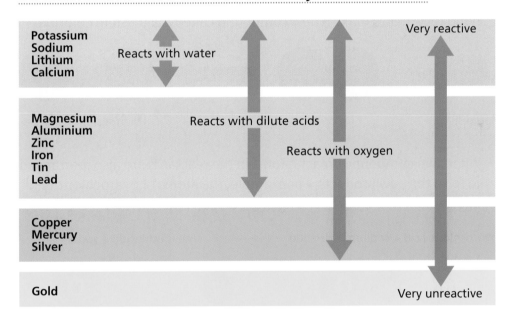

↻ **Fig. 14.2.8**
The reactivity series of metals

Investigating the reactivity of metals

Using the reaction between water and the metals listed below and the reaction between the same metals and a dilute solution of hydrochloric acid, plan, design, carry out and write up an investigation to list these metals in order of reactivity (with the most reactive metal first and the least reactive metal last): magnesium, copper, calcium, zinc.

1. What variable will you change? What variables will stay the same?
2. How will you make sure this is a fair test?
3. Write a word equation for the reactions of each of these elements with water.
4. What gas is released when a metal and an acid react?
5. Write a word equation for the reactions of each of these elements with dilute hydrochloric acid.

Atoms in Reactions

Learning Intentions

In this topic we are learning to:

- Explain how atoms in elements can be rearranged to form new substances.
- Recognise the difference between ionic and covalent bonding.
- Investigate the properties of ionic and covalent substances.

Rearranging Atoms

The law of conservation of mass tells us that the total mass of reactants in a chemical reaction always equals the total mass of the products. This is because atoms are not destroyed in a chemical reaction, they are just rearranged.

- When two elements react together to form a compound, atoms of the different elements combine with each other. For example, when magnesium reacts with chlorine, the magnesium and chlorine atoms bond together to make a new compound called magnesium chloride.

➲ **Fig. 14.3.1**
The rearrangement of atoms when hydrochloric acid reacts with sodium hydroxide

Magnesium   Chlorine   Magnesium chloride

- When two compounds react, atoms in the reactants are also rearranged to form the new products. For example, the atoms of hydrochloric acid and sodium hydroxide rearrange to form salt and water.

hydrochloric acid + sodium hydroxide ⟶ sodium chloride + water

➲ **Fig. 14.3.2**
How the atoms of each reactant rearrange to form the products salt and water

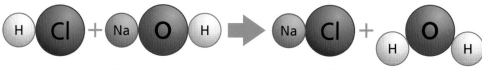

Sum of atoms of reactants = 5   Sum of atoms of products = 5

Figures 14.3.1 and 14.3.2 show that the total sum of the atoms in the reactants and the sum of the atoms in the products are the same. As a result, the mass also stays the same.

Chemical Bonds

We know that elements combine with each other to form compounds. To form a compound, the atoms of one element bond with the atoms of other elements.

Compounds form because they are more stable (have lower energy) than the atoms of the elements they are made of.

Atoms form bonds using the electrons in the outer shells only. These outer electrons can be shared between atoms in a bond or they can be transferred from one atom to another atom.

- An ionic bond occurs when one atom loses electrons and another atom gains these electrons.
- A covalent bond occurs when atoms share electrons.

During bonding, atoms lose, gain or share electrons so they can gain a full outer shell. Atoms that have a full outer shell are stable and do not react.

Ionic Bonding

All neutral atoms have equal numbers of protons and electrons. As the number of positive charges is equal to the number of negative charges, the atom has an overall neutral charge.

When an atom loses or gains an electron, it becomes an **ion**. An ion is a charged atom.

- If an atom gains an electron, it has an extra negative charge so the overall charge on the ion is negative. For example, $Cl + e^- \rightarrow Cl^{-1}$.
- If an atom loses an electron, it has fewer negative charges than positive charges so the overall charge of the ion is positive. For example, $Na \rightarrow Na^{+1} + e^-$.

All the elements on the periodic table are either metals (such as sodium or iron) or non-metals (such as chlorine or oxygen).

- Most non-metals will gain electrons to have a full outer shell and form negative ions.
- Most metals will lose electrons to have a full outer shell and form positive ions.

When metals and non-metals react, they form an **ionic bond**. An ionic bond is a force of attraction between oppositely charged ions in a compound.

Look at the two following examples of ionic bonding.

1. How sodium and chlorine react

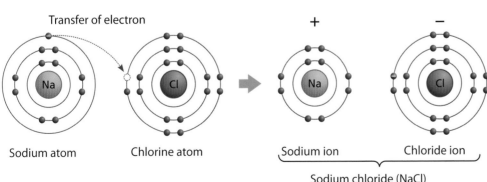

Transfer of electron

Sodium atom   Chlorine atom   Sodium ion   Chloride ion

Sodium chloride (NaCl)

The sodium atom has one electron on its outer shell. It will lose this electron to achieve a full outer shell.

The chlorine atom has seven electrons in its outer shell. It will gain an electron to achieve a full outer shell.

On losing an electron, the sodium atom becomes positively charged. It is now a sodium ion.

On gaining an electron, the chlorine atom becomes negatively charged. It is now a chloride ion.

↻ **Fig. 14.3.3**
An ionic bond between sodium and chlorine to form sodium chloride

2. How magnesium and oxygen react

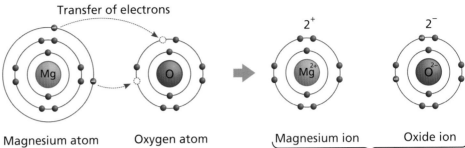

Transfer of electrons

Magnesium atom   Oxygen atom

Magnesium ion   Oxide ion

Magnesium oxide (MgO)

⮕ **Fig. 14.3.4**
An ionic bond between magnesium and oxygen to form magnesium oxide

| The magnesium atom has two electrons in its outer shell. It will lose these to achieve a full outer shell. | The oxygen atom has six electrons in its outer shell. It will gain two electrons to achieve a full outer shell. | On losing two electrons, the magnesium atom becomes positively charged. It is now a magnesium ion. | On gaining two electrons, the oxygen atom becomes negatively charged. It is now an oxide ion. |

A grain of salt

1 2³

In one grain of salt there are approximately 1,200,000,000,000,000,000 atoms, half of which are sodium atoms.

In an ionic bond, metal and non-metal ions combine with one another to produce an orderly arrangement of ions called a **crystal lattice**.

⮕ **Fig. 14.3.5**
A sodium chloride (salt) crystal lattice

Covalent Bonding

A **covalent bond** is formed when pairs of electrons are shared between two atoms. The shells containing the outer electrons overlap and this allows atoms to share electrons.

Look at the two following examples of covalent bonding.

1. Water

When electrons are shared by hydrogen and oxygen atoms to form water, two hydrogen atoms share one electron each with an oxygen atom.
The three atoms gain a full outer shell by sharing electrons and a water molecule is formed.

⮕ **Fig. 14.3.6**
How electrons are shared by hydrogen and oxygen atoms to form water

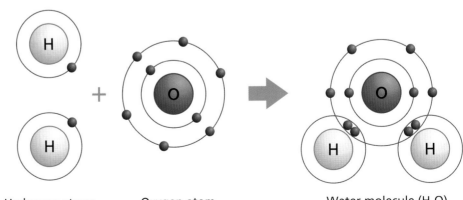

Hydrogen atoms   Oxygen atom   Water molecule (H_2O)

2. Methane

Methane is another substance that has covalent bonding between the elements that make it up. Each methane molecule has four hydrogen atoms covalently bonded to a carbon atom.

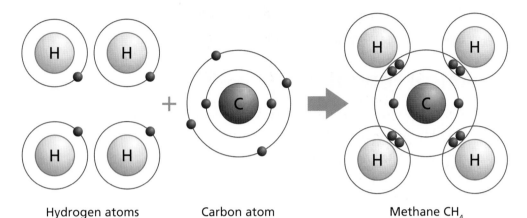

Hydrogen atoms   Carbon atom   Methane CH_4

↻ **Fig. 14.3.7**
How electrons are shared by hydrogen and carbon atoms to form methane

Investigating the properties of ionic and covalent compounds

Copy and complete the table for the substances listed to identify each substance as an ionic or covalent compound: sugar, urea, washing soda crystal, table salt and benzoic acid.

1. Research the melting point of each compound.
2. Plan how you will test if each substance will conduct electricity.
3. Did your predicted bond type match up with the actual bond type? If not, explain why.
4. Each compound listed is found in everyday substances around the home. List an everyday substance that contains the compounds you tested.

Name of substance being tested	State at room temperature	Melting point	Does it conduct electricity?	Predicted bond (based on collected data)	Actual bond (based on verifying data from a reliable source)	Everyday use
Sugar						

Properties of Ionic and Covalent Substances

The properties of ionic and covalent substances are usually the opposite of each other. The table below lists the properties of ionic and covalent substances.

Ionic substances	Covalent substances
Usually solids	Usually liquids or gases
Have high melting points and boiling points	Have low melting points and boiling points
Conduct electricity in liquid form or if they dissolve in water	Do not conduct electricity

Properties of materials are determined by the bonding that holds that material together.

Chemical Formulae

Key Words

Chemical formula
Coefficient
Subscript
Valency

Coefficient and subscript

Coefficient is the number in front of the formula. It indicates the number of molecules or ions of each kind involved in the reaction.

Subscript is the number to the lower right of the chemical symbol. It indicates the number of atoms of that element found in the compound.

Chemical Formulae

The name of a compound is useful as it usually tells us some of the elements that the compound contains.

Every compound has a **chemical formula** (when we talk about more than one formula, we refer to them as formulae).

Chemical formulae are put together using the chemical symbols for the elements that make up the compound.

A chemical formula shows the ratio of atoms of each element in the compound. For example:

- The chemical formula for water is H_2O. This formula shows that for every oxygen atom there are two hydrogen atoms.

- The chemical formula for carbon dioxide is CO_2. The formula shows that for every carbon atom there are two oxygen atoms.

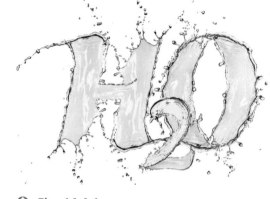

🎧 **Fig. 14.4.1**
The 2 in H_2O is a subscript

When writing a chemical formula, the numbers of atoms in the compound should be on the right-hand side of the chemical symbol and written as subscript (in a smaller size). If we put '2' in front of a formula it means we have two molecules. For example, $2H_2O = (H_2O + H_2O)$.

Chemical formulae

Copy and complete the table by giving the name of the elements that make up the following substances and the ratio for each element in the compound: sodium chloride (NaCl), silver chloride (AgCl), carbon dioxide (CO_2), magnesium oxide (MgO), lead iodide (PbI_2), aluminium chloride ($AlCl_3$)

Example:

Name of compound	Chemical formula	Elements present	Ratio of elements present
Sodium sulfide	Na_2S	Sodium Sulfur	Na : S 2 : 1

Writing Chemical Formulae: Ionic Compounds

To predict the chemical formula of ionic compounds, you first need to find out the charge on an ion using the periodic table.

Using the periodic table to predict what ions are formed

Using the example as a guide, write out the electronic configurations for the atoms listed below. Use the configurations to predict the type of ion (positive or negative) that the atom will form.

> **Example:**
>
> Electronic configurations of sodium: 2, 8, 1
>
> It will lose 1 electron and become $[2, 8]^{+1}$
>
> Sodium ion = Na^{+1}

- Group 1: Lithium and potassium
- Group 2: Magnesium and calcium
- Group 6: Oxygen and sulfur
- Group 7: Fluorine and bromine

Can you spot a trend that connects the periodic table to the ions formed by the atoms of the elements?

The periodic table can be used in constructing the chemical formulae for compounds that form between metals and non-metals.

Naming compounds

When naming a compound formed between a metal and a non-metal:

- The name of the metal always comes first.
- The name of the non-metal follows and its ending is changed to '–ide'.

For example, sodium and chlorine combine to make sodium chloride.

A compound is always neutral. This means the charges of the ions in the compound must balance.

When writing the chemical formula for an ionic compound, you need to work out the correct ratio of ions that will give an overall neutral charge for the compound.

Look at the following two examples of how to use the periodic table to work out chemical formulae for ionic compounds.

1. Potassium iodide (KI)

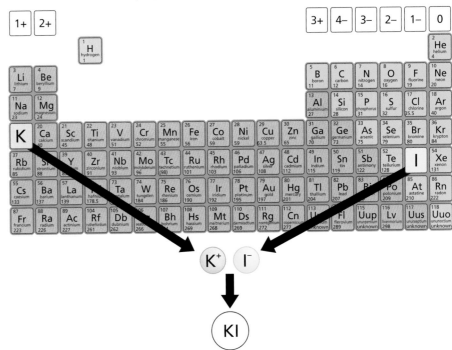

Fig. 14.4.2
How to use the periodic table to work out the chemical formula of potassium iodide

2. Magnesium iodide (MgI₂)

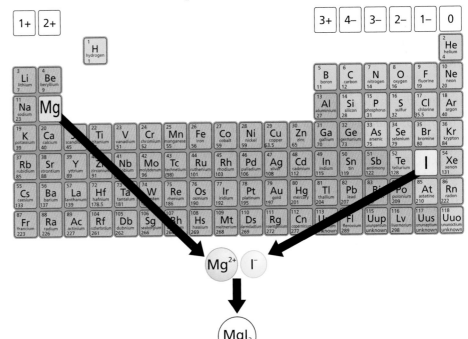

Fig. 14.4.3
How to use the periodic table to work out the chemical formula for magnesium iodide

Constructing the chemical formula of ionic compounds

1. 2³

1. List the elements used to form each of these products:
   - Sodium chloride
   - Sodium sulfide
   - Potassium oxide
   - Barium sulfide
   - Calcium oxide
   - Magnesium chloride
2. Using the periodic table, construct the chemical formula for each of the products listed in question 1.
3. Using the periodic table, write the name and formula of three other compounds not in the above list.

Writing Chemical Formula: Covalent Compounds

When writing the chemical formula of a covalent compound, you need to satisfy the valency of that element. **Valency** is the combining power of the element. It is the number of bonds that elements need to form in a compound.

Figure 14.4.4 shows the combining powers of each group of elements on the periodic table. From this, you can see that carbon has a combining power of 4. This means carbon needs to form four bonds.

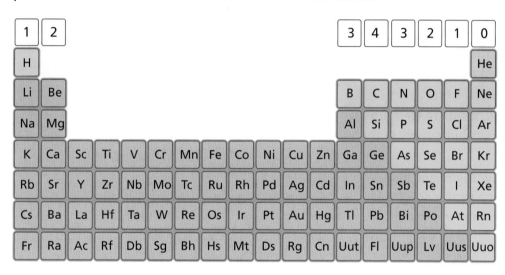

⊆ **Fig. 14.4.4**
Combining powers of element groups on the periodic table

For example, when carbon bonds with another element, it needs to create four bonds with that element. Oxygen has a combining power of two. The building blocks in Fig. 14.4.5 show how carbon and oxygen combine to form carbon dioxide.

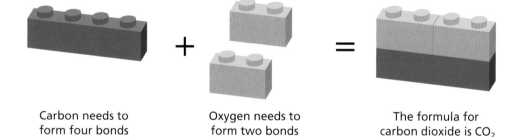

Carbon needs to form four bonds

Oxygen needs to form two bonds

The formula for carbon dioxide is CO_2

⊆ **Fig. 14.4.5**
Building blocks used to model the covalent bonding in carbon dioxide (CO_2)

Constructing the chemical formula of covalent compounds

Using Fig. 14.4.4, construct the chemical formula for each of these compounds:

- Water (compound of oxygen and hydrogen).
- Methane (compound of carbon and hydrogen).
- Ammonia (compound of nitrogen and hydrogen).
- Hydrogen sulfide (compound of hydrogen and sulfur).
- Carbon tetrafluoride (compound of carbon and fluorine).

Chapter Summary

- There are different types of chemical reactions: oxidation, neutralisation, electrolysis and decomposition.
- Oxidation reactions happen when a substance reacts with oxygen. For example, combustion reactions and corrosion (rusting) of metals.
- Decomposition reactions break down a substance into simpler compounds or elements. Heat is often used to bring about decomposition.
- In a chemical reaction, the total mass of all the reactants always equals the total mass of the products. This is known as the law of conservation of mass.
- During combustion reactions, a substance burns with oxygen in the air and gives out energy in the form of heat and light.
- A compound that contains hydrogen and carbon is called a hydrocarbon. When hydrocarbons are burned, carbon dioxide and water vapour are produced.
- You need three conditions for fire: fuel, heat and oxygen.
- When metals react with water, a metal oxide or metal hydroxide and hydrogen gas are formed.
- When metals react with oxygen, a metal oxide is formed.
- Corrosion is the gradual weakening of metals by chemical reaction with their environment.

- Iron reacts with water and oxygen in the air to form iron oxide (rust).
- By comparing how easily metals react with air, water and dilute acid, scientists have developed an order of reactivity of metals. This is called the reactivity series.
- To form a compound, the atoms of one element form bonds with the atoms of other elements.
- Atoms form bonds using only the electrons in their outermost shell.
- Ionic bonding occurs when one atom loses electrons and another atom gains electrons. Covalent bonding occurs when atoms share electrons.
- An ion is a charged atom. It may be positive or negative.
- A compound is always neutral and so the charges of the ions in the compound must balance.

Go to your Portfolio to check what you have learned in this chapter.

The BIG Challenge

It has been suggested that salt speeds up the rusting of iron. This may be a problem for car owners who live by the sea and during the winter when salt is used to grit roads. Remember, salt dissolved in water lowers the freezing point of water.

Design and carry out an investigation to test the hypothesis 'Salt speeds up iron rusting'. If possible, use time-lapse photography to record the changes that take place during the investigation.

Take the chapter 14 quiz on educateplus.ie.

Questions

1. Copy and fill in the blanks:

a. _____ reactions occur when a substance reacts with oxygen. _____ and _____ are examples of _____ reactions.

b. A _____ is a compound that contains hydrogen and carbon.

c. When a fuel burns it gives out _____ in the form of _____ and _____ .

d. The three conditions needed for a fire are _____ , _____ and _____ .

e. When alkali metals react with water, a metal _____ and _____ gas are formed.

f. When metals react with oxygen, a _____ _____ is formed. Rust is the oxide of _____ .

g. An _____ bond is formed when atoms lose and gain _____ .

h. A _____ bond is formed when atoms _____ electrons.

i. An _____ is a charged atom. Ions can have a _____ or a _____ charge.

j. When an atom loses an electron, it has a _____ charge. When an atom gains an electron, it has a _____ charge.

2. Provide an explanation for each of the following:

a. Gold can be dug out of the earth as a pure metal (element).

b. The noble gases were the last gases to be discovered.

3. Which rust prevention method would you use in each of the following and why?

a. Protecting a lawnmower in the winter.

b. Protecting a car bumper.

c. Protecting iron gates.

4. What term would you use to describe the following reactions? Choose from oxidation, decomposition or combustion.

a. Copper + oxygen → copper oxide
   ($2Cu + O_2 → 2CuO$)

b. Methane + oxygen → carbon dioxide + water
   ($CH_4 + 2O_2 → CO_2 + 2H_2O$)

c. Water → hydrogen + oxygen
   ($2H_2O → 2H_2 + O_2$)

d. Hydrogen peroxide → water + oxygen
   ($2H_2O_2 → 2H_2O + O_2$)

5. Suggest a reason for the following:

a. Aeroplanes are made of aluminium and not steel.

b. Silver coins are not made of pure silver.

c. Bicycles and cars are painted.

d. The roofs of sheds are often galvanised.

6. The following image shows the set-up for an investigation into how iron nails rust.

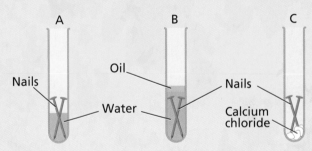

a. In which of the test tubes will the iron nails rust?

b. Why was the water in test-tube B boiled and then covered with a layer of oil?

c. What is the function of the calcium chloride?

d. How did the students ensure this was a fair test?

7. Use the periodic table to write the chemical formula for each of the following compounds:

a. Beryllium chloride

b. Aluminium chloride

c. Barium bromide

d. Lithium nitride

e. Potassium sulfide

f. Aluminium oxide

g. Magnesium nitride

8. Why does sugar in water not conduct electricity but salt in water does?

Working as a Scientist

Communicating Science

Formulae and Equations

Chemical formulae and equations are used by scientists to explain what happens during chemical reactions.

Chemical equations show the bonds that are broken and formed when atoms are rearranged during a chemical reaction. They tell the scientist what chemicals are involved in a reaction and the products that have been formed. They also tell the scientist how much of each reactant is needed in the reaction and how much product will be formed.

There are two types of equation:

- Word equations. For example:

> Hydrochloric acid + sodium hydroxide → sodium chloride + water

- Chemical equations. For example: $HCl + NaOH \rightarrow NaCl + H_2O$

Use what you have learned about formulae and equations in this chapter to complete the following tasks.

Identifying the parts of a chemical equation

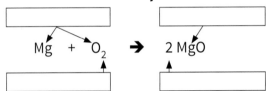

1 **Label the chemical equation above using the following labels:**
  - Product
  - Reactants
  - Subscript
  - Coefficient

Linking subscripts and coefficients

2 **In boxes a–e below**

  i. Circle each subscript in the chemical formula.
  ii. Draw a square around each coefficient.
  iii. Answer the questions related to each chemical formula.

a.
$$O_2$$
What does the O represent?

_____

b.
$$CO_2$$
How many atoms of each element are there?

C = _____ O = _____

c.
$$5H_2$$
How many atoms of hydrogen are there?

d.
$$2Na_2SO_4$$
How many atoms of each element are there?

Na = _____ S = _____ O = _____

e.
$$2C_2H_6$$
How many atoms of each element are in the formula shown?

C = _____ H = _____

Building a model to explain chemical equations

Equipment: Nuts and bolts, a cup.

- Put some nuts and bolts in the cup. Count the number of each present and record in the table.

- Now imagine that the nuts and bolts react with each other. The product that you are to make consists of two nuts on each bolt. Your goal is to make as many of the product as possible.

3 **Copy and complete the following table.**

Item		How many?
a.	Nuts	
b.	Bolts	
c.	Nut/bolt product	
d.	Nuts left over	
e.	Bolts left over	

Fig. 14.6.1

4 **Write out a word equation (use your own words for the reactant and product) for this reaction.**

5 **Using N as the symbol for the nuts and B as the symbol for the bolts, write out a chemical equation for this reaction.**

6 **If you were given 14 nuts, how many bolts would you need to make the maximum quantity of product? How much product would you make?**

7 **If you produced 23 products, how many nuts and bolts did you start with?**

When balancing an equation, it is important to ensure that you have the same number and type of atoms before and after the reaction has taken place. This is because matter cannot be created or destroyed.

A balanced equation has the same type and the same number of each atom on the left-hand side and the right-hand side of the arrow.

8 **Write a word equation for the reaction in question 5. Then write a balanced chemical equation for the same reaction.**

Balancing chemical equations

9 **Balance the chemical equation for each of the following reactions.**

a. ☐ Mg + ☐ O_2 → ☐ MgO

b. ☐ CF_4 + ☐ Br_2 → ☐ CBr_4 + ☐ F_2

c. ☐ H_2O_2 → ☐ H_2O + ☐ O_2

Physical World

The physical world is at the heart of everything. Physics helps us understand the world beyond us, the world around us and the world inside us.

The physical world is the world of matter and energy. As we study the physical world, we will learn about force, acceleration, sound, light, heat and radioactivity.

The physical world explains how things 'work', from computers to particle accelerators. It also helps us to understand the wonders of nature – the movement of the tides, the eruption of volcanoes, how our eyes see and gravity.

◯ **Fig. 1**
Knowledge of the physical world can help us to understand the wonders of nature

Physicists need to be good problem solvers. They have to ask questions and be accurate. This can lead to new discoveries. Nuclear fusion and renewable energy from the Sun are examples of amazing advances in the physical world.

⊂ **Fig. 2**
Physics helps explain how things 'work'

⊃ **Fig. 3**
Solar energy is a form of renewable energy

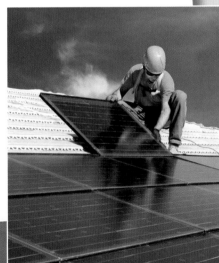

What you may already know:

- Energy from the Sun gives our planet heat and light.
- Some quantities can be measured, such as temperature, time, length and mass.
- Distance, time, speed, acceleration and force are all related to motion.
- Electricity can power devices, such as electrical appliances in your home, your mobile phone and even some cars.
- Magnets can stick to some metals and to each other.
- There are different sources of power, such as batteries, nuclear power and wind power.

Code Breaker

Crack the code to reveal the name and well-known quote of a scientist who is famous for developing our understanding of the physical world.

e	f	i	n	o	p	s	t
:-)	@	XX	!	#	%	$	XY

L:-)ar! @r#m   y:-)$XY:-)rday.   LXXv:-)   @#r   XY#day.   H#%:-)

_____ _____ _____.   _____ ___ _____.

@#r   XY#m#rr#w. Th:-)   XXm%#rXYa!XY   XYhXX!g   XX$

___ _____.   ____ _____   _____ ___

!#XY   XY# $XY#%   qu:-)$XYXX#!XX!g.

____ ___ _____ _____.

Alb:-)rXY   EXX!$XY:-)XX!

_____ _____

Think BIG

- How is energy used and changed in the physical world?
- Is time travel possible?
- Why is the sky blue?
- How can modern physics help to make a sustainable planet Earth?

In **Physical World** you will learn about:

Chapter 15 Physical quantities that can be measured and how to measure them.

Chapter 16 Energy – what it is, its different forms and how it is used and transferred through different processes.

Chapter 17 Types of motion and how forces can affect objects.

Chapter 18 Magnetism and electricity – causes, effects and uses.

Chapter 19 How light, sound and heat affect how we see, hear and feel in the physical world.

Chapter 20 How new discoveries and technologies in the physical world have changed science, the environment and society.

Chapter 15

Measuring the Physical World

What you may already know:

- Some quantities can be measured, such as time, length, area, volume and speed.

- To measure things we use instruments, such as a stopwatch, a ruler, a measuring jug or even a Garda speed gun.

What you will learn in this chapter:

- SI units are the standard units of measurement in most countries.

- The difference between basic and derived units.

- Physical quantities that we can measure and the ways we can measure them.

- The difference between random errors and systematic errors when taking measurements.

Think BIG

- Why do we measure and have units?

- Why are there 24 hours in a day?

Puzzler

Can you crack this code?

The first letter of each image spells out a key word you will come across in this chapter. Use the hints provided if you need to, or revisit the Puzzler after you finish this chapter.

1.
Planet between Saturn and Neptune

2.
Scientist famous for an apple falling on his head

3.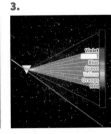
Colour between blue and violet in a rainbow

4.
Used to measure temperature

5.
Human-made or natural objects that orbit planets

1. _____
2. _____
3. _____
4. _____
5. _____

SI Units

Learning Intentions

In this topic we are learning to:

- Explain what is meant by physical quantity.
- Identify SI units of measurement for different physical quantities.
- Compare basic SI units with derived SI units.

Key Words

Quantity
Physical quantity
Measuring
Metric system
SI units
Derived units

🎧 Fig. 15.1.1

How many living things can you count in the above picture? If you answered ten, you are correct. If you answered three cows, two sheep, one fox and four humans, you are also correct. The animals can be counted together but your natural instinct might have been to group them based on the numbers of different 'things'.

In the same way, the physical world is made up of different things that we measure based on what they are.

An exact amount or number of things is called a **quantity**. A **physical quantity** is a quantity that can be measured.

The physical world is interested in the measurement of physical quantities, ways of **measuring** them and the relationships between these quantities.

People and Science

William Thomson, also known as Lord Kelvin, was an Irish mathematician, physicist and engineer. He is known for developing the value for absolute zero, the lowest known temperature in the universe. The SI unit of temperature, the Kelvin, is named in his honour.

🎧 Fig. 15.1.2
Lord Kelvin

'Quantity'

ⓐⓑⓒ

The word 'quantity' comes from the Latin word *quantus,* meaning 'how great, how much'.

I often say that when you can measure what you are speaking about, and express it in numbers, you know something about it; but when you cannot measure it, when you cannot express it in numbers, your knowledge is of a meagre and unsatisfactory kind.

Basic Units

By the 1960s, many scientists all over the world had agreed to use the same system of measuring physical quantities, called the **metric system**. This international system paved the way for the **SI units** of measurement that are widely used today.

The full SI system has seven basic units of measurement. We will look at five of them. The quantities and their units of measurement are listed in the table below.

Physical quantity	Symbol	SI unit of measurement (and symbol)
Length	l	metre (m)
Time	t	second (s)
Mass	m	kilogram (kg)
Temperature	T	kelvin (K)
Electric current	I	amperes, or amps for short (A)

◯ **Fig. 15.1.3**
Basic SI units

Problems can occur when people do not agree on a common system of units.

Researching units

Do some research to find out the answers to the following questions:

1. What are the two other SI units not listed in the table above?
2. Where did imperial units of measurement come from?
3. What makes a unit a basic unit?
4. Why are there 24 hours in a day?

Derived Units

Some other physical quantities are measured in **derived units**.

Derived units are units that are calculated by combining basic units in a specific way.

For example, the unit for speed is metres per second. It is derived by dividing the basic unit of distance (metres) by the basic unit of time (seconds).

$$\text{Speed} = \frac{\text{Distance}}{\text{Time}} = \frac{\text{Metres}}{\text{Seconds}} = \text{metres per second, or m/s}$$

Other common derived units are density, power, voltage and resistance. We will learn more about these units in later chapters.

Recognising division in units

When you see the word 'per' between two basic units, it means the first unit has been divided by the second one. For example, 'metres per second' tells us that speed is calculated by dividing the unit for distance (metres) by the unit for time (seconds).

A forward slash (/) can also be used to mean 'per' or 'divided by'. For example, metres per second and m/s mean the same thing.

Using your *Formulae and Tables* booklet, find the formula for each quantity in the following table.

Physical quantity	Unit	Found by dividing ...
Speed	m/s	Distance by time
Density	kg/m³	_____ by _____
Power	Watts (W)	_____ by _____
Voltage	Volts (V)	_____ by _____
Resistance	Ohms (Ω)	_____ by _____

People and Science

Scottish scientist **James Watt** made improvements to the steam engine, which marked an important moment in the Industrial Revolution.

The concept of 'horsepower' to describe the power of different engines was developed by Watt.

➲ **Fig. 15.1.4**
Old Bess, an engine made by Watt, in the Science Museum in London

Famous symbols

Some symbols for units are represented by capital letters, such as newtons (N), joules (J), watts (W) and kelvins (K). These units have been named in honour of key scientists who made discoveries in the area related to that physical quantity. For example, the unit of power, the watt, is named after James Watt.

Fun Fact

The definition of 'time' has troubled people for thousands of years. It is accepted as a physical quantity that allows us to order events in the past, present or future. The German physicist Albert Einstein famously said that 'the only reason for time is so that everything doesn't happen at once'. How would you define time?

Measuring Length and Area

Learning Intentions

In this topic we are learning to:

- Describe how to use various instruments for measuring length.
- Measure and calculate the area of a regular and irregular shape.

The instrument you choose to measure with depends on the scale and size of the quantity you are trying to measure.

For example, if you are trying to measure the length of a football field, a ruler from your pencil case might not be the best tool. Or if you are trying to measure the length of the centre circle on a football field, a straight object such as a metre stick would not accurately measure the curve of the line.

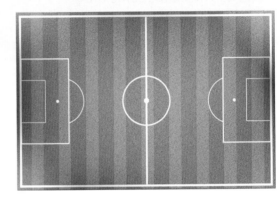

Fig. 15.2.1
Overhead view of a football field

Measuring Length

The SI unit for **length** is metres (m). There are many instruments that can be used to measure different lengths.

- For measuring the length of straight lines, you could use a **ruler**, a **metre stick**, a measuring tape or a **trundle wheel**.

- For measuring the length of curved lines, you could use an **opisometer** (for short lines) or a trundle wheel (for long curved lines).

- For measuring widths, thicknesses and lengths of small objects, you could use a **Vernier calliper** or a **micrometer**.

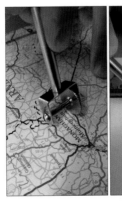

Fig. 15.2.2
A worker measuring distances with a trundle wheel as part of work to lay a new water pipe

Fig. 15.2.3
An opisometer is traced along the curved line. It is then placed next to a ruler and drawn back to its zero point in a straight line. The length of this straight line is the same as the length of the curved line

Fig. 15.2.4
A Vernier calliper being used to measure the diameter of a bolt

Fig. 15.2.5
A micrometer being used to measure the thickness of a coin

Plan, design, carry out and write up an investigation to answer the following question: if you drew a straight line with a brand-new biro until it ran out, how long would the line be?

Where am I?

Using a scaled map of Ireland and an opisometer, can you work out where this picture might have been taken?

⟱ Fig. 15.2.6

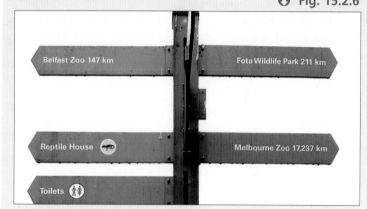

Measuring Area

Area is the amount of space taken up by a two-dimensional shape. The SI unit for area is metres squared (m^2).

If a shape has regular dimensions, its area can be found using a standard equation from your *Formulae and Tables* booklet. For example:

- Area of a square = length x breadth
- Area of a circle = π x radius x radius (πr^2)

If a shape has irregular dimensions (such as your hand or a leaf), its area is more difficult to find. One way of finding the area of irregular shapes is to trace them onto a sheet of graph paper, as shown in Fig. 15.2.7.

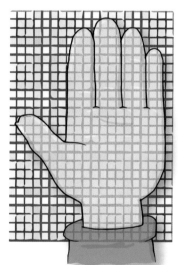

For example, the number of squares covered by your hand = 867.

Each square has an area of 1 mm^2.

So, the total area of your hand =

867 x 1 mm^2 = 867 mm^2

🎧 **Fig. 15.2.7**
Calculating the area of your hand

Areas at school, areas at home

Carry out the following tasks and present your data in a suitable table.

1. Find three items in the school laboratory that have a regular shape. Using appropriate measurement instruments, calculate their areas.

2. Find some objects at home that have an irregular shape. Trace their outline onto graph paper and use the method described in Fig. 15.2.7 to find their area. Having carried out this method, consider the following:

    a. Do you think this is an accurate way of finding the area of an irregular shape?

    b. Can you suggest any ways to make this method more accurate?

    c. Can you suggest any other methods that could be used?

Measuring Mass and Volume

Key Words

Mass
Scales
Electronic mass balance
Spring balance
Volume
Graduated cylinder
Meniscus
Overflow can

Learning Intentions

In this topic we are learning to:

- Define mass and volume.
- Describe ways to measure the mass of different objects.
- Outline the correct use of a graduated cylinder and investigate how to measure the volume of regular- and irregular-shaped objects.

Measuring Mass

Mass is the amount of matter in an object.

The SI unit for mass is the kilogram (kg). In the school laboratory, a lot of masses will be smaller quantities and are measured in grams (g).

Some of the instruments that can be used for measuring mass are:

- Bathroom **scales** for measuring the mass of a person.

- An **electronic mass balance** for measuring the mass of a beaker of water.

- A **spring balance** for measuring the mass of an apple or a banana.

Fig. 15.3.1
A person on a bathroom scale

Fig. 15.3.2
A beaker of water on an electronic mass balance

Fig. 15.3.3
A weight hanging from a spring balance

Measuring Volume

The **volume** of an object is the amount of space it takes up. The SI unit for volume is the cubic metre (m^3). A lot of the volumes you come across in the laboratory will be smaller quantities and are measured in cubic centimetres (cm^3).

Measuring volume depends on the shape and size of the object being measured.

- If you want to measure the volume of a regular shape – such as a wooden block or a cylinder – use a ruler to measure its dimensions. The volume of the block in Fig. 15.3.4 can be calculated using the following formula.

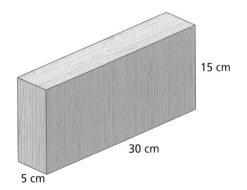

15 cm
30 cm
5 cm

Fig. 15.3.4
A wooden block

Volume = length x breadth x height
Volume = 30 x 5 x 15 = 2,250 cm^3

- If you want to measure the volume of a liquid, use a **graduated cylinder**. When liquids are poured into a graduated cylinder, the surface of the liquid does not appear to be level. The centre point of the liquid appears to be lower than the edges touching the cylinder. This bowl shape is known as a **meniscus**.

Many meniscus meanings!

The word 'meniscus' is also used to describe a part of the knee joint in humans. Find out why.

- If you want to measure the volume of a small object with an irregular shape, place it in a graduated cylinder with a known volume of water. You can then record the new level of the water. The difference between the levels is the volume of the object.

- If you want to find the volume of an irregular shaped object that will not fit into a graduated cylinder (for example, a large stone), it can be placed in an **overflow can** filled with water. As the stone is lowered into the water, the water will spill out of the can and is collected by the graduated cylinder. The volume of water collected is the volume of the stone.

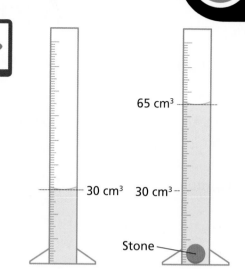

65 cm³

30 cm³   30 cm³

Stone

The volume of the stone
= 65 – 30 = 35 cm³

🎧 **Fig. 15.3.5**
Measuring the volume of an irregular object using a graduated cylinder

Overflow can

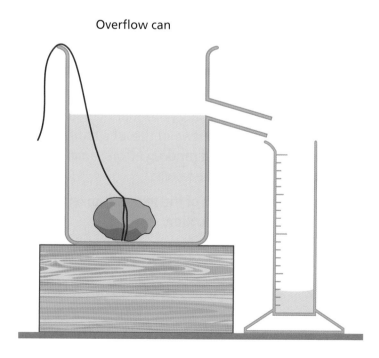

How to use a graduated cylinder

To get an accurate reading for the volume of a liquid from a graduated cylinder, you need to take the reading at eye level from the bottom of the meniscus, as shown in Fig. 15.3.7.

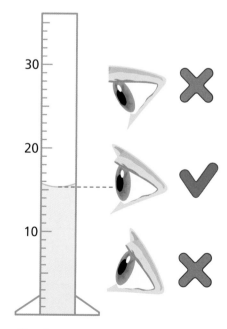

🎧 **Fig. 15.3.7**
The correct way to read from a graduated cylinder

Accuracy in Measurements

Key Words

Random errors
Average
Outlier
Systematic errors
Zero error

Learning Intentions

In this topic we are learning to:

- Distinguish between random and systematic errors.
- Reflect on how random and systematic errors can be reduced.

We measure physical quantities to collect a set of numbers for the unit being measured. When we have a large amount of these numbers, we have collected a set of data.

We collect sets of data for physical quantities for the following reasons:

1. To gather evidence that can be used to test a hypothesis.
2. To get numerical evidence to explain why something works the way it does.
3. To find patterns and relationships between the physical quantities being measured.
4. To find out when the data does not turn out the way we expect it to.

It is very important that the data we collect is accurate. If we do not measure physical quantities in the correct way, we end up with inaccurate data. When this happens, it is known as an error in the measurement.

There are two main sources of errors when taking measurements: random errors and systematic errors.

◔ **Fig. 15.4.1**
A graph showing outliers

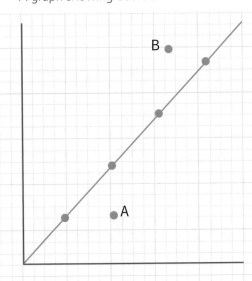

Random Errors

Random errors cause specific readings to be too high or too low.

Random errors are caused by taking a measurement the wrong way or by a difference in the reaction times of two people taking a measurement.

They often happen when a large number of readings have been taken and only one or two of these readings do not fit with the others. To avoid random errors, an **average** (or mean) of the data should be taken.

When compared to the rest of the readings taken, a random error will stand out as an **outlier**.

For example, in the graph in Fig. 15.4.1 the data collected at A and B are outliers.

Spotting random errors

Make a list of the types of random errors that could occur:

a. When you measure the length of a curved line.

b. When you are reading the volume of a liquid from a graduated cylinder.

Systematic Errors

Systematic errors cause all readings to be above or below the right value.

Systematic errors can happen when the measuring instrument is faulty or has not been set correctly, or when a person takes every measurement the wrong way.

A **zero error** is a type of systematic error. It happens when you use an instrument that has not been set to zero. This may be because of wear and tear (for example, the ends of a metre stick wearing away) or forgetting to reset an instrument (such as an electronic balance).

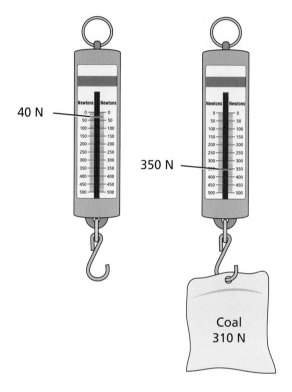

↻ **Fig. 15.4.2**
A worn metre stick

↻ **Fig. 15.4.3**
The spring balance on the left should read zero, but because of a systematic error it reads 40 N with nothing attached to the hook. Now every reading will be heavier by 40 N. The actual weight of the bag of coal is 310 N, but the balance reads 350 N

Zeroing an Electronic Balance

Most electronic balances have a button on the front that says 'zero' or 'tare'.

When you turn on the balance, press this button once before you use the balance. This will reset the reading on the balance to zero.

↻ **Fig. 15.4.4**
Zeroing an electronic balance

Chapter Summary

- A physical quantity is a quantity that can be measured.
- SI units are the accepted units of measurement for physical quantities.
- There are two types of units: basic units and derived units.
- The SI unit for time is seconds (s).
- The SI unit for length is metres (m).
- A ruler and a metre stick can be used to measure the length of straight lines.
- An opisometer and a trundle wheel can be used to measure the length of curved lines.
- A Vernier calliper and a micrometer can be used to measure the width, thickness and length of small objects.
- Area is the amount of space taken up by a two-dimensional shape.
- The SI unit for area is metres squared (m^2).
- Mass is the amount of matter in an object.

- The SI unit for mass is the kilogram (kg).
- Instruments that can be used to measure mass include bathroom scales, an electronic mass balance and a spring balance.
- The volume of an object is the amount of space it takes up.
- The SI unit of volume is the cubic metre (m^3).
- A graduated cylinder can be used to measure the volume of a liquid.
- When using a graduated cylinder, read at eye level and from the bottom of the meniscus.
- To measure accurately, it is important to avoid errors.
- Random errors cause specific readings to be either too high or too low.
- Systematic errors cause all readings to be above or below the right value.
- A zero error is a type of systematic error that happens when an instrument has not been set to zero.

The BIG Challenge

A group of American tourists plan to visit Ireland. They have emailed Fáilte Ireland, the tourism organisation, to say they are confused by the measurements and units used here.

You have been hired by Fáilte Ireland to help the tourists to safely find their way around Ireland. Give a presentation to your classmates about your ideas, paying particular attention to the following:

- The differences between the types of measurement systems used in the USA and in Ireland.
- The physical quantities they should be aware of and where they might see them (think of road signs, maps, food packaging, weather reports and so on). Make sure you mention time, distance, speed, mass and temperature. (Take some photos to include in your presentation of the places where you commonly see these quantities used.)
- The SI units for these quantities, but also the other types of units they may come across.
- How to carry out conversions from the units used in the USA to those used in Ireland.

Go to your Portfolio to check what you have learned in this chapter.

Take the chapter 15 quiz on educateplus.ie.

Questions

1. Copy and fill in the blanks:

   a. The physical world is interested in the measurement of physical _____, ways of _____ them and the _____ between them.

   b. By the 1960s, many scientists had agreed on a common system of measurement of physical quantities called the _____ _____. This paved the way for the _____ _____ of measurement.

   c. The SI unit for time is the _____, the SI unit for length is the _____ and the SI unit for mass is the _____.

   d. A unit that has been produced from combining basic units is known as a _____ _____.

   e. To measure accurate widths, thicknesses and lengths, you can use a _____ _____.

   f. The _____ of an object is a measure of how much matter is in that object.

   g. The amount of space an object takes up is known as its _____.

   h. If you want to measure the volume of a liquid, you can use a _____ _____. Make sure to take your readings at _____ _____ and from the _____ of the _____.

   i. When measuring with a faulty technique, or when there is a difference between the reaction times of two people taking measurements, this is known as a _____ _____. When this type of error occurs, the data will stand out as an _____.

   j. _____ _____ cause all readings to be above or below a certain value.

2. Describe the appropriate instruments and method for measuring the following:

   a. The diameter of a golf ball.

   b. The area of a dog's foot.

   c. The volume of a box of matches.

3. Over the course of one day, make a list of everywhere that you see units. Make a note of where you see them and what they are measurements of.

4. Use your *Formulae and Tables* booklet to complete the following table:

Physical quantity	Symbol	SI unit of measurement ( )
Length		
		Second (s)
Mass		
Temperature		
		Amperes, or amps for short (A)
Speed		
		Metres per second squared (m/s²)
		Volts (V)

5. Pádraig wants to see if the leaf area of plants in his garden changes as he moves closer to the garden hedge.

   a. Write a hypothesis that Pádraig could test in this investigation.

   b. Plan an investigation that Pádraig could carry out to test this hypothesis.

   c. Make a list of the equipment that Pádraig could use and explain how they are used.

   d. Draw a table that Pádraig could use to present the data from this investigation.

6. Using appropriate measurement instruments, measure the volume of

   a. The science laboratory.

   b. A golf ball.

   How many golf balls can you fit into the science laboratory?

7. If a 70 kg man was made of 50 cent coins, how much money would he be worth? Use appropriate measurement instruments to help you find out the answer.

Working as a Scientist

Communicating Science

Mars Climate Orbiter

In 1998, the Mars Climate Orbiter, the first weather satellite to travel between planets, was launched in the United States by the National Aeronautics and Space Administration (NASA). It was expected to orbit (move in a circle around) Mars at a safe distance, but it broke apart after moving too close to the planet and entering the upper atmosphere. The fault happened because one part of the mission team was using imperial units of measurement (lbs, mph) to guide the orbiter, while the other part of the team was using SI units.

1 Read the news report below from CNN.com and write down the key points.

2 Think about the following issues and write down your responses.

   a. Who was at fault? Why?

   b. What was at fault? Why?

   c. What suggestions might have been offered?

3 Compare your views with those of your lab partner. Create a summary of both your views and present it to the class. Record the feedback on your presentation.

By Robin Lloyd
CNN Interactive Senior Writer

MAIN PAGE
WORLD
U.S.
LOCAL
POLITICS
WEATHER
BUSINESS
SPORTS
TECHNOLOGY
SPACE
HEALTH
ENTERTAINMENT
BOOKS
TRAVEL
FOOD
ARTS & STYLE
NATURE
IN-DEPTH
ANALYSIS
myCNN

Headline News brief
news quiz
daily almanac

(CNN) – NASA lost a $125 million Mars orbiter because a Lockheed Martin engineering team used English units of measurement while the agency's team used the more conventional metric system for a key spacecraft operation, according to a review finding released Thursday.

The units mismatch prevented navigation information from transferring between the Mars Climate Orbiter spacecraft team at Lockheed Martin in Denver and the flight team at NASA's Jet Propulsion Laboratory in Pasadena, California.

Lockheed Martin helped build, develop and operate the spacecraft for NASA. Its engineers provided navigation commands for Climate Orbiter's thrusters in English units although NASA has been using the metric system predominantly since at least 1990.

After a 286-day journey, the probe fired its engine on

🔊 Fig. 15.6.1
Mars Climate Orbiter

news quiz
daily almanac

MULTIMEDIA:
video
video archive
audio
multimedia showcase
more services

E-MAIL:
Subscribe to one of our news e-mail lists.
Enter your address:

[ ] **go**

Or:
Get a free e-mail account

DISCUSSION:
message boards
chat
feedback

CNN WEB SITES:
myCNN.com CNNSI
allpolitics CNNfn

AsiaNow
En Español
Em Português
Svenska
Norge
Danmark
Italian

FASTER ACCESS:
europe
japan

September 23 to push itself into orbit. The engine fired but the spacecraft came within 60 km (36 miles) of the planet – about 100 km closer than planned and about 25 km (15 miles) beneath the level at which it could function properly, mission members said...

The Mars Climate Orbiter and Polar Lander were designed to help scientists understand Mars' water history and the potential for life in the planet's past. There is strong evidence that Mars was once awash with water, but scientists have no clear answers to where the water went and what drove it away.

Error points to nation's conversion lag

Lorelle Young, president of the US Metric Association, said the loss of Climate Orbiter brings up the 'untenable' [weak] position of the United States in relation to most other countries, which rely on the metric system for measurement. She was not surprised at the error that arose. 'In this day

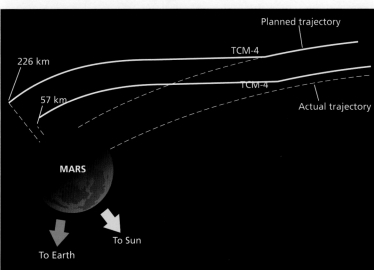

🎧 **Fig. 15.6.2**
The planned versus the actual trajectory of the Mars Climate Orbiter

and age when the metric system is the measurement language of all sophisticated science, two measurements systems should not be used,' Young said. 'Only the metric system should be used because that is the system science uses.' She put blame at the feet of Congress [the United States government] that she said has squeezed NASA's budget to the point that it has no funds to completely convert its operations to metric. 'This should be a loud wake-up call to Congress that being first in technology requires funding,' she said, 'and it's a very important area for the country.'

---

4 **You are a chief science adviser to the US government. The President has been asked to give a speech on national television explaining the disaster to the public. With your lab partner, write the speech that you would advise the President to give. Pay attention to the following:**

a. **The differences between imperial and metric systems of measurement.**

b. **The types of physical quantities involved in the motion of the orbiter.**

c. **A summary of who and what was at fault.**

d. **The importance of teamwork and communication in science.**

e. **Advice for future missions.**

Chapter 16

Energy

What you may already know:

- The Sun lights and heats our planet.
- We need energy to do things, for machines to move and for lights to turn on.
- There are costs for heating a home and running a car.
- Sources of energy include fossil fuels, wind power and solar energy.

What you will learn in this chapter:

- What energy is and where energy comes from.
- Different forms of energy.
- The law of conservation of energy.
- How certain objects and devices can store and transfer energy.
- Energy conversions that can be seen in nature, in industry, in the home and in the science laboratory.
- What efficiency means in energy conversion devices.
- How to design, build and test a device that transforms energy from one form to another.

Think BIG

- Why does Earth need a sun?
- Why do we insulate houses?

Puzzler

Can you crack this code?

The first letter of each of these images spells out a key word that you will come across in this chapter. Use the hints provided if you need to, or revisit the Puzzler after you finish this chapter.

1.	2.	3.	4.	5.
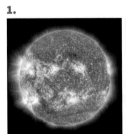				
Earth revolves around it	Pacific and Atlantic are the largest	Type of light that makes white glow	Source of power in Fukishima power station	How far something travels

1. _____   2. _____   3. _____   4. _____   5. _____

What is Energy?

In this topic we are learning to:

- Explain what energy is.
- Illustrate ways that energy can be stored.
- State the law of conservation of energy.

What Can Energy Do?

Energy makes many things possible. For example, energy allows a stereo to play music, rain to fall from the sky, a light bulb to glow and a computer to process information.

In all of these cases the common factor is that **work** is done. In physics, work is done when a force moves an object.

Energy is the ability to do work.

The SI unit for energy is the joule (J).

Key Words

Work
Thermal
Chemical
Light
Sound
Kinetic
Potential
Nuclear
Magnetic
Electrical
Law of conservation
 of energy

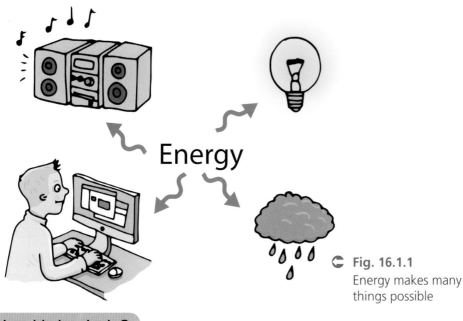

Energy

◁ **Fig. 16.1.1**
Energy makes many things possible

What else does energy do? **a b c**

Fill in the blanks.

Energy allows:

A car to _____.

A fire to _____.

A person to _____.

A _____ to
_____?

To get an idea of how big a joule is, here are some everyday examples:

- A joule is the amount of energy needed to raise the temperature of 1,000 cm³ of cool air by 1 °C.
- A joule is the amount of energy needed to raise a small apple one metre off the ground.
- As you read this book, you transform approximately 100 J of heat energy every second.

Using these figures, carry out the following tasks:

1. Calculate the amount of energy needed to raise the temperature of the air in the school laboratory by 1 °C.
2. Calculate how much heat energy is generated by all the people in your class in five minutes while they are sitting down doing a test.

People and Science

James Prescott Joule, an English brewer, is known for developing the law of conservation of energy. He studied heat and its relationship to mechanical work.

The SI unit of energy, the joule (J), is named in his honour. Joule was fascinated by electrical energy and experimented by giving electric shocks to his brothers!

⊃ **Fig. 16.1.2**
James Prescott Joule

Stored Energy

Energy is like money. You can store money in your pocket or in the bank. When you want to buy something, you transfer this money for goods or services. In the same way, certain objects store energy. Different things store energy in different ways, as shown in the mind map below.

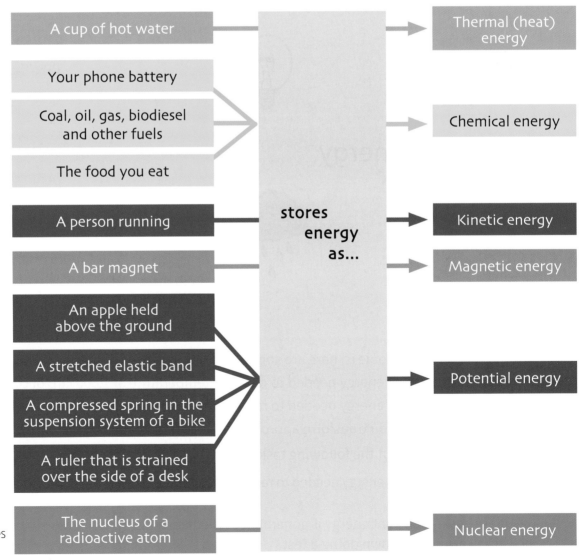

⊃ **Fig. 16.1.3**
Energy stores
mind map

Forms of Energy

As you can see from the mind map on page 274, energy exists in a number of forms. Consider Fig. 16.1.4.

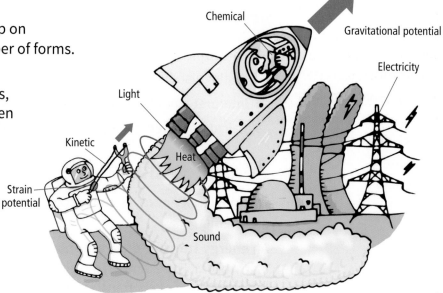

- Fuels, such as coal, oil and gas, contain **chemical** energy. When these fuels are burned, the energy is transferred as **thermal** (heat) energy, as well as **light** and **sound**.

- Chemical energy in the rocket fuel is used to move the rocket. This form of energy is known as **kinetic** energy. Any moving object has kinetic energy.

- The food in the astronaut's sandwich is 'fuel' too. It contains chemical energy. This energy is transferred in our bodies in various forms, such as heat and kinetic energy.

- As the rocket climbs higher, it gains **potential** energy. Potential energy is the energy an object has due to its shape or position. An object can have this form of energy due to its position against gravity. Gravity pulls objects towards the Earth. The higher up the rocket goes, the more it goes against gravity and the more potential energy it gains. An object can also have potential energy if it is stretched or strained. For example, the astronaut on the ground holds a pebble in the stretched elastic band of a catapult. This is strain potential energy.

- The power station in the background uses **nuclear** energy in radioactive atoms to heat steam. This steam gains kinetic energy, which is used to turn turbines.

- Turbines contain coils of wire and a magnet. The kinetic energy of the steam and the **magnetic** energy of the magnet are changed into **electrical** energy.

Fig. 16.1.4
Energy exists in various forms

GO Learn more about how fuels burn in Chemical World 14.1

GO Learn more about how our bodies get energy from food in Biological World 2.2

GO Learn more about nuclear energy in Earth and Space 24.2

Conservation of Energy

When one form of energy changes to another form of energy, we say it has been converted.

Energy must appear from somewhere and you cannot end up with less energy than you started with. Energy can be stored, transferred usefully or dissipated. This is known as conservation of energy.

The **law of conservation of energy** states that energy cannot be created or destroyed, but it can change from one form to another.

Remembering energy

Using the first letter of each type of energy, write a mnemonic to help you remember them.

Energy Transfers

Learning Intentions

In this topic we are learning to:

- Distinguish between useful and waste energy conversions.
- Interpret models for representing energy transfers.
- Calculate the efficiency of different devices.

Energy Transfer Diagrams

We know that energy is always conserved. However, not all energy transfers are useful.

An **energy transfer diagram** shows the useful energy transfers taking place in a process. For example, the energy transfer diagram in Fig. 16.2.1 shows the conversion of chemical energy in a battery to light when the battery is used to power a filament bulb.

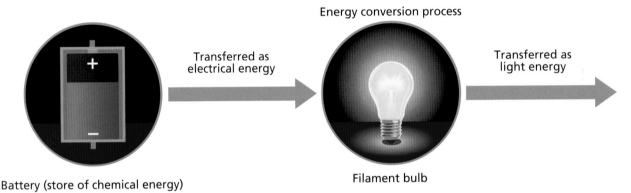

Energy conversion process

Transferred as
electrical energy

Transferred as
light energy

Battery (store of chemical energy)

Filament bulb

○ **Fig. 16.2.1**
Energy transfer diagram
for a filament bulb

Figure 16.2.1 shows only the **useful energy transfers** that take place. It is important to note that the bulb also gets hot. Energy transfers that are not useful are known as **waste**. In this case, the thermal (heat) energy is waste.

Sankey Diagrams

A more accurate way of showing all of the energy transfers going on in the bulb is to draw a **Sankey diagram**.

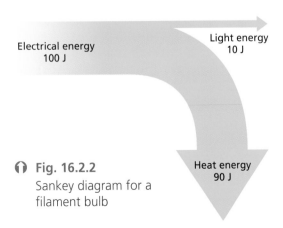

Electrical energy
100 J

Light energy
10 J

Heat energy
90 J

○ **Fig. 16.2.2**
Sankey diagram for a
filament bulb

In a Sankey diagram, the thicker the arrow is, the more energy there is involved in the process. A typical Sankey diagram for a filament bulb is shown in Fig. 16.2.2.

It is clear from Fig. 16.2.2 that most of the energy transfer in this bulb is in the form of heat rather than light.

Unwanted heat energy can be transferred through different devices and processes. In this case, the energy is transferred to the area around the bulb and heats the room. When this happens, we say that the energy is **dissipated** in the form of heat.

To reduce the amount of heat energy dissipated by light bulbs, scientists have developed energy saving bulbs. These bulbs need less electrical energy to work and dissipate less heat energy.

'Dissipate'

The word 'dissipate' comes from the Latin word *dissipat*, meaning 'scattered'. Why do you think this is relevant when talking about energy?

'Dissipate' has multiple meanings. Find out what these meanings are and compare them to the energy meaning.

Efficiency

The ideal light bulb would convert all its electrical energy into light energy, but this is not realistic. To measure how close we can get to 100 per cent energy transfer in a device, we calculate its **efficiency**.

$$\% \text{ Efficiency} = \frac{\text{Useful energy transferred}}{\text{Total energy}} \times \frac{100}{1}$$

For example, the electrical energy transferred in the filament bulb in Fig. 16.2.2 is 100 J. The useful output of light energy is 10 J.

$$\% \text{ Efficiency} = \frac{10}{100} \times \frac{100}{1} = 10 \% \text{ efficient}$$

Investigating heat loss in light bulbs

A student wants to compare the amount of heat 'lost' by three different light bulbs: a filament bulb, a light-emitting diode (LED) bulb and a compact fluorescent light (CFL) bulb. Plan, design, carry out and write up an investigation to make this comparison.

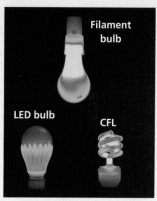

🎧 **Fig. 16.2.3**
The brighter the colour of the bulb, the more heat energy dissipated.

Rate those bulbs

1. Consider the Sankey diagrams for the types of bulb shown in Fig. 16.2.4.

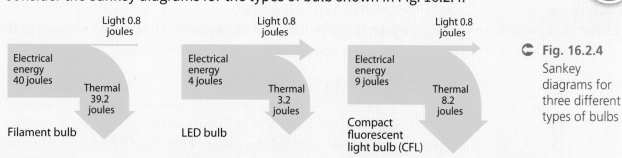

Filament bulb: Light 0.8 joules, Electrical energy 40 joules, Thermal 39.2 joules

LED bulb: Light 0.8 joules, Electrical energy 4 joules, Thermal 3.2 joules

Compact fluorescent light bulb (CFL): Light 0.8 joules, Electrical energy 9 joules, Thermal 8.2 joules

🔄 **Fig. 16.2.4** Sankey diagrams for three different types of bulbs

2. Rate the thermal energy (heat) saving ability of the bulbs in order of best to worst.
3. Calculate the percentage efficiency of each bulb.

Energy transfer and Sankey diagrams

Energy transfer and Sankey diagrams are two ways of modelling the transfer of energy through different devices and processes. In groups, discuss each model.

1. What is good about them?
2. Are they missing anything? If so, what?
3. Can you come up with a different way of representing energy transfer?

Energy Transfer in the Home

Learning Intentions

In this topic we are learning to:

- Explain what is meant by power.
- Calculate the power of different electrical appliances.
- Outline steps that can be taken to make homes more energy efficient.

Most of our daily energy use takes the form of heat and electrical energy in machines, such as vacuum cleaners, kettles and washing machines. These machines are commonly known as home appliances.

All machines transfer energy from one form to another, but some can do it quicker than others. For example, a more powerful vacuum cleaner will suck up dirt quicker than a less powerful one.

Power

Power is the rate at which energy is transferred from one form to another. In the more powerful object, energy is transferred at a faster rate. This measure of how much energy is transferred per second in a machine is known as its power rating. The SI unit for power is **watts** (W).

Power can be calculated using the following formula:

$$\text{Power} = \frac{\text{Energy (J)}}{\text{Time (s)}}$$

Unit of power = W

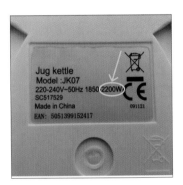

● **Fig. 16.3.1**
Power rating label on a kettle

The label in Fig. 16.3.1 shows that the kettle has a power rating of 2,200 W. This means that for every second the kettle is on, it converts 2,200 J of electrical energy into heat energy.

A single watt is a small amount of power and it is more common to see power ratings on appliances written in kilowatts (kW).

Watts to kilowatts

To convert watts to kilowatts, divide the number of watts by 1,000. For example, the power of the kettle in Fig. 16.3.1 written in kilowatts is:

2,200 W ÷ 1,000 = 2.2 kW

Now write the power of the following in kilowatts:

- 3,000 W electric heater
- 100 W light bulb
- 1,440 W hairdryer

Counting Electricity

The term for a unit of electricity is a **kilowatt-hour** (kWh). This is calculated by multiplying the power of each appliance used by the number of hours you used them for. For example, if a 3,000 W electric heater was on for one hour, the number of electrical units used would be 3 kW x 1 hour = 3 kWh.

When you get an electricity bill, you are charged according to the number of units of electricity you have used since your last bill. You are then charged in euros per unit of electricity.

Counting up the energy

A washing machine has a power rating of 500 W. It is used for three hours a day in a family home.

1. Calculate how many kilowatt hours of energy the washing machine is using up over the course of a week.

2. If each unit of electricity is charged at €0.14, calculate the cost of running the washing machine for a week.

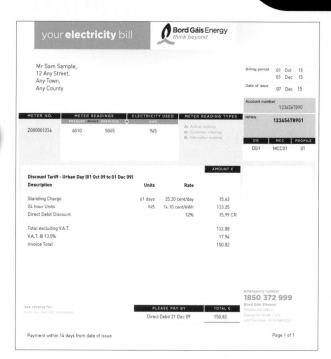

O Fig. 16.3.2
An electricity bill

Reducing 'Energy Loss' in the Home

Although you might hear about 'energy loss', it is important to remember that energy cannot be lost or disappear – it is transferred into unwanted forms or dissipated in various ways. However, this can lead to an increase in energy bills.

All modern homes for sale or rent in Ireland come with a Building Energy Rating (BER) Certificate. The BER shows how much energy a home uses. This is called an **energy rating**. The scale of the BER goes from A to G. A is the best rating.

To increase a home's energy efficiency and reduce electricity bills, a number of steps can be taken:

- Use fewer appliances, or use appliances for a shorter time.

- Use energy efficient appliances that need less electricity to produce the same useful energy output. For example, CFLs instead of filament bulbs.

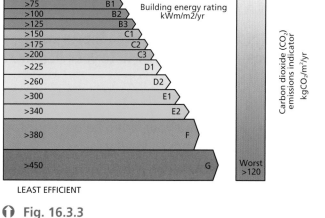

O Fig. 16.3.3
The BER scaling for home energy efficiency

- Insulate the house to prevent heat energy dissipating through the walls, roof, floor, doors and windows.

- Insulate the hot water cylinder with a lagging jacket to prevent heat loss.

- Monitor energy use with energy meters.

Staying warm

Plan, design, carry out and write up an investigation to compare the difference in heat loss from a hot water cylinder with and without a lagging jacket.

Chapter Summary

- Energy is the ability to do work or move something.
- The SI unit for energy is the joule (J).
- Energy can be stored in certain objects and can also be transferred into other forms.
- The law of conservation of energy states that energy cannot be created or destroyed, but can only be changed from one form to another.
- Energy can exist as chemical, light, sound, heat, gravitational potential, strain potential, electrical, magnetic and nuclear energy.
- Energy transfers can be both useful and wasteful.
- An energy transfer diagram is a way of representing the useful energy transfers that can take place in a device or process.
- A Sankey diagram is a way of representing the useful and wasteful energy transfers that can take place in a device or process.

- The efficiency of an energy transfer tells us how much energy input appears as useful energy output:

$$\% \text{ Efficiency} = \frac{\text{Useful energy transferred}}{\text{Total energy}} \times \frac{100}{1}$$

- Power is the rate at which energy is transferred from one form to another.

$$\text{Power} = \frac{\text{Energy (J)}}{\text{Time (s)}}$$
$$\text{Unit of power} = \text{W}$$

- Electrical power units are measured in kilowatt-hours (kWh).
- You can improve the energy rating of a home by taking measures to reduce waste energy output, such as using energy efficient appliances and insulating the house.

The BIG Challenge

In groups of three, make a short video (approximately two minutes long) to present to your classmates called 'Energy Use in My Everyday Life'.

Tips

- Storyboard your video before you start. Think about what you want to show and why.
- Share the video with your classmates. Discuss what parts of the video were good and suggest ideas for how it could be improved.

Some things you could include in your video:

- The appliances in your home or school and the energy transfers that take place in them.
- The ways in which your home or school is energy efficient.
- The ways you could improve the energy efficiency of your home or school.
- Your everyday use of energy (including appliances and devices, heating, food).

Go to your Portfolio to check what you have learned in this chapter.

Take the chapter 16 quiz on educateplus.ie.

Questions

1. Copy and fill in the blanks:

   a. Energy is the _____ to do _____.

   b. The SI unit for energy is the _____.

   c. The law of conservation of energy states that energy cannot be _____ or _____, but it can be _____ from one _____ to another.

   d. When a fuel is burned in a rocket, it releases _____ energy, as well as _____ and _____.

   e. A ball raised off the ground has _____ energy. A stretched elastic band has _____ _____ energy. All moving objects have _____ energy.

   f. The energy stored in the _____ of atoms is known as _____ energy.

   g. When unwanted _____ energy is transferred in devices and processes, we say that the energy is _____.

   h. The rate at which _____ is transferred in a device is known as its _____ and is measured in _____.

2. Copy the Venn diagram and place the following items in the correct places to represent the types of energy stored in them:

- A mobile phone held to your ear
- A sandwich
- Petrol
- A television on a table
- A human body

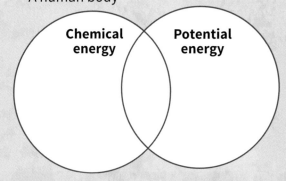

3. a. Describe where and how energy is stored in an MP3 player.

   b. Explain what happens to the energy stored in the MP3 player when it is switched on.

4. Using energy transfer diagrams, describe the energy transfers that happen when:

   a. You cook a burger on a charcoal barbecue.

   b. You send a text message.

   c. You start a car.

   d. You light a Bunsen burner.

   e. A tennis ball rolls off the desk and hits the floor.

   f. A pencil rolls off the desk and hits the floor.

5. An electric motor with an input energy of 1,000 J transfers 300 J of this energy into kinetic energy.

   a. Calculate the % efficiency of the motor.

   b. What happens to the rest of the energy?

6. Calculate the power generated when:

   a. A kettle converts 60,000 J of electrical energy into heat in 30 seconds.

   b. A runner converts 5,000 J of chemical energy into kinetic energy in 40 seconds.

   c. A ball falling off a cliff converts 8,000 J of potential energy into kinetic energy in two seconds.

7. A 100 W light bulb is only 5 per cent efficient. Using a Sankey diagram, explain in detail what this means.

8. If the cost of a unit of electricity is €0.14, complete the following table:

Appliance	Power rating	Amount of time used per day	Units in kWh	Cost of running per day
Shower	9,500 W	1 hour		
Hairdryer		40 minutes		€1.24
Kettle		2 hours	4.4	

Working as a Scientist

Investigation Design

Energy Conversion Device

Jean and Fintan designed and built an energy conversion device that transforms energy from one form to another to perform a function. The materials they used were:

- A large elastic band connected between two supporting columns (e.g. the legs of a laboratory chair) to create a catapult.
- A piece of cardboard taped to the middle of the elastic band.
- A toy car held in the cardboard and pulled back different distances.

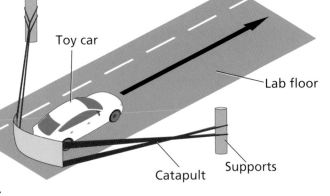

🎧 **Fig. 16.5.1**
The set-up

They wanted to see how the device worked to move the car across the laboratory floor. Your challenge is to advise them about how to carry out the task in a scientific way.

1 **What are the dependent and independent variables in this investigation?**

2 **What would the controls be in this investigation?**

Jean and Fintan pulled the car back in the elastic catapult a set number of distances and released it, allowing it to roll across the laboratory floor each time. They repeated this ten times, stretching the elastic by one centimetre more each time.

3 **Describe the measurements Jean and Fintan would take in this investigation and the instruments they would use. How would they reduce errors? Which errors are random errors and which are systematic errors? How would you reduce both types of errors? Remember, scientists change only one variable at a time.**

Jean and Fintan's teacher reminded them that it is important to note any observations they made during the investigation and not just the measurements. She asked what they had noticed in terms of energy transfer when they pulled the catapult back and let the car go.

4 **What useful energy transfers would the students have observed?**

5 **Would the students have observed any waste energy transfers? If so, what would they be?**

6 **Sketch a Sankey diagram of the energy transfers taking place in this investigation.**

Jean and Fintan collected the following table of data for this investigation:

Distance the catapult was pulled back (cm)	Average distance travelled by car (cm)	Distance the catapult was pulled back (cm)	Average distance travelled by car (cm)
1	5.2	6	30
2	10	7	35.1
3	17	8	40.5
4	17	9	45
5	24.9	10	50.3

7 Identify the outliers in the data. Are these a result of random or systematic errors?

8 Suggest a suitable graph to present the relationship between the distance the catapult was pulled back and the distance travelled by the car.

9 What would you conclude to be the relationship between the distance the band was pulled back and the distance travelled by the car?

This catapult is a device that converts strain potential energy in the elastic band into kinetic energy in the object it fires. Some energy is 'lost' in the form of sound and heat (caused by friction between the wheels of the car and the floor, the body of the car and the air). To make this device more efficient would mean that, for the same amount of strain potential energy, there would be more of it converted into kinetic energy and less converted into sound and heat.

10 Discuss the set-up of this investigation with your lab partner and come up with a list of ways that you could make this energy transfer more efficient.

11 Now think of a device you could make that would transform energy from one form to another.
   a. What forms of energy are involved?
   b. How are you going to make the device?
   c. How are you going to test the device?
   d. What steps could you take to improve the efficiency of the device?

Object Catapult Technology

Object catapult technology is used to launch fighter jets from aircraft carriers as a form of assisted take-off. A tow bar is attached to the plane's nose gear, which is connected to two catapult cylinders, each about the length of a soccer pitch. Hot steam is pumped into these cylinders, building up pressure.

When enough pressure has been built up, the pistons in the cylinder are forced forward at high speed. The pilot blasts the plane's engines and the plane is pulled forward, reaching speeds of 0 to 266 kilometres per hour in just two seconds.

🎧 **Fig. 16.5.2**
Fighter jet launch

12 Make a table listing the similar and different energy transfers this type of launcher would have compared to the elastic catapult used in Jean and Fintan's investigation.

13 Come up with some advantages of steam-driven catapults over the elastic catapult used in this investigation.

14 The US military are researching the possibility of electromagnetic aircraft launchers. Research this technology and find out some advantages it may have over steam-driven launchers.

Chapter 17

Motion

What you may already know:

- Acceleration, speed, time and distance are linked with motion.
- Different objects float or sink in water.

What you will learn in this chapter:

- Different types of motion.
- How to analyse the motion of different objects.
- What forces are and what they can do.
- How balanced and unbalanced forces affect motion.
- Why objects float and sink.

Think BIG

- What causes objects to move?
- Do you think humans will ever run the 100-metre sprint in less than nine seconds?

Puzzler

Can you identify this animal?

Hint: it is the world's fastest land mammal, reaching speeds of up to 112 km/h!

Types of Motion

There are different types of basic motion (movement), including:

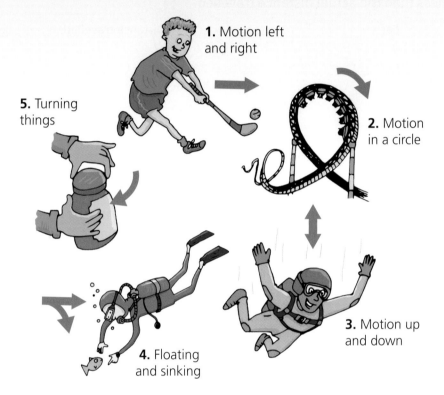

1. Motion left and right

5. Turning things

2. Motion in a circle

4. Floating and sinking

3. Motion up and down

Distance, Speed and Time

Every type of motion is linked to a number of variables:

- **Distance**: measured in metres (m).
- **Speed**: the distance an object travels in a given time, measured in metres per second (m/s).
- **Time**: measured in seconds (s).

The equation for speed is:

$$\text{Speed} = \frac{\text{Distance travelled (m)}}{\text{Time taken (s)}}$$

$$\text{Unit of speed} = \text{m/s}$$

Distance, speed and time are **scalar** quantities. Scalar quantities have a magnitude (size). They do not take place in any direction. For example, the speedometer in a car tells you how fast the car is going but gives no information on the direction the car is moving in.

Key Words

Distance
Speed
Time
Scalar
Vector
Displacement
Velocity
Distance–time graph

↻ **Fig. 17.1.1**
Different types of motion

Calculating distance

Using the equation for speed, if a person runs 20 m in 4 seconds, then their speed would be calculated as:

$$\frac{20}{4} = 5 \text{ m/s}$$

Now you try! If a person is driving a car at a constant speed of 20 m/s for 5 minutes (300 s), what distance would they cover?

Displacement and Velocity

'Magnitude'

In the physical world, the word 'magnitude' refers to the size or amount of a physical quantity. The word comes from the Latin *magnus*, meaning 'great'.

Vector quantities have both magnitude and direction.

Two vector quantities that control the motion of objects are:

- **Displacement** is the distance an object travels in a certain direction. For example, 50 m north east. It is also the shortest distance between a starting and a finishing point. For example, if a person was travelling on a hilly road between point A and point B, as shown in Fig. 17.1.2, their displacement is still only the shortest distance from A to B. This is much less than the actual distance travelled.

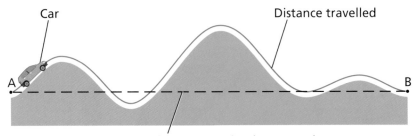

➲ Fig. 17.1.2

Displacement = 3 km (or 3,000 m)

Time taken = 10 mins (or 600 secs)

Despicable vector

There is a character called Vector in the film *Despicable Me*. Look him up online to see why this is a well-deserved name.

- **Velocity** is the speed of an object and the direction it is travelling in. For example, 100 km/h south. Velocity can be calculated by dividing the displacement of an object by the time taken for that displacement to take place. The equation for velocity is:

$$\text{Velocity} = \frac{\text{Displacement}}{\text{Time taken}}$$

For example, the velocity of the car in Fig. 17.1.2 would be calculated as:

$$\text{Velocity} = \frac{\text{Displacement}}{\text{Time taken}} = \frac{3,000}{600}$$

$$V = 5 \text{ m/s east}$$

Distance versus displacement

A person drove from Patrickswell in County Limerick to Killaloe on the Tipperary–Clare border using the route shown on this map.

Using the scale on the map and appropriate measurement instruments, calculate:

1. The distance travelled.

2. The displacement of the driver.

3. The velocity, if the journey took 28 minutes. Why is it safe to assume that the velocity was not this exact value for the entire journey?

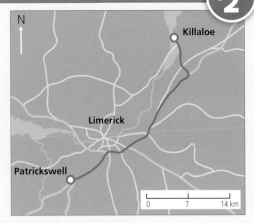

🎧 Fig. 17.1.3
Scaled map showing a journey from Patrickswell to Killaloe

Distance–Time Graphs

A **distance–time graph** shows the distance something travels over the time taken to travel that distance.

The y-axis of a distance–time graph shows the distance travelled, and the x-axis shows the time taken.

Look at the distance–time graph in Fig. 17.1.4. It represents 25 seconds of a student's bicycle journey to school.

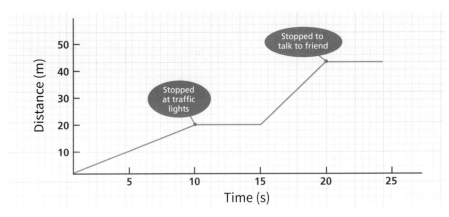

⋂ **Fig. 17.1.4** Distance-time graph

The student is travelling at a steady pace until he reaches a set of traffic lights after ten seconds. He stops at the lights and then continues on his journey. He then stops again to talk to a friend.

There are two types of motion shown in this distance–time graph:

- Objects moving at a constant speed produce a straight line distance–time graph, showing that they are covering the same distance every second.

- Objects that are stationary (not moving) cause the line on the distance–time graph to stay horizontal. This is because although the distance does not change, time continues on the x-axis.

A distance–time graph can be used to calculate the speed of an object. The slope of a distance–time graph tells us the speed of an object.

$$\text{Slope} = \frac{\text{Change in distance}}{\text{Change in time}} = \text{Speed}$$

For example, the average speed of this student until he came to the traffic lights was:

$$\text{Average speed} = \frac{\text{Total distance travelled}}{\text{Time taken}} = \frac{20}{10} = 2 \text{ m/s}$$

Changing Speeds

Learning Intentions

In this topic we are learning to:

- Consider what it means for an object to accelerate.
- Measure and calculate accelerations.
- Predict the motion of objects experiencing accelerations.

Acceleration

Objects do not always move at a constant speed. They speed up and slow down.

When speed changes over time, it is called **acceleration**.

The formula for acceleration is:

$$\text{Acceleration} = \frac{\text{Change in speed (m/s)}}{\text{Time taken (s)}}$$

$$\text{Unit of acceleration} = \text{m/s/s, or m/s}^2$$

For example, if the speed of a car changes from 15 m/s to 25 m/s in four seconds, then the acceleration of the car can be calculated as:

$$\text{Acceleration} = \frac{\text{Change in speed}}{\text{Time}} = \frac{(25-15)}{4} = \frac{10}{4} = 2.5 \text{ m/s}^2$$

This means that every second, the speed of the car is increasing by 2.5 m/s:

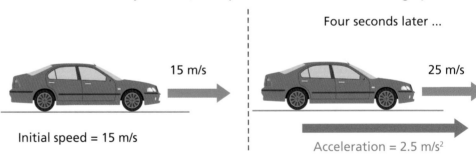

Four seconds later ...

15 m/s

25 m/s

Initial speed = 15 m/s

Acceleration = 2.5 m/s²

◔ Fig. 17.2.1

Final speed = 25 m/s

Acceleration is a vector quantity, so it takes place in certain directions. This means that acceleration can also be described as how quickly velocity changes.

$$\text{Acceleration} = \frac{\text{Change in velocity}}{\text{Time taken}}$$

Speeding up or slowing down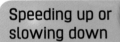

An acceleration that causes the speed of an object to increase is simply known as acceleration. An acceleration that causes the speed of an object to decrease is known as a deceleration.

Using this knowledge, what do you think the function of an accelerator in a car is?

Fun Fact

Fleas can accelerate 50 times faster than a space shuttle

◔ Fig. 17.2.2
A flea

Showing Changing Speeds on a Distance–Time Graph

When an object does not move at a constant speed, using a straight line to represent its motion on a distance–time graph is not realistic. A curved line more accurately suggests the type of motion that is taking place.

Look at Fig. 17.2.3.

(a)

(b)

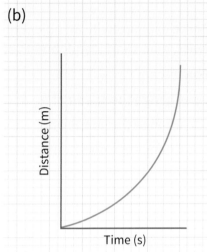

↻ **Fig. 17.2.3**
(a) A person dropping an apple from a building

(b) A distance–time graph for the motion

- The distance the apple falls every second changes as the journey progresses (a).

- The curve of the distance–time graph for this motion shows us that for every second of the motion, the object is covering a larger distance (b).

This graph shows that the apple's speed is getting greater with time. In other words, the apple is accelerating.

Visualising acceleration

The car shown in Fig. 17.2.1 has an acceleration of 2.5 m/s², meaning that for every second of its journey its speed is increasing by 2.5 m/s. Using this information, complete the table below for the car's distance travelled and its speed at every second of its journey, starting at a speed of 15 m/s:

Time	Speed	Distance = speed x time
0	15	0
1	17.5	17.5
2		
3		
4		

Use these values to draw two graphs:

1. The speed of the car against time.

2. The distance of the car against time.

In both graphs, put time on the x-axis. What do the shapes of these graphs tell you about the motion of the car?

Forces: Pushes and Pulls

Key Words

Force
Contact forces
Non-contact forces
Interaction pair
Newton meter
Force meter

Learning Intentions

In this topic we are learning to:

- Classify forces as contact and non-contact.
- Describe various interaction pairs.
- Demonstrate a way to measure forces.

Forces lingo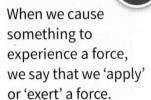

When we cause something to experience a force, we say that we 'apply' or 'exert' a force.

Force explains why an object moves the way it does, why things stretch, twist, tear, snap, bend, break, speed up, slow down and change shape.

Forces can:

- Change the speed of an object (causing it to accelerate or decelerate).
- Change the shape and size of an object.
- Change the direction an object is moving in.

Sometimes a single force can do more than one of these things.

Feeling forces

Find ten objects at home or in the school laboratory and exert push and pull forces on them. The objects could include a football, a piece of modelling clay, a rubber band, a paper clip and a yoghurt carton. Fill in a table with the following headings to describe how the objects react to the forces:

Item	Reaction to pushing	Reaction to pulling	Reaction to squeezing	Reaction to twisting

Contact and Non-contact Forces

There are many forces in everyday life. These can be grouped into categories according to whether they are **contact forces** or **non-contact forces**:

Contact forces   Two objects have to be in contact for these forces to occur

Pushes and pulls: applied forces, when you tackle somebody in a rugby match, when you throw a shot putt	Friction: helps you to walk, slows cars down on roads, slows landing modules down when they re-enter Earth's atmosphere from space	Support forces: the force that keeps you upright when you stand on the ground or sit on a chair, the upthrust that keeps a boat floating in water	Tension: pulls a bungee jumper back up, allows a person to climb up a rope	Surface tension: keeps insects floating on water

Non-Contact forces   The two objects do not have to be in contact for these forces to occur

Gravity: pulls objects towards the Earth, keeps the Earth orbiting around the Sun and holds the universe together	Magnetic forces: pull on metals (such as iron, nickel and cobalt)	Electrostatic forces: when the hairs on your arm are attracted to a TV screen, when lightning strikes

Fig. 17.3.1
What type of force is being experienced in each picture?

Fig. 17.3.2
Forces are exerted in pairs when a person jumps off the ground

Forces in Pairs

Think about the forces being applied when the boy jumps off the ground in Fig. 17.3.2.

- The boy pushes the ground down: this is the force the boy exerts on the ground.

- The ground pushes the boy up: this is the force the ground exerts on the boy.

These forces happen in a pair. This is known as an **interaction pair**.

Describing the interaction pair

There is a second interaction pair happening when the boy jumps. Copy the following sentences and circle the correct word to describe this second interaction pair:

- Gravity pulls the boy (up/down). This is the force of the (Earth/boy) on the (Earth/boy).

- The boy pulls the Earth (up/down). This is the force of the (Earth/boy) on the (Earth/boy).

What happens next?

Two ice skaters place their hands together and ice skater A pushes on ice skater B. Predict what will happen to ice skater B when ice skater A pushes. Explain why you made this prediction.

Fig. 17.3.3

Measuring Forces

Forces can be measured in the laboratory using a **newton meter**. This is also known as a spring balance. Forces can also be measured digitally using a **force meter**.

Remember, the SI unit for force is the newton (N).

Taking readings

A student applies a pulling force and measures it with a newton meter. What is the value of this force?

Fig. 17.3.4
A newton meter being pulled

291

Forces: Moving Faster and Slower

Key Words

Balanced
Equilibrium
Unbalanced
Dynamic equilibrium
Friction
Drag forces
Lubrication
Streamlining

Learning Intentions

In this topic we are learning to:

- Compare balanced and unbalanced forces.
- Discuss useful and nuisance friction effects.
- Explore streamlining in nature and technology.

Know your forces

Draw a diagram of a rocket taking off and use labelled arrows to represent the forces acting on the rocket.

In Fig. 17.4.1, the dog and person are both tugging on the toy with equal force. Because of this, they do not move, as the forces cancel each other out. The forces are **balanced**.

The toy is said to be in **equilibrium**. Equilibrium is a state of balance between opposing forces.

If the dog began to exert a greater force, he would pull the person to the left. The forces would then be **unbalanced**. Unbalanced forces cause objects to speed up, slow down or change direction.

Pulling force of dog   Pulling force of person

🎧 **Fig. 17.4.1**
Balanced forces

Balanced but Moving

An object can have balanced forces acting on it when it is moving. Consider a car driving along a road.

🎧 **Fig. 17.4.2**
The force driving the rocket upwards is greater than the force pulling it downwards. As a result, the rocket takes off.

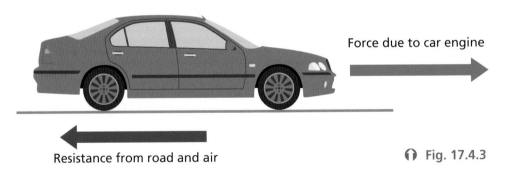

Force due to car engine

Resistance from road and air

🎧 **Fig. 17.4.3**

The car in Fig. 17.4.3 is being driven forward by the force of the engine, while its motion is being resisted by its grip on the road and by the air.

In this case, the forces are equal but the car continues to move with a constant speed. This is known as **dynamic equilibrium**.

Another example of dynamic equilibrium is when a skydiver falls at a steady speed from the sky after opening their parachute.

Friction

Friction is a force that opposes motion when two objects are placed in contact.

Friction can be:

- Useful: allowing for grip when you walk, run and climb or when you apply the brakes on a bike or in a car.

- A nuisance: opposing motion when trying to move things or slowing down the moving parts of machines.

Friction does not only happen when solids are in contact. When you wade through water, it is harder than walking the same distance on land. This is known as water resistance. Likewise, playing a match into the wind is tougher than if it is a calm day. This is an example of air resistance. Water and air resistance are examples of **drag forces**.

Fig. 17.4.4 Friction allows for grip when braking and running

Fig. 17.4.5 An athlete can use a resistance chute to increase the amount of drag force holding them back while running, thereby making them work harder over shorter distances

Parachutes away!

The Irish Defence Forces want you to investigate the effect of the shape and size of a parachute on landing speed. Use string, a toy soldier and a material of your choice to form different-shaped and different-sized parachutes. Plan, design, carry out and write up this investigation. Think of how you will present your findings to the Irish Defence Forces in a convincing, scientific way.

Fig. 17.4.6 Waxing a surfboard reduces friction

Visualising drag forces

Using the particle theory from Chemical World 9.1, draw diagrams that explain why a person experiences greater drag force when moving through water than when moving through air.

Reducing the Force of Friction

Lubrication is used to reduce the friction between two solids. Examples of lubricants are oil and wax. Oiling the chain of a bicycle can reduce friction and make it easier to move the bike forward. Surfers can wax their surfboards to reduce the friction between the board and the water.

Drag forces in wind and air can also be reduced by **streamlining**. Animals, such as cheetahs and dolphins, are streamlined to help them move easily through the air and water. Some of the best natural examples of streamlining have been imitated in modern sport. For example, hi-tech swimsuits were developed to imitate a shark's skin. The suits helped swimmers move smoothly through the water.

Fig. 17.4.7 Olympic swimmer Matt Welsh wearing the Speedo Fastskin swimsuit, designed to reduce drag in the same way a shark's skin does

293

Forces: Changing Shapes

Key Words

Deform
Compress
Stretch
Reaction
Elastic
Elastic limit

🎧 **Fig. 17.5.1**
An athlete landing on a crash mat after a high jump and a person standing on a table

GO Learn more about the properties of solids in Chemical World 9.1

Learning Intentions

In this topic we are learning to:
- Describe how solids support weight.
- Model how forces deform objects.

Look at the two images in Fig. 17.5.1. The athlete collapses into the crash mat, while the person appears to stand firm on the table.

In fact, a person does collapse into the table, but the amount is so small that we cannot see it. If a person was dropped from a height onto the table we may see this collapse, but it would more likely be a snap or break because the molecules of the wood in the table are rigid.

The crash mat changes shape in a way that we can see. In both cases, whether we see it or not, the weight of the person will **deform** the object. When forces **compress** or **stretch** objects, they deform them.

When a person stands on the table, their weight compresses the particles of the table, pushing them closer together. The bonds joining the particles push back against the person to support their weight. This is shown in Fig. 17.5.2.

⤷ **Fig. 17.5.2**
3D molecular structure being compressed

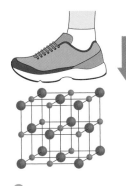

① Foot applies force (weight) on solid

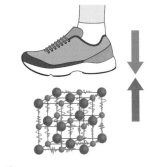

② Bonds between the particles compress and push back against the foot

The force applied by the table in response to the weight of the person is known as a **reaction** force.

This is another example of an interaction pair.

Elastic Objects

Any object that is able to restore its shape after it has been stretched or compressed is an **elastic** object.

Springs, elastic bands and bungee cords are elastic.

⤷ **Fig. 17.5.3**
Elastic objects apply forces to restore their shape

At some point, however, you will be able to extend elastic objects to a point where they will not restore their shape. This point is known as the **elastic limit**.

⮒ **Fig. 17.5.4**
A spring before and after being extended beyond its elastic limit

What is the relationship?

Extension of spring (cm)	Force applied by weights in pan (N)
0	0
2	0.5
4	1.0
6	1.5
8	2.0
10	2.5
12	3.0
13	3.5
14	4.0

The set of data in this table was recorded in an investigation where students extended a spring by adding weights to a pan. Using the data:

1. Plot a suitable graph. Determine from the graph when the elastic limit of the spring was reached.

2. Up to the point where the elastic limit was reached, could you suggest what the relationship was between the extension of the spring and the force applied by the weights in the pan?

Crash!

Using the particle theory (see Chemical World 9.1) and your understanding of compressing forces, work with your lab partner to design a poster explaining why a tackle bag is used in sports training rather than allowing people to run into wooden tables.

- What function do you want the bag to perform?
- What states of matter exist within the bag?

Fun Fact

Golf balls are designed to compress when struck with the golf club. They apply a force to restore to their normal shape in flight, allowing them to reach speeds upwards of 280 km/h.

⮑ **Fig. 17.5.5**
A golf ball deformed by a club

295

Forces: Pressure

Learning Intentions

In this topic we are learning to:

- Measure and calculate pressures.
- Outline how pressure varies in liquids and gases.
- Explain what is meant by atmospheric pressure.

When you cut bread, push a thumbtack into wood or even stand on the floor, you apply a force. This force is applied over an area. The smaller the area, the more concentrated the force will be.

The amount of force over a unit of area is known as **pressure**.

Pressure is calculated using the following equation:

$$\text{Pressure} = \frac{\text{Force applied (N)}}{\text{Area it is applied over (m}^2)}$$

$$\text{Unit of pressure} = \text{N/m}^2$$

Pressure

Based on what you know, try to answer the following questions in groups:

1. Why do we cut bread with the sharp side of a knife?
2. You can push a thumbtack into a piece of wood, but cannot push your thumb into the wood. Why?
3. Why do tractors have very wide tyres?

Depending on the situation, you may want a high or a low pressure. For example:

- Snowshoes increase the area a person's body weight is spread over. This reduces pressure, preventing the person sinking into the snow.
- The spikes on running shoes concentrate body weight over a smaller area. This increases pressure, making the shoes sink into the track and increasing the runner's grip.

◑ Fig. 17.6.1
Snowshoes and running shoes distribute body weight differently

Pressure in Solids

A person weighing 500 N stands on their two feet. If the area of each foot is 0.018 m², the pressure exerted on the ground can be calculated as:

$$\text{Pressure} = \frac{\text{Force}}{\text{Area}} = \frac{500}{(2 \times 0.018 \text{ m}^2)} = 13{,}888.88 \text{ N/m}^2$$

If the same person was standing on one stiletto heel with an area of 0.0001 m², then the pressure exerted would be:

$$\text{Pressure} = \frac{\text{Force}}{\text{Area}} = \frac{500}{0.0001} = 5{,}000{,}000 \text{ N/m}^2$$

Elephants and stilettos

Which would you rather stood on your foot?

a. A person weighing 600 N and wearing a pair of stilettos. The person stands on your foot with the stiletto heels, each of which has an area of 0.0001 m².

b. An elephant weighing 38,000 N standing on one foot of area 0.12 m².

Explain your answer.

⮞ **Fig. 17.6.2**

Describe the relationship

Copy the following sentences and circle the correct words to describe the relationships:

- A force applied over a (small/large) area results in a (big/small) pressure.

- Pressure is a measure of (force/area) per unit (force/area). Pressure is measured in (newtons per metre squared/newton metres).

Fun Fact

Jellyfish stings are one of the fastest cellular processes in nature. The pressure generated when a jellyfish releases its stinging barbs into its prey is more than 15 giga N/m². That is the same as the pressure exerted by a high-speed bullet!

⮞ **Fig. 17.6.3**
When a jellyfish releases its barbs into its prey, more than 15 giga N/m² of pressure is generated

Pressure in Liquids

🎧 **Fig. 17.6.4**
The polystyrene cup on the left was the same as the cup on the right before being taken underwater to a depth of around 3,000 metres by the deep-sea research vessel *Alvin*

Why do your ears 'pop' when you dive to the bottom of a swimming pool?

This is because of the pressure the liquid puts on your eardrums. The size of this pressure depends on how deep you are in the water. Pressure in liquids increases with depth. This means that the bottom of something in a liquid will always feel more pressure than the sides because this point is the deepest.

The polystyrene cup that was brought to the bottom of the ocean in Fig. 17.6.4 has not been squashed flat. This is because liquids, at a given depth, exert pressures equally in all directions. They do this because they can flow.

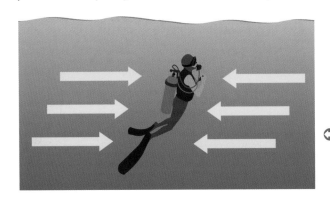

🔄 **Fig. 17.6.5**
At a given depth, pressure is exerted on a diver equally in all directions

Testing pressure and depth

Using a plastic bottle of water, plan, design, carry out and write up a demonstration that shows pressure in liquids increases with depth.

Powering with liquids

Hydraulics use liquid pressure to work machinery. The apparatus in Fig. 17.6.6 shows how hydraulics work. Pressure is applied to the small piston in syringe A and the liquid between the two syringes pushes on the large piston B.

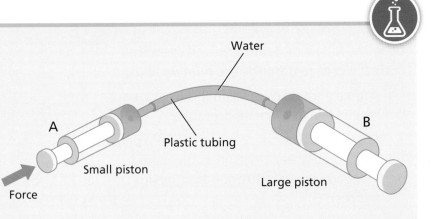

🎧 **Fig. 17.6.6**
Hydraulic apparatus

Using the $\boxed{\text{Pressure} = \dfrac{\text{Force}}{\text{Area}}}$

formula and your knowledge of liquids, predict which piston will experience the larger force.

1. Build this apparatus in class and test it for a range of forces. Remember, you will need to come up with a way of measuring:

   a. The force applied to the pistons.

   b. The area of the pistons.

2. Record your results for a range of data in a clear way.

3. Explain why your predictions did or did not match your results.

Pressure in Gases

How does a balloon inflate?

As gas particles move around, they collide with other objects and with each other. In other words, they exert a force. This force, applied over an area, causes **gas pressure**. The faster the gas particles move, the more force they exert so the greater the pressure is.

If you compress gas particles into a small space, such as a balloon, the number of collisions will increase over a small area. This increases the gas pressure inside the balloon, causing it to inflate.

 Learn more about compressing gases in Chemical World 9.1.

🎧 **Fig. 17.6.7**
When a balloon is blown up, the particle collisions increase

Pressure at high speeds

The air pressure in the tyres on Formula 1 cars is reduced before the start of a race. Due to heat generated by friction, the tyres can reach up to 100 °C during a race. Explain why the tyres are not inflated fully at the start of a race.

Atmospheric Pressure

We are at the bottom of a sea of air, which is above and around us. This air exerts a pressure known as **atmospheric pressure**.

Just as pressure increases with depth in liquids, the pressure of the atmosphere is greatest at ground level. The pressure decreases as you climb higher above the ground.

The atmospheric pressure at the summit of Mount Everest is one-third of the pressure at sea level. That means only one-third of the oxygen is available to climbers.

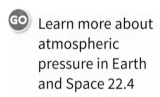 Learn more about atmospheric pressure in Earth and Space 22.4

Fig. 17.6.8
Mount Everest

Forces: Floating and Sinking

Key Words

Density
Buoyancy
Upthrust
Archimedes' principle

Learning Intentions

In this topic we are learning to:

- Measure and calculate density.
- Evaluate the relationship between density and floating bodies.
- Illustrate how bodies experience upthrust.

Remember your units!

The SI unit for density is kg/m^3, but for the size and mass of objects you will come across in school, you will probably use g/cm^3.

Density

To find out if something will float or sink in water, you need to know its **density**.

Density is a measure of how much matter is in a substance compared to how much space it takes up.

Density is the ratio of mass to volume. The formula for density is:

$$\text{Density} = \frac{\text{Mass (kg)}}{\text{Volume (m}^3)}$$

$$\text{Unit of density} = \text{kg/m}^3$$

What happens next?

A can of Coca-Cola and a can of Diet Coke, both of equal volume, are placed into a large container of water.

1. Predict what happens next, explaining your reasoning.
2. Carry out this test at home and record your observations.
3. Explain why your observations did or did not match your prediction.

⊃ **Fig. 17.7.1**

Polystyrene
Cork float
Methylated spirits
Corn oil
Plastic building block
Water
Rubber tubing
Sugar syrup
Glass marble

Finding water density

The density of pure water is 1 g/cm^3. Using appropriate instruments, prove that this is correct.

If a material has a mass of 120 g and a volume of 150 cm^3, its density is calculated as:

$$\text{Density} = \frac{\text{Mass}}{\text{Volume}}$$

$$\text{Density} = \frac{120}{150} = 0.8 \text{ g/cm}^3$$

This material will float in water because it has a density less than water. If its density was greater than the density of water, it would sink.

◠ **Fig. 17.7.2**
Different density liquids and materials

Describing density

Copy the following sentences and circle the correct word to explain the link between floating, sinking and density:

- A (less/more) dense material will float in a (less/more) dense liquid.
- A (less/more) dense material will sink in a (less/more) dense liquid.

Using this knowledge and Fig. 17.7.2, make a list of materials that would float in sugar syrup.

Buoyancy

Buoyancy is another factor that affects if an object will float.

We know that pressure in liquids increases with depth. The force as a result of this pressure is known as **upthrust**. If the upthrust is large enough, it will keep an object afloat, or buoyant.

Archimedes' principle states that an object placed in water will feel an upthrust equal to the weight of the water it displaced.

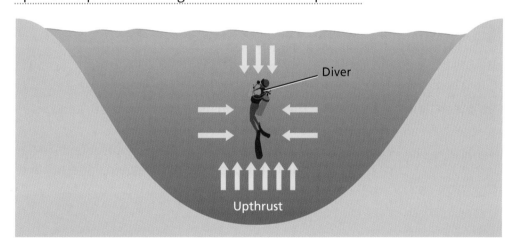

Diver

Upthrust

⟳ **Fig. 17.7.3** Upthrust in a liquid

Overflowing cup?

A glass is filled with ice and water to the top, as shown.

1. When the ice melts, which of the following things do you think will happen to the level of the water?
    a. It will go down.
    b. It will stay the same.
    c. The glass will overflow.
2. Discuss the possible reasons for your answer with your lab partner.
3. Set up this investigation at home or in school.
4. Record your observations and explain why they did or did not match your predictions.

Why do boats float?

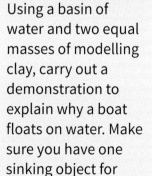

Using a basin of water and two equal masses of modelling clay, carry out a demonstration to explain why a boat floats on water. Make sure you have one sinking object for comparison.

Chapter Summary

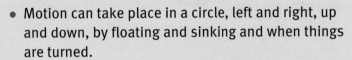

- Motion can take place in a circle, left and right, up and down, by floating and sinking and when things are turned.

- $$\text{Speed} = \frac{\text{Distance (m)}}{\text{Time (s)}}$$

- A scalar quantity has magnitude (size) only. Speed is a scalar quantity.

- A vector quantity has magnitude and direction. Velocity is a vector quantity.

- The slope of a distance–time graph tells us the speed of an object.

- $$\text{Acceleration} = \frac{\text{Change in speed (m/s)}}{\text{Time (s)}}$$

- If an acceleration takes place in the same direction as an object is moving, that object speeds up. If it takes place in the opposite direction, it slows down or decelerates.

- Forces can change the shape and size of an object and/or the speed and direction it is moving in.

- Forces work in pairs known as interaction pairs.

- When a force is applied to an object, it can deform that object by bending, stretching or compressing it.

- Any object that can restore its shape after it has been stretched or compressed is known as an elastic object.

- When the forces on an object are balanced, the object is said to be in equilibrium.

- Unbalanced forces cause objects to speed up, slow down or change direction.

- Friction is a force that opposes motion when two objects are placed in contact. It is a resistance to motion.

- Water and air resistance are forms of friction. They are known as drag forces.

- Friction can be reduced by lubrication and streamlining.

- $$\text{Pressure} = \frac{\text{Force (N)}}{\text{Area (m}^2)}$$

- $$\text{Density} = \frac{\text{Mass (kg)}}{\text{Volume (m}^3)}$$

- Pressure in liquids increases with depth.

- The air around us exerts a pressure known as atmospheric pressure.

- Upthrust is the force that an object feels in liquid due to the pressure of the liquid underneath it.

The BIG Challenge

The human desire to go faster, climb higher and reach further can be seen in humankind's attempts to break speed and distance records.

For example:

- The record for highest freefall jump, broken by Dr Alan Eustace in 2014.

- The record for fastest sprint over 100 m and 200 m, broken by Usain Bolt in 2009.

- The record for fastest land speed in a vehicle, broken by ThrustSSC in 1997.

Create a poster about these amazing achievements. The poster should mention the distance, time, speed and accelerations achieved in each case.

Go to your Portfolio to check what you have learned in this chapter.

?

Take the chapter 17 quiz on educateplus.ie.

Questions

1. Copy and fill in the blanks:

a. The speed of an object can be calculated by dividing _____ travelled by _____ taken.

b. A _____ quantity has magnitude only, whereas a _____ has both magnitude and _____.

c. The _____ of a distance–time graph tells us the _____ of the object.

d. Acceleration can be calculated by dividing change in _____ by _____.

e. When an acceleration takes place in the same direction an object is moving in, the object _____ _____. When the acceleration takes place in the opposite direction, the object _____ _____. This is also known as _____.

f. Forces can change an object's shape, _____, _____ and _____.

g. Any object that is able to restore its shape after it has been _____ or _____ is known as an _____ object. Examples include _____ and _____ _____.

h. _____ is a force that occurs when two objects are placed in _____. It is a _____ to motion.

i. Pressure in liquids increases with _____.

j. The air around us exerts a pressure known as _____ _____.

2. If you could drive to the Sun at a speed of 88.5 km/h, it would take around 193 years. Based on these figures, calculate how far away we are from the Sun.

3. Use labelled diagrams to explain the force interaction pairs occurring when:

a. You are sitting upright on your laboratory chair.

b. A child bounces up and down on a trampoline.

c. You kick a rugby ball.

d. A chef cuts an onion with a knife.

e. A rocket takes off from a space centre.

f. A landing module enters the Mars atmosphere.

4. Copy the Venn diagram and insert the letters for the following forms of motion into the correct position.

a. Driving a car from Waterford to Cork.

b. A skateboarder skating through a half-pipe.

c. Riding a rollercoaster.

d. Running on a treadmill.

e. A space rocket taking off from the Earth.

f. Hitting a tennis ball horizontally across a tennis net.

g. A hockey puck sliding across the ice.

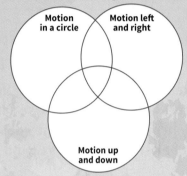

5. If a Formula 1 car can accelerate from rest at 25 m/s^2, calculate how fast it would be moving after 10 seconds.

6. Copy the funnel diagrams and place the names of the relevant contact and non-contact forces discussed in this chapter in the correct funnel.

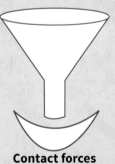 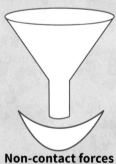

Contact forces   **Non-contact forces**

7. Copy and complete this table:

Object	Density (g/cm^3)	Mass (g)	Volume (cm^3)
A		180	25
B	3.9		15
C		72	90
D	35	70	

Which of the objects listed would:

a. Float.

b. Sink in water.

Working as a Scientist

Asking Questions and Making Predictions

Buckle up! Investigating the Physics of Seat Belts

You have most likely been a passenger in a car or bus before and have hopefully used a seat belt. The Irish Road Safety Authority (RSA) says that 'seat belts are your best protection in accidents and it is especially important that any child in your vehicle be protected by the safety restraint appropriate to their size and weight'.

> **Step 1:** Prior knowledge and experience

Before starting any investigation, it is useful to make a note of all the relevant information you already know. This will help you to make decisions and also predictions about what you will test.

1 **Make notes about everything you know about car safety. What types of safety features do cars have? What do these safety features do? Now think about seat belts. Why are they needed? How are they designed? How do they work? Are there different types of seat belts? What factors would affect the way they work in a crash?**

> **Step 2:** Asking questions

To increase awareness amongst young people, your local youth group has asked you and your lab partner to write a blog on the importance of wearing seat belts. They want you to create an investigation to show what would happen in crash tests with and without wearing a seat belt.

2 **What do you think you should test to show what would happen if you did or did not wear a seat belt in a crash? What would you expect to be the outcome from a crash where you did or did not wear a seat belt? Make a list of other questions you might ask.**

> **Step 3:** Developing a line of inquiry

The youth group want you to continue with the task as follows:

- Make a crash test dummy out of modelling clay.
- Design a vehicle and place the dummy in it.
- Slide the vehicle down a ramp to simulate a crash. You will have to think of a way to arrange the apparatus so it will cause a collision.
- Note the damage to the crash test dummy.
- Use sticky tape to make a seat belt for the dummy.
- Repeat the investigation with the dummy strapped in the seat belt.

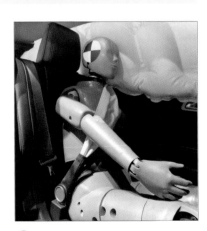

🎧 Fig. 17.9.2

Think about how you might proceed from here. Remember, a scientist only changes one variable at a time.

3 How are you going to design the vehicle and arrange the equipment? It might be helpful to draw a diagram and make a full list of the materials you need.

4 What variables will you have to keep the same to make this a fair test?

5 What measurements will you take and what instruments will you need to take those measurements?

6 Is there anything else you will need to do to ensure accuracy?

7 How will you go about presenting your data?

8 Based on your knowledge and experience, make a list of predictions for the outcome of this investigation. Explain your reasons for these predictions.

Step 4: Observations in the real world

Now you need to carry out the investigation. Remember to record your results in a clear way and to note any observations you make. It might be a good idea to record the collisions using a camera or video to compare to any other data you might collect.

⟳ Fig. 17.9.3
Suggested set-ups for investigation

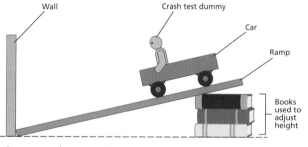

Suggested set-up 1

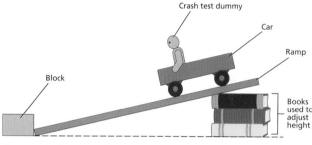

Suggested set-up 2

Step 5: Presenting and interpreting data

Now that you have obtained your data, you need to present it in a way that will help explain your findings to teenagers.

9 Would a table of results alone show what you want to communicate in the blog?

10 Do you need to draw a graph or a chart? If so, decide on the type that suits what you are trying to show.

11 Are there any limitations to the method used in this investigation? If so, what are they?

12 Based on the evidence, summarise your conclusions about the impact of wearing and not wearing a seat belt. Link this back to what you learned about motion in this chapter:

- **Balanced and unbalanced forces**
- **Acceleration**
- **Forces and shapes**

13 Now write the blog. Think about the importance of communicating this information in a way that the teenage readers of the blog will relate to and understand.

Chapter 18

Magnetism and Electricity

What you may already know:

- Many things run on electricity: home appliances, the internet, mobile phones, satellites and even some cars.
- Switches can be used to turn things on and off.
- Batteries can be used to power different devices.
- Magnets can attract or repel each other.

What you will learn in this chapter:

- How magnets work and uses of magnets.
- What static electricity is and its effects.
- The components of an electric circuit and different ways to wire a circuit.
- What is meant by current, potential difference and resistance.
- How electricity is supplied to homes.

Think BIG

- How do smartphones, touchscreens, Wii controllers and computers work?
- How do we know which way is north and which way is south?

Puzzler

Can you crack this code?
The first letter of each image spells out a key word that you will come across in this chapter. Use the hints provided if you need to, or revisit the Puzzler after you finish this chapter.

1.

This force keeps cars on the road

2.
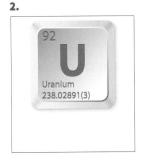
A radioactive element on the periodic table

3.
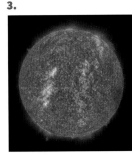
The star at the centre of our solar system

4.
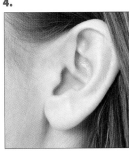
The organ you use for hearing

1. _____

2. _____

3. _____

4. _____

Magnetism

Learning Intentions

In this topic we are learning to:

- Investigate the properties of magnets.
- Evaluate the nature and role of magnetic fields.
- Illustrate magnetic field lines using a plotting compass.

A **magnet** is a piece of metal that attracts other materials.

Magnets can only attract certain materials. These are called **magnetic materials**. Magnetic materials include iron, cobalt and nickel. Magnets can only be made from these materials.

These magnetic materials can also be mixed with other metals as alloys to make magnets. For example, steel, which contains iron and carbon.

GO Learn more about alloys in Chemical World 10.5

Magnetic Poles

The magnetic force of attraction is strongest at both ends of a magnet. These ends are called **poles**.

Magnets have a north pole and a south pole.

Like poles repel each other. Unlike poles attract each other.

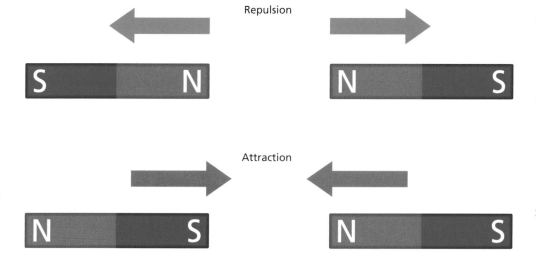

Key Words

Magnet
Magnetic materials
Poles
Magnetic field
Magnetic field lines
Compass

Describing the poles

Copy the following sentences and circle the correct word to describe the magnetic poles in question:

- A north pole will repel a (north/ south) pole.
- A south pole will attract a (north/ south) pole.

➲ Fig. 18.1.1
Attraction and repulsion in bar magnets

Seeing magnets interact

Place two bar magnets in a plastic pocket and under a sheet of paper with a north pole facing a south pole. Next, scatter some iron filings on top of the sheet of paper. Draw a diagram of what you see. Repeat this task for two south poles facing each other. Note your observations.

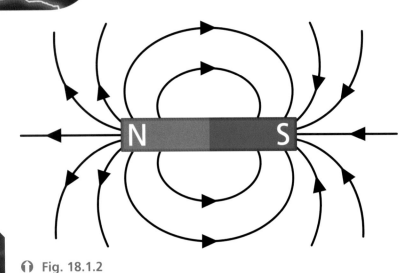

🔊 **Fig. 18.1.2**
Magnetic field lines

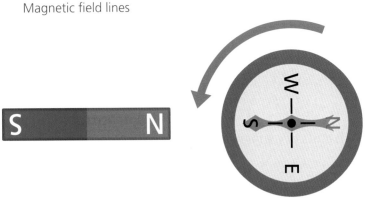

Magnetic Fields

A **magnetic field** is the space around a magnet that exerts a force on magnets and magnetic materials.

Like all forces, magnetic forces have direction. The directions of forces in a magnetic field are represented by **magnetic field lines**.

The direction of these lines can be seen if you place a **compass** near enough to a magnet so it will experience a magnetic force.

A compass is a small magnet that moves freely to show direction. The direction the compass needle points is the direction of the magnetic field lines.

Magnetic field lines always run from the north to south pole of the magnet.

↺ **Fig. 18.1.3**
A compass needle can be moved by a magnet

Seeing magnetic fields

1. Place a bar magnet inside a plastic pocket folder. Next, place a sheet of paper on top of the plastic folder. Scatter some iron filings on top of the sheet of paper.

2. Draw a diagram of what you see. Can you identify where the magnetic field is at its strongest?

Using a plotting compass

A plotting compass is a small compass that you will most likely find in the school laboratory. Using a plotting compass, plan, design, carry out and write up an investigation to verify that the picture of the magnetic field lines in Fig. 18.1.2 is correct.

↺ Fig. 18.1.4

Linking ideas

Compare the magnetic field lines in Fig. 18.1.2 with your observations when you sprinkled iron filings over the bar magnet. Based on your comparison, write a statement describing the relationship between the strength of magnetic fields and the distance between the magnetic field lines.

The Earth's Magnetic Field

The Earth's core contains a circulating liquid of molten iron and nickel. This circulation creates a large magnetic field around the planet. This field is at its strongest at the geographic north and south poles.

GO Learn more about the Earth's core in Earth and Space 22.1

The Earth behaves as if there is a huge bar magnet going through its centre. The magnetic poles run in the opposite direction to the geographic poles. This is why a compass points north – its north pole is attracted to the magnetic south pole.

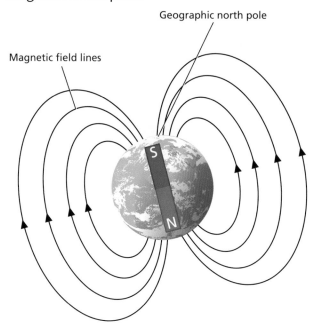

Fun Fact

Have you ever wondered how birds know which direction to fly in when they migrate? The answer may be in their beaks. The nerve branches in their upper beaks contain lots of iron, which scientists think they use to measure the strength and direction of the Earth's magnetic field. This is known as a biological magnetometer.

🎧 Fig. 18.1.5
The geographic north pole is near to the magnetic south pole and vice versa

The Earth's magnetic field is very important for:

- Navigation: compasses rely on their attraction to the magnetic poles to give us geographic directions.

- Protection: the Earth's magnetic field protects the planet from large streams of energy from the Sun called solar winds. Without it, these winds would strip away the ozone layer surrounding the planet, which protects us from harmful ultraviolet radiation.

The Earth's magnetic field deflects cosmic rays towards the north and south poles. Here, they cause the atmosphere to glow in beautiful colours known as aurorae.

GO Learn more about the Earth's atmosphere in Earth and Space 22.4

⇩ Fig. 18.1.6
The Northern Lights, aurorae borealis

What is Electricity?

Key Words

Current electricity
Static electricity
Charged particles
Conductors
Insulators

Learning Intentions

In this topic we are learning to:

- Demonstrate that electricity is a form of energy.
- Investigate the differences between conductors and insulators.
- Distinguish between static and current electricity.

Electricity is a form of energy. We know it is a form of energy because it can be converted into other forms of energy and because it can cause objects to move.

⊃ **Fig. 18.2.1**
Electricity can be converted into other forms of energy. Can you identify the energy transfers taking place in these two pictures?

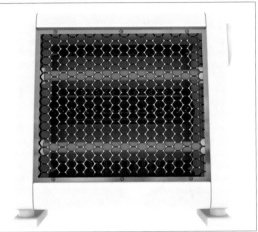

Prove it!

Work with your lab partner to plan, design, carry out and write up investigations to test the following hypotheses:

- Electricity can be converted to other forms of energy.
- Electricity can move things.

Before you begin, write a prediction of what you think the outcome of each investigation will be. After you record your observations, explain why you think they did or did not match your predictions. In each case, list the energy conversions taking place.

Safety note: do not turn on any electrical power source without asking your teacher to inspect your work first.

Fun Fact

The electricity needed to light up the Las Vegas strip each night could provide enough power for a town of 25,000 residents.

How much?

1. Work in groups of three to calculate the total amount of time all the students in your class use the following items on a daily basis:
   - Mobile phone
   - Television
   - Laptop or tablet computer
2. Present your results in an appropriate way on a poster.
3. Do you think your figures are accurate? Why/why not?
4. Did any of the results surprise you? Which ones? Why?

Electricity Flow

There are two types of electricity.

- **Current electricity** is a steady flow of charge though wires and circuits.
- **Static electricity** involves electric charge collecting in one place and sometimes suddenly jumping from one place to another.

We will learn more about both types of electricity later in the chapter.

Conductors and Insulators

One thing static and current electricity have in common is that under certain conditions both forms of electricity involve the movement of **charged particles**.

Certain substances will allow charged particles to flow through them freely. These substances are known as electrical **conductors**. Metals such as copper are good conductors.

Other substances do not allow charged particles to flow through them easily. These substances, such as rubber and plastic, are known as electrical **insulators**.

A day without electricity

Imagine that you have to spend a day with absolutely no electricity. Write a diary entry describing what your day was like.

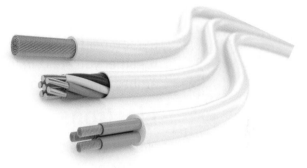

🎧 **Fig. 18.2.2**
Copper is a good electrical conductor, so it is used for wires. Plastic is a good insulator, so it is used for the protective casing around electrical wires

Conduct or insulate?

A group of students wanted to prove that copper is a conductor and plastic is an insulator. They connected a piece of copper to a battery using metal crocodile clips and conducting wires. A battery provides energy to move charged particles, causing electricity to flow. They also connected a bulb and a switch as shown in Fig. 18.2.3.

1. Predict what happens when the switch is closed.
2. The students replaced the piece of copper with a plastic rod. Predict what happens when the switch is closed. Explain the reasons for your predictions.
3. Set up this circuit in school and test these items for yourself.
4. Collect other items from home or school that you believe to be either conductors or insulators of electricity.
5. List the items in a table alongside your prediction of whether or not they conduct electricity.
6. Test the items and record your observations in the same table. Explain why your predictions did or did not match your observations.

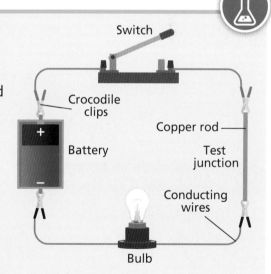

🎧 **Fig. 18.2.3**
Investigation set-up

Safety note: *do not turn on any electrical power source without asking your teacher to inspect your work first.*

Static Charges

Key Words

Negative

Positive

Learning Intentions

In this topic we are learning to:

- Discuss how objects can be charged by friction.
- Investigate the interaction between like and unlike charged particles.

In 600 BC, the Ancient Greeks realised that rubbing amber with fur caused the two to be attracted to each other. They also noticed that the rubbed piece of amber could attract light substances, such as hair, and that it could even spark if it was rubbed for long enough.

This effect happens because of friction between the amber and the fur. Remember that friction is a contact force, so when you rub two objects together you are bringing those objects into contact. When the fur and amber come into contact they become charged with static electricity.

Electrons

How does the charging happen? Electrons play an important role in electricity. When you rub the amber on the fur, you are physically 'knocking' electrons off one object and onto the other. In this case, electrons are transferred from the fur to the amber.

⬤ **Fig. 18.3.1**
Electrons transferring between fur and amber

Electrons have a negative charge, that means:

- If an object gains electrons, it becomes **negative**.
- If an object loses electrons, it becomes **positive**.

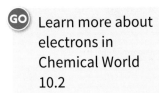

GO Learn more about electrons in Chemical World 10.2

'Electron'

The origin of the term 'electron' is from the Greek word *ēlektron* meaning 'amber'.

Electricity gets its name from 'electron'.

Relive the Greek discovery

1. Gather the following materials:
   - Amber (ask your geography teacher if you can borrow a piece)
   - A biro
   - A balloon

2. Now rub the materials off the sleeve of your jumper, a good substitute for fur. Next, hold the item close to your hair. What do you observe?

3. Can you explain what happened? What does this say about the nature of:
   a. The items listed above?
   b. Your jumper?

Movement Between Charges

As we know, movement suggests that a force is being exerted. This force has a magnitude and direction (it is a vector) and its direction depends on the types of charges involved.

There are two types of static charges: positive charges (+) and negative charges (–). These charges can attract or repel each other in much the same way as the poles of magnets.

- A negative charge repels a negative charge: these are the same type of charge, or like charges.

- A negative charge attracts a positive charge: these are the opposite type of charge, or unlike charges.

- A positive charge repels a positive charge: these are the same type of charge, or like charges.

> Like charges repel. Unlike charges attract.

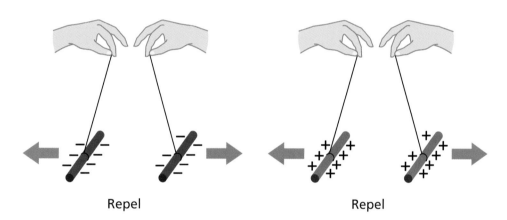

Repel   Repel   Attract

♁ **Fig. 18.3.2**
How like and unlike charges interact

Explaining charging 12³

Using your knowledge of subatomic structure and the balance of protons and electrons in atoms, show the electron configuration for a sodium atom that has lost two electrons. How does this explain why items that lose electrons become positively charged?

Electric water

1. Turn on a tap in the laboratory so that a thin stream of water flows.

2. Rub a polythene rod off your jumper (rubbed polythene becomes negatively charged).

3. Bring the rod close to the stream of water.

4. Repeat this task using a piece of cellulose acetate (an overhead projector plastic sheet). This takes on a positive charge when rubbed.

5. Record your observations. What do these results tell you about the charges present in water?

Charges — moving or not? 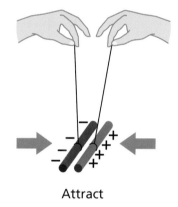 a b c

Using your knowledge of the subatomic structure, draw a diagram to explain the statement: 'In static electricity, it is only the negative charges that move'.

Effects of Static Electricity

Key Words

Lightning
Cumulonimbus clouds
Discharge
Lightning conductors
Earthing

Learning Intentions

In this topic we are learning to:
- Examine how lightning occurs and how lightning conductors work.
- Outline some uses of static electricity.

Lightning is one of the most visible and spectacular effects of static electricity.

The starting point for lightning is in **cumulonimbus clouds**, also known as 'thunderheads'. These clouds carry a positive charge on top and a negative charge below. Friction between ice particles and water droplets within the clouds causes this charge.

Look at Fig. 18.4.1. The charge built up between the cloud and the ground causes a **discharge** of giant sparks, which is lightning.

◑ **Fig. 18.4.1**
How lightning happens

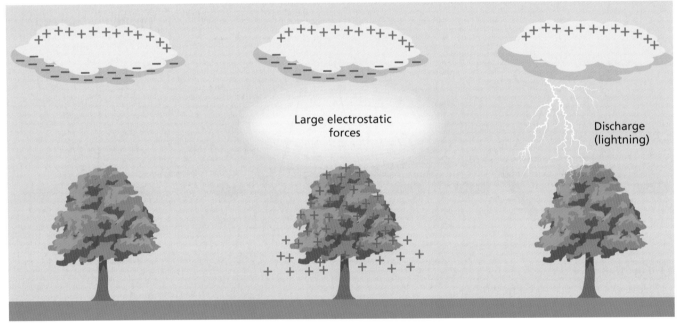

Large electrostatic forces

Discharge (lightning)

1 There is a negative charge at the bottom of the cloud

2 Positive charge is generated

3 When the charge is large enough, the cloud discharges in a bolt of lightning

Lightning Conductors

Lightning will be more likely to strike taller or more pointed objects, such as trees. It happens especially if the object is a good conductor, such as a metal aerial.

To prevent these unwanted strikes, **lightning conductors** are used. They are often placed on the tallest building in a town. Lightning conductors are normally connected to a large metal plate below the ground.

When electricity travels through an object into the ground, it is known as **earthing**. An earthed object cannot build up a charge.

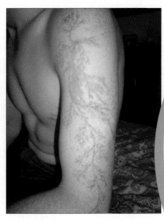

⋂ **Fig. 18.4.3**
Lichtenberg figures

> ### Fun Fact
> Lightning flashes more than three million times a day worldwide – that's about 40 times a second! The bolt of electricity seen in a lightning fork is moving at about 100 million km/h. Fig. 18.4.3 shows the marks on a person struck by lightning. These marks are known as Lichtenberg figures.

⋂ **Fig. 18.4.2**
The Clock Gate in Youghal, County Cork, is one of the tallest structures in the town. Its lightning conductor is wide, thick and made of copper. Why do you think it has these features?

Static Electricity at Work

The properties of static electricity can be useful. The table below describes some of the ways static electricity is used.

Use	How it works
Forensics	Objects in a crime scene can be placed above a charged metal wire covered in a fine black powder to reveal fingerprints.
Electrostatic painting	Electrostatic paint is charged in such a way that it sticks to the surface of cars or bicycles when it is sprayed. This reduces the amount of paint needed to cover a surface.
Cling film	As cling film is unrolled, electrons are pulled from the roll onto the sheet of film, making it negatively charged. As it is wrapped around an item, an attractive force is exerted, making the film 'cling'.
Touchscreen technology	Some touchscreens have a sheet of electric charge running across them. Where the screen is touched, a small discharge occurs. This is detected by the hardware of the phone or tablet, which communicates with the operating system to perform a function, such as opening an app.

Static in everyday life

With your lab partner, draw up a list of ways you have experienced static electricity in your everyday life.

Electric Circuits

Key Words

Components
Circuit diagram
Current
Ammeter

Learning Intentions

In this topic we are learning to:
- Explain what is meant by electric current.
- Plan, design and build simple electric circuits.
- Model the basic operation of an electric circuit.

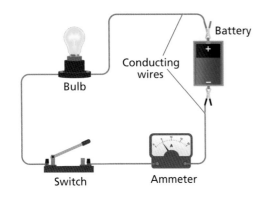

🎧 **Fig. 18.5.1**
A complete simple circuit

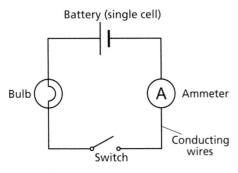

🎧 **Fig. 18.5.2**
The same circuit drawn in a circuit diagram

Building circuits

Using equipment supplied by your teacher, build electric circuits that:
- Give out light.
- Make noise.
- Move things.

Take a photograph of what your circuit looks like and draw a circuit diagram.

Safety note: do not turn on any electrical power source without asking your teacher to inspect your work first.

Electric circuits are part of many devices we use every day, from a circuit board in a computer to a toaster.

In all of these devices, electrical energy is converted into other forms. This happens when electrical energy passes through objects in the circuit called **components**. For example, a battery, a speaker or a motor.

Symbols in Electricity

Components can be drawn as they look (as in Fig. 18.5.1) or they can be represented more simply by using symbols. We use these symbols in a **circuit diagram** (as in Fig. 18.5.2).

Some circuit symbols are shown in the table below. They can also be found in your *Formulae and Tables* booklet.

Component	Function	Symbol
Battery (single cell)	Provides energy to move charges around a circuit	
Switch	Completes a circuit when closed, turns it 'on'. Breaks a circuit when open, turns it 'off'	
Bulb	Converts electrical energy to light energy	
Buzzer	Converts electrical energy to sound energy	
Motor	Converts electrical energy to kinetic energy	

Moving Charges

An electric circuit must be complete to work. For example, if there was a break in the circuit shown in Fig. 18.5.1, the bulb would not give out light.

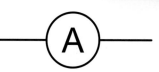

When a circuit is complete, charged particles in the metal wires of the circuit start to move.

Where do moving charges come from? The surprising answer is that they have been there all the time. The electrical wires of a circuit are made up of atoms, which contain electrons. Electrons are the charges involved in the flow of electric charge through metals.

Current is the rate of flow of charge per second. The SI unit for electric current is the ampere, or amp for short. Its symbol is the letter A. Current in a circuit can be measured using an **ammeter**.

The particles of a solid are vibrating a small amount all the time. When you connect a source of energy, such as a battery, into a circuit you cause all of these charges to move in one direction. The energy in the battery 'pushes' the charges.

The Three Effects of Electricity

Electric current can have three effects:

1. Heating. For example, in electric kettles and heaters.
2. Magnetic. For example, in electromagnets.
3. Chemical. For example, in the electrolysis (splitting) of water.

◉ Fig. 18.5.3
The circuit symbol for an ammeter

GO Learn about the electrolysis of water in Earth and Space 22.3

A model for electric circuits

We cannot see what goes on inside electric circuits when a current flows. A model to explain what is going on can be created by using a loop of rope pulled around by one person and passing through another person's hands.

1. Using this model, come up with a presentation for your class that explains the following aspects of an electric circuit:
   - The battery is the source of energy in the circuit.
   - The energy of the battery is converted into other forms when it passes through components.
   - A circuit needs to be complete in order for electric current to flow.
   - The charges are already in the wire.
   - Current is the rate of flow of charge.
   - The current begins to flow at all points at the same time.
   - The current needs a component to flow through.

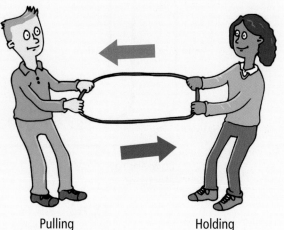
Pulling   Holding

2. Scientists use models to help explain what is happening when a current flows. Is this a good model for representing electric circuits? Is it missing anything? Is there anything you could add, change or do differently to improve this model?

◉ Fig. 18.5.4
The rope model

Potential Difference and Voltage

Learning Intentions

In this topic we are learning to:

- Model potential difference in electric circuits.
- Identify different sources of potential difference.

We know that batteries are a source of electrical energy in a circuit, but only when it is in a complete circuit. Why? How is this energy put into action?

Figure 18.6.1 shows how a battery transfers energy to electrons and moves them around a circuit.

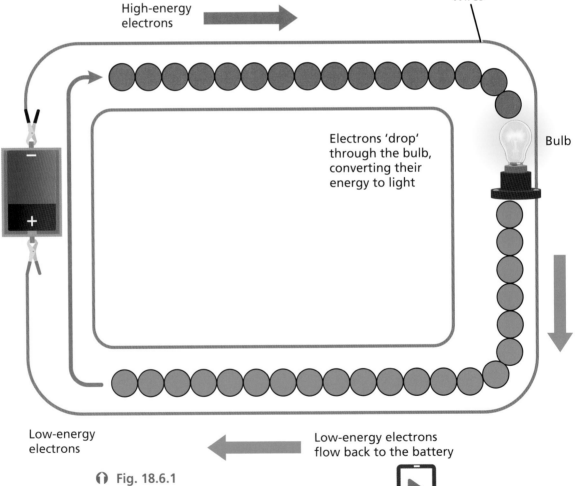

High-energy electrons

Wires

Battery gives energy to electrons – it 'lifts' them in energy

Electrons 'drop' through the bulb, converting their energy to light

Bulb

Low-energy electrons

Low-energy electrons flow back to the battery

🎧 **Fig. 18.6.1**
Electrical energy conversion in an electrical circuit

1. The battery gives energy to the electrons – it 'lifts' them in energy.
2. These high-energy electrons 'drop' through the bulb and convert their energy to light.
3. The low-energy electrons flow back to the battery.

This is why the circuit must be complete: the battery must be connected to the components in a circuit to allow the charges to drop through them and convert their energy.

When there is a point of high electrical energy and a point of low electrical energy in a complete circuit, we say that there is a difference in electrical potential energy between those points. This is known as **potential difference**.

Potential difference provides the energy that pushes electrons around a circuit. It is needed to make a current flow.

⌒ Fig. 18.6.2
The circuit symbol for a voltmeter

Measuring Potential Difference

Potential difference is also called **voltage**. The SI unit for voltage is **volts**. The symbol for voltage is the letter V.

A **voltmeter** is used to measure the potential difference across a component. In other words, it measures the 'drop' in energy as energy travels through a component and is converted to other forms.

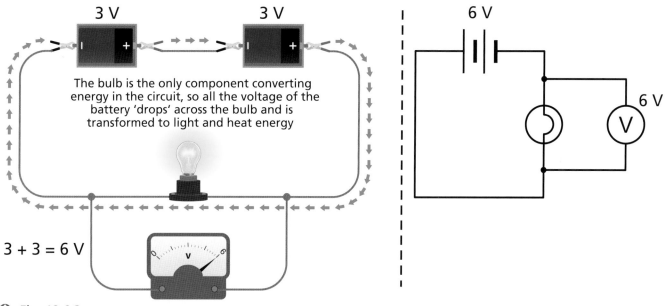

The bulb is the only component converting energy in the circuit, so all the voltage of the battery 'drops' across the bulb and is transformed to light and heat energy

3 V 3 V 6 V

3 + 3 = 6 V 6 V

⌒ Fig. 18.6.3
Potential difference in a circuit being measured using a voltmeter

Conservation of energy and mass in electric circuits

Using the law of conservation of energy and law of conservation of mass, discuss the following statement with your lab partner: 'Energy and mass are not "lost" when electrons flow in a circuit.'

See Physical World 16.1 for a reminder about the law of conservation of energy and Chemical World 9.5 for a reminder about the law of conservation of mass.

Cells and Batteries

When we talk about electric components, one 'battery' on its own is called a cell. Two or more cells stacked together are called a **battery**.

Cells and batteries are sources of electrical potential energy. They can transfer their chemical energy into electrical energy.

The flow of electric current is from the positive (+) to the negative (–) end of a battery.

GO Learn about the electrolytes in Earth and Space 22.3

- A **simple cell** (or single cell) is made up of two different metals, called **electrodes**, placed in a chemical. This chemical can be in the form of a liquid or a paste called an **electrolyte**.

⊃ **Fig. 18.6.4**
A simple cell can be made from a copper and zinc plate (electrodes) placed in dilute sulfuric acid solution and connected to a bulb

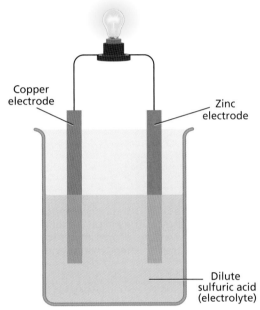

Copper electrode

Zinc electrode

Dilute sulfuric acid (electrolyte)

- The more cells connected to each other in a battery, the greater the potential difference of the battery.

↺ **Fig. 18.6.5**
The circuit symbol for a battery made up of many simple cells

⊃ **Fig. 18.6.6**
A car battery has many electrodes placed in a liquid chemical

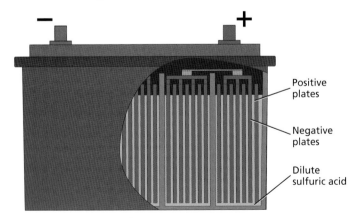

Positive plates

Negative plates

Dilute sulfuric acid

A chemical reaction happens inside every cell or battery. This leads to a build-up of positive charges at one electrode and negative charges at another electrode.

If these electrodes are connected by wires to a bulb, they now have a point of low energy to 'drop' to. In other words, we have created a potential difference and the charge can flow.

Types of Battery

There are two main types of battery:

1. A **primary cell** or battery is one that cannot be recharged once it is used up.

2. A **secondary cell** or battery can be recharged and used again. Most of the batteries we use today are rechargeable. For example, the battery in your mobile phone has to be recharged.

Although secondary cells usually cost more to buy, they are more cost-effective over time as they can be used again. Rechargeable batteries also benefit the environment as the disposal of batteries contributes to pollution.

Fig. 18.6.7
Rechargeable batteries

Fruit and veg voltage

Fruits and vegetables, such as lemons and potatoes, can be used as a source of chemical energy (a battery) in powering a simple alarm clock. By placing a galvanised nail into one end of a potato and a piece of copper wire in the other, and then connecting to the power terminals of the clock, you will have created a circuit that will allow the clock to work.

Plan, design, carry out and write up an investigation to compare the effects of changing (a) metal types and (b) fruit/vegetable type on the voltage produced across two different metals, when the electrolytes are fruits and/or vegetables.

Fig. 18.6.8
A potato alarm clock

Fun Fact

Electric eels can generate potential differences of up to 600 volts for hunting and self-defence – this is nearly three times the voltage supplied to a family home!

Fig. 18.6.9

Series and Parallel Circuits

Key Words

Series

Parallel

Learning Intentions

In this topic we are learning to:

- Distinguish between the wiring of components in series and parallel circuits.
- Compare voltages and currents in series and parallel circuits.

There are two ways of connecting components in electric circuits:

- When components are connected in a single loop with each other and the battery, they are connected in **series**.
- When components are connected in different branches, they are connected in **parallel**.

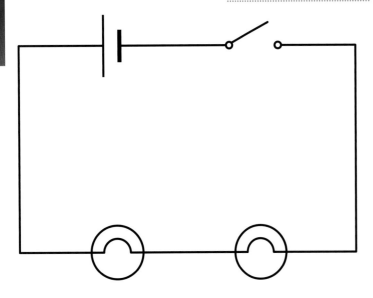

◑ **Fig. 18.7.1**
A series circuit

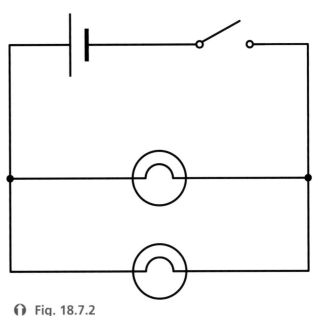

◑ **Fig. 18.7.2**
A parallel circuit

Series and parallel

Read the following statements and discuss with your partner whether the lights involved are wired in series or parallel:

1. When a single bulb breaks on a set of Christmas tree lights, all the lights go out.

2. One of the bulbs in the headlights of a car breaks but the other stays on.

3. A televison, cooker and washing machine can be operated independent of each other.

In the series circuit in Fig. 18.7.1, if one bulb blows then the other goes out too. This is because they are connected in a single loop with each other. If one of the bulbs blows in the parallel circuit in Fig. 18.7.2, the other can stay on as it is still connected in a complete circuit to the battery.

- Ammeters measure the current flowing through a circuit, so they have to be connected in series with components.
- Voltmeters measure the potential difference across a component. This means they must be connected across a component in parallel to measure the difference in energy between one side and the other.

Current and Voltage in Series Circuits

In a series circuit:

- The current is the same at all points.
- The voltages across all of the different components sum to the voltage of the battery in the circuit.

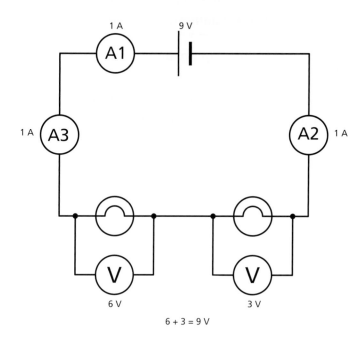

↻ **Fig. 18.7.3**
Each of the ammeters – A1, A2, and A3 – record the same current of 1 A. The voltages in this circuit add up to a total of 9 V – this is equal to the voltage of the battery

Current and Voltage in Parallel Circuits

In a parallel circuit:

- The current of each separate branch of the circuit sums to the value of the series current in the overall circuit.
- The voltage across components on the same branch is equal.

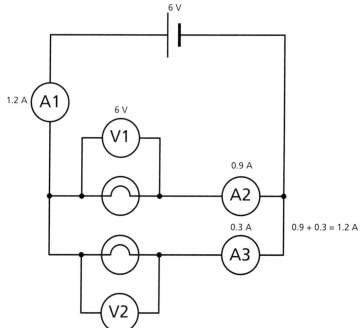

↻ **Fig. 18.7.4**
The current recorded on ammeters A2 and A3 sum to the value of the current recorded on ammeter A1. This is the value of the series current in the overall circuit. The voltmeters V1 and V2 record the same value. This value, 6 V, is the same as the voltage of the single cell battery

Resistance

Key Words

Resistance

Ohm

Ohmmeter

Variable resistor

Resistor

⋒ **Fig. 18.8.1**
Lower currents flow in a games console wire than in an electric hob

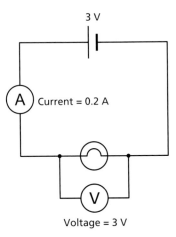

⋒ **Fig. 18.8.2**

Learning Intentions

In this topic we are learning to:

- Appreciate what resistance means.
- Calculate voltage, current and resistance in electric circuits.
- Investigate the factors that affect the resistance of a component.

Resistance is a measure of how difficult it is for an electric current to pass through a substance.

The SI unit for electrical resistance is the **ohm**. Its symbol is the Greek letter omega, Ω. Resistance can be measured with an **ohmmeter** connected in series.

Calculating Voltage, Current and Resistance

Different components in circuits offer different degrees of resistance to the current. For example, the current flowing through a games console is a lot lower than the current flowing through the filament of an electric cooker. The difference is due to the resistance of the wires.

So, the electric current that flows depends not only on the voltage of the battery but also on the resistance of the components that the current must flow through.

Current can be calculated using the equation:

$$\text{Current (A)} = \frac{\text{Voltage (V)}}{\text{Resistance } (\Omega)}$$

In Fig. 18.8.2, the ammeter measures the current flowing through the bulb to be 0.2 A. The bulb is the only component connected in the circuit so the voltage across it is equal to the voltage of the single cell battery, 3 V. The resistance of the bulb can be calculated as:

$$\text{Current} = \frac{\text{Voltage}}{\text{Resistance}}, \text{ so Resistance} = \frac{\text{Voltage}}{\text{Current}}$$

$$\text{Resistance} = \frac{3}{0.2}$$

$$\text{Resistance} = 15 \ \Omega$$

When components are connected in series, their resistances combine. This can cause a decrease in the overall current flowing in a circuit for a given voltage.

Bright bulbs?

Build the circuit in Fig. 18.7.1 on page 322. Now connect two more bulbs of the exact same type (rating) in series.

1. Before you switch on the circuit, predict what will happen to the brightness of the bulbs.
2. Now switch on the circuit and record what you see. Did your predictions match your observations? Why/why not?
3. Explain what is happening to the total current in the circuit and why.

Using Resistance

Resistance can be a nuisance as it leads to a loss of energy from a battery. However, resistance also has important functions:

- Appliances, such as kettles, cookers and toasters, use high-resistance coils of wire to generate large quantities of heat.
- Some devices, such as laptops and mobile phones, need resistors in their circuit boards as their components will only operate with very small currents.
- Certain devices can vary their resistance. These variable resistors can be used to adjust the volume in stereos and MP3 players.

What is the resistance?

1. An electric motor has a current of 3 A flowing through it and is connected in series to a 12 V battery. What is the resistance of the motor?
2. Calculate the resistance of each bulb in the series circuit shown in Fig. 18.7.3 on page 323.

Varying resistance

You will find two types of **variable resistor** in the school laboratory: a rheostat and a potentiometer. If you study metalwork or technology, you may have used potentiometers to control the size of the current in any electrical devices you have built.

Using one of these devices, design and build an electric circuit that demonstrates how you can increase and decrease the volume of a buzzer.

🔊 **Fig. 18.8.3**
A rheostat

🔊 **Fig. 18.8.4**
A potentiometer

Resistance and Charges

Resistance slows down moving charges. In a metal wire, these moving charges are electrons. As the electrons move, they collide with the material of the component as they try to pass through it.

Any component that slows down moving charges is known as a **resistor**.

How much a resistor slows down the current passing through it depends on:

- Length: the longer a resistor is, the harder it is for charges to get from one side to the other and so the greater the resistance.
- Temperature: when you heat particles, you give them more energy and they move faster. Electrons are more likely to hit fast-moving particles. This means charges are slowed down when the resistor is hotter. Note that some components, such as thermistors, decrease their resistance with increased temperature.
- Nature of material: conductors allow charges to pass through them easily and have a low resistance. Insulators do not allow charges to pass through them easily and have a high resistance.

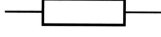
🔊 **Fig. 18.8.5**
Circuit symbol for a resistor

Testing resistance

Plan, design, carry out and write up an investigation to test the following hypotheses:

1. The resistance of a metal wire increases with temperature.
2. The resistance of a metal wire increases with length.

Make sure to vary only one thing at a time and to collect a range of data.

Electricity in the Home

Key Words

Live
Neutral
Alternating current
Direct current
Diodes
Forward biased
Reverse biased
Light-emitting diode (LED)
Fuse

GO Learn more about how power stations generate electricity in Earth and Space 24.1

⤳ **Fig. 18.9.1**
A power station is like a big battery. Appliances are connected across this circuit in parallel

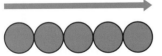

Alternating current: charges constantly move forwards and backwards

Direct current: charges move in one direction only

🎧 **Fig. 18.9.2**
Direct versus alternating current

Learning Intentions

In this topic we are learning to:

- Illustrate how appliances are connected to the mains supply.
- Distinguish between alternating current and direct current.
- Investigate the role of a fuse wire.

An electrical power station is just like a giant battery providing homes with electrical energy. This energy is transported to houses through two main electrical wires – the **live** wire and the **neutral** wire. All devices in a house connect across these two wires in parallel. This is why it is possible to turn one device off while keeping others on.

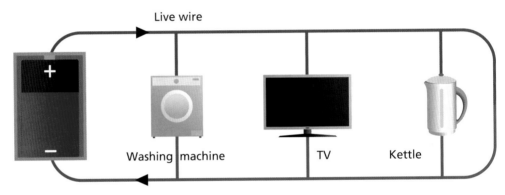

Live wire

Washing machine   TV   Kettle

Neutral wire

Electrical power

1₂³

The electrical power of an appliance can be calculated using the current flowing through and the voltage across an appliance:

> Electrical power (W) = voltage (volts) x current (amps)

For example, if a component is connected to a 50 V supply and the current flowing through it is 2 A, its electrical power is calculated as:

> 50 x 2 = 100 W

Now you try! Using the equation, calculate the power of a kettle connected to a 220 V mains supply if there is a current of 10 A flowing through it.

Alternating and Direct Current

Electricity is generated in power stations in the form of **alternating current**, or a.c. This means the electrons in the wire are constantly changing direction every one-fiftieth of a second.

Alternating current is generated in power stations and transmitted into homes at a potential difference of 220–240 V. This is known as the mains voltage.

Direct current, or d.c., flows in one direction only.

Diodes

Many everyday appliances run on d.c. These appliances can convert a.c. from the mains into d.c. using **diodes**. Diodes are components that allow current to flow in one direction only.

- When the positive end of the diode is connected to the positive end of the battery, it is said to be **forward biased**. This allows current to flow.

- If the negative end of the diode is connected to the positive end of the battery, this is known as **reverse biased** and no current flows.

Because a.c. is constantly changing direction, current only flows when it is forward biased. Mobile phone chargers, for example, contain many diodes that convert the mains electricity into d.c.

A **light-emitting diode (LED)** is a diode that emits light when current flows through it. LEDs come in a range of colours and can be used to show if devices are on or off. LEDs require a very small current. They must be connected in series with a resistor to stop damage by too large a current.

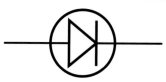

Fig. 18.9.3
Circuit symbol for a diode

Fig. 18.9.4
LEDs

LEDs lighting the future

Research LED technology under the following headings:

1. Advantages of LEDs over filament bulbs.
2. Advances in LED lighting.
3. LED televisions.
4. Future uses of LEDs.

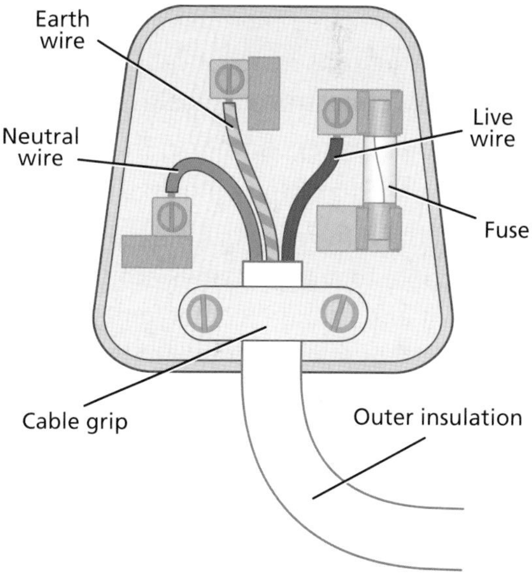

Electrical Safety

The live wire in a house circuit is high in electrical energy and the neutral wire is low.

If a fault develops that exposes the live wire, it can cause a nasty electric shock.

The **fuse** wire is a safety measure that prevents this from happening. A fuse is connected in a standard three-pin plug as in Fig. 18.9.5.

If an appliance is faulty, this can lead to the current in the circuit becoming too large. The fuse has a thin piece of wire running through it, designed to melt if the current goes above a set value. When the fuse wire melts, it breaks the circuit and cuts off the electricity. Fuses are connected to the live wire as this is high in electrical energy.

The earth wire will draw a large current through the plug if an appliance is faulty. This helps the fuse wire to melt.

The fuse box of a house contains other circuit breakers that help to cut off the electrical supply if there is a fault in an appliance.

Earth wire

Neutral wire

Live wire

Fuse

Cable grip

Outer insulation

Fig. 18.9.5
A three-pin plug

Fig. 18.9.6
Circuit breakers

Chapter Summary

- A magnet is a piece of metal that attracts other materials.
- Magnets have a north pole and a south pole. Like poles repel each other. Unlike poles attract each other.
- A magnetic field is the space around a magnet that exerts a force on magnets and magnetic materials.
- Electricity is a form of energy. It can be converted into other forms of energy and can move things.
- Conductors allow electric charges to move through them easily. Insulators do not.
- Objects can be charged with static electricity by friction.
- There are two types of charges – positive charges and negative charges. An object that gains electrons is negatively charged. An object that loses electrons is positively charged.
- Like charges repel. Unlike charges attract.
- Lightning is a natural effect of static electricity.
- Potential difference is a measure of the energy available to move charges around an electric circuit and through components. When they move through the components, the energy of the charges is converted into other forms.
- When components are connected in a single loop with each other and the battery, they are connected in series. When components are connected in different branches, they are connected in parallel.

- Current is the same at all points in a series circuit. The voltages across all components sums to the source voltage of the cell or battery powering the circuit.
- Voltage is the same across all parallel branches and the currents in each individual branch sum to the value of the series current in the overall circuit.
- Resistance is a measure of how difficult it is for an electric current to pass through a substance. Its unit is the ohm and it can be measured using an ohmmeter.
- The relationship between voltage, current and resistance can be represented with the equation:

$$\text{Resistance } (\Omega) = \frac{\text{Voltage (V)}}{\text{Current (A)}}$$

- The resistance of a material depends on its length, temperature and nature.
- Electric current can have a heating, magnetic and chemical effect.
- Electrical power can be calculated using the equation:

$$\boxed{\text{Electrical power (W)} = \text{voltage (V)} \times \text{current (A)}}$$

- Alternating current constantly changes direction. Direct current flows in one direction only.
- Diodes can be used to convert a.c. to d.c.
- A fuse wire is a safety device that breaks a circuit if there is an electrical fault.

The BIG Challenge

Why do different electrical appliances have different current and voltage values written on them?

1. Plan, design, carry out and write up two investigations to clearly show the relationship between the current flowing through and the voltage across:

    a. A metal wire at a constant temperature.

    b. A filament bulb.

2. There is a physical law that explains the relationship between current and voltage. Research this law and link what it says to your findings.

Go to your Portfolio to check what you have learned in this chapter.

Take the chapter 18 quiz on educateplus.ie.

Questions

1. Copy and fill in the blanks:

   a. Electricity is a form of _____. It can be converted into other forms of _____ and can _____ _____.

   b. A substance that allows electric charge to flow through it easily is known as a _____. A substance that does not allow electric charge to flow through it easily is known as an _____.

   c. There are two types of static charges called _____ and _____ charges. Like charges _____. Unlike charges _____.

   d. When you rub a pen off your hair, you are _____ charges onto the pen. This is charging by _____.

   e. Electric current is a flow of electric _____. It is measured in _____ and can be measured using an _____ connected in _____.

   f. Potential _____ is a measure of the energy available to _____ charges around an electric circuit and through components, where their energy is converted into other forms.

   g. Current is the _____ at all points in a series circuit and voltages _____.

   h. A fuse wire is a safety device that _____ a circuit if there is an electrical _____.

   i. Resistance is a measure of how difficult it is for an electric _____ to pass through a _____.

   j. Appliances can convert a.c. to _____ using _____. These are components that allow current to flow in _____ only.

2. Based on your knowledge of the behaviour of static charges, explain why:

   a. A Perspex rod can be charged easier than a copper rod.

   b. If you clean a window with a dry cloth on a dry day, it will soon become dusty.

   c. If you pull cling film off a roll and bring it close to your arm, it makes the hairs on your arm stand up. This does not happen when you use aluminium foil.

   d. It may be dangerous to raise an umbrella during a thunderstorm.

   e. As some drugs used to put patients to sleep during surgery are explosive, the floor tiles in an operating theatre are made of a conducting material.

   f. Aeroplanes need to be earthed through a static port when they land.

3. Explain why an electric cable has copper on the inside and is surrounded by plastic.

4. A student has set up the following circuit. She records the current at 0.6 A. After about ten minutes of leaving the bulb on, she notices that the current has dropped to 0.5 A. Explain why this happens. Make reference to current, voltage and resistance in your answer.

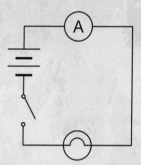

5. Electricians working with high-voltage power lines wear suits lined with silver wire of a very low resistance. Using your knowledge of electricity and resistance, explain why these suits are an important safety feature for these workers.

6. Why are the on/off switches for electric showers sometimes operated by pulling strings instead of pressing a switch with your finger?

7. Identify 1, 2, 3 and 4 in the diagram below.

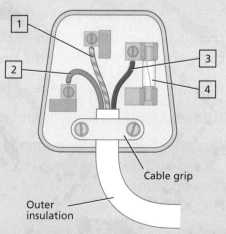

Cable grip

Outer insulation

Working as a Scientist

Making and Recording Observations

Electronic Systems in Action: Making Scores Count

Electronic systems are performing useful tasks all around us. These tasks can range from a function as simple as turning off a kettle when it boils to landing an aeroplane on autopilot.

For electronic systems to work correctly, they sometimes need to be able to sense changes in the environment and respond to these changes.

Sensors that detect a change in their surroundings can input this change to an electronic system. A process within the electronic system then takes place, leading to a function taking place, such as turning on a light, an alarm buzzer, a motor and so on. This function is the output of the system.

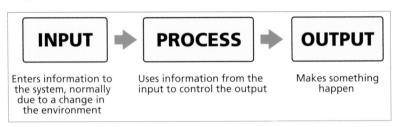

🎧 Fig. 18.11.1

Robert and Louise are basketball players. Their team has been playing well in competition, but their level of accuracy in scoring points is a concern. To investigate this, their coach asks them to design an electronic system that will keep track of the number of points they score in training compared to the number of shooting chances they have. They design a circuit containing the following components:

- Input: a light sensor, which is a light-dependent resistor (LDR). The resistance of this device decreases when the intensity of light shining on it increases.
- Process: a computer microprocessor that detects the light level input from the light sensor.
- Output: a rate counter that registers one count every time the circuit detects a break in the beam of light.

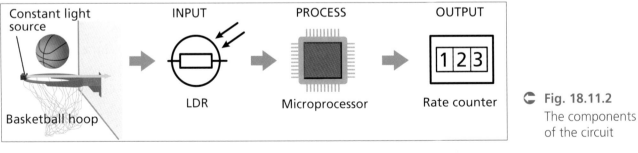

🔄 Fig. 18.11.2
The components of the circuit

1 Compare the workings of an electronic system to the workings of the nervous system in the human body. What are the similarities and differences?

2 Describe what happens when a basketball passes through the hoop.

3 Using the input/process/output model, describe this electronic system.

The students want to test the performance of the system for four different types of scoring shots: a swish, a slam dunk, a backboard score and a 'toilet bowl' (a shot where the ball rolls around the ring then drops in).

They take 30 shots of each type and collect data to compare the number of shots actually scored to the number of counts registered on the electronic rate counter. They found the following:

- For 30 swish shots scored, the rate counter registered 30 counts.
- For 30 slam dunks scored, the rate counter registered 18 counts.
- For 30 backboard shots scored, the rate counter registered 25 counts.
- For 30 toilet bowl shots scored, the rate counter registered 38 counts.

The students also observed that there were 17 occasions when the ball hit the rim but popped out again, not going into the net. However, the rate counter registered six of these misses as scores.

4 **Discuss different ways that Robert and Louise could present their results. Are there any calculations they could do to show the accuracy of their system for the different types of shots?**

◯ Fig. 18.11.3
Robert and Louise

5 **Write a paragraph that summarises the performance of the electronic system. For which type of shot did the system work the best? Why? For which type of shot did the system have the poorest performance? Why? Could you offer any advice on improving the performance of this system?**

Hawk-Eye Technology

Hawk-Eye technology has become very popular in sports for detecting the position of a ball in games. It uses a number of high-speed video cameras that focus on the ball.

A large number of image frames taken by these cameras builds up a record of the path the ball has travelled. This is inputted to the processing technology of the Hawk-Eye software. Based on the rules of the game being played, the Hawk-Eye can tell if a shot was in or out, or a score was over the line or not.

◯ Fig. 18.11.4
Hawk-Eye technology in action at a GAA match

6 **Discuss the advantages of Hawk-Eye technology over the system Robert and Louise designed for detecting scores.**

7 **Can you suggest any disadvantages of Hawk-Eye technology? It might be useful to do some research on Hawk-Eye technology to inform your views.**

Chapter 19

Seeing, Hearing, Feeling

What you may already know:

- Swimming pools can sometimes appear to be shallower than they actually are.
- White light is made up of seven colours, the colours of the rainbow.
- Sounds that are too loud are bad for your ears.
- Body temperature is measured with a thermometer.

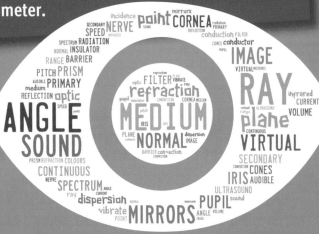

What you will learn in this chapter:

- How light can be reflected off different surfaces to form images.
- The bending of light as it goes from air into glass, water or your eye.
- How white light can be dispersed and why objects have colours.
- How sounds are created and heard.
- The ways that heat can be transferred through substances.
- How heating and cooling affects substances.
- What temperature is and how to measure it.

Think BIG

- Is there a cure for blindness?
- What is a sonic boom?
- Where are the hottest and coldest places on Earth?

Puzzler

Can you crack this code?

The first letter of each of these images spells out a key word that you will come across in this chapter. Use the hints provided if you need to, or revisit the Puzzler after you finish this chapter.

1.	2.	3.	4.	5.

A shape with parallel sides	Appears in the sky after a rain shower	As Buzz Lightyear might say, 'To ___ and beyond!'	A luminous celestial body	Neil Armstrong was the first person to walk on this in 1969

1. ___
2. ___
3. ___
4. ___
5. ___

Bouncing Light

Learning Intentions

In this topic we are learning to:

- Demonstrate that light is a form of energy.
- Conduct an investigation on the reflection of light off mirrors.

Light is a form of energy. We know this because it can be changed into other forms of energy and can move things.

Light can travel through a vacuum. This is why the light of the Sun can shine on Earth through the vacuum of space.

Light can also travel through solids, liquids and gases, as long as they are transparent (i.e. you can see through them). Glass, air and water are examples of substances that light can pass through.

Reflection

Light travels in straight lines. When light hits a surface, it bounces off the surface. The bouncing of light off a surface is called **reflection**.

There are two types of reflection:

1. Diffuse reflection: when light bounces off a rough surface in all directions.
2. Regular reflection: when light bounces off a smooth surface in one direction.

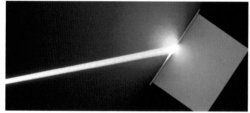

Fig. 19.1.2
Light bouncing off white card is an example of diffuse reflection

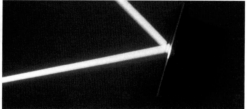

Fig. 19.1.3
Light bouncing off a mirror is an example of regular reflection

Mirrors are able to reflect light in a regular way because they are smooth and shiny. A **plane mirror** is specially designed to achieve a high level of regular reflection.

Key Words

Reflection
Plane mirror

GO Learn more about how light travels in Earth and Space 23.1

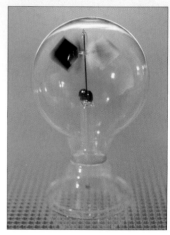

Fig. 19.1.1
A Crooke's radiometer is a device that shows how light can move things. What energy conversion is taking place here?

Prove light is a form of energy

Plan, design, carry out and write up an investigation that proves light is a form of energy.

Seeing the light!

Plan, design, carry out and write up an investigation to find out the relationship between the angles at which light strikes and bounces off a plane mirror. Consider the following:

1. How are you going to measure the different angles?
2. What way will you position the mirror to make this a fair test?
3. How many readings are you going to take?
4. How are you going to present your results in a way that shows the relationship clearly?

Bending Light

Key Words

Medium
Refraction
Pupil
Iris
Cornea
Lens
Retina
Optic nerve

Learning Intentions

In this topic we are learning to:

- Evaluate a model for refraction of light.
- Investigate the refraction of light through different solids.
- Describe how our eyes allow us to see.

Why does a straw look broken when it is placed in a glass of water?

When light strikes the straw, the light is reflected and travels to our eyes. On its way to our eyes the light moves through water, the glass and air. As the light travels from one substance or **medium** to another, it changes direction.

The bending of light as it passes from one medium to another is called **refraction**.

A Model for Refraction

Because light travels so fast, it is hard to see why it bends when it moves from one medium to another.

A simple example can help to model how this happens. Consider a car driving along a normal road surface at speed, through a patch of mud and then back onto the normal road surface again.

Fig. 19.2.1
The top of the straw looks normal in the air, but the glass of water appears to break it. This is due to refraction

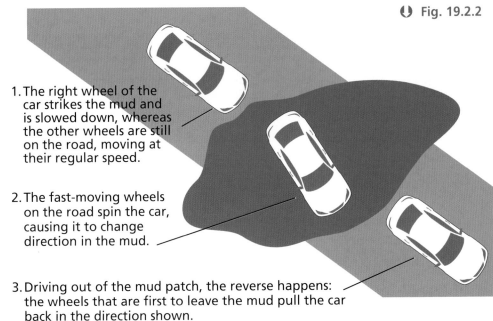

Fig. 19.2.2

1. The right wheel of the car strikes the mud and is slowed down, whereas the other wheels are still on the road, moving at their regular speed.

2. The fast-moving wheels on the road spin the car, causing it to change direction in the mud.

3. Driving out of the mud patch, the reverse happens: the wheels that are first to leave the mud pull the car back in the direction shown.

Refraction From Air to Glass and Glass to Air

Fig. 19.2.3
Light waves slow down when they enter a denser medium

Light can be slowed down when it travels into a glass block from the air. This is because the glass is denser than air. The denser a transparent substance is, the slower light travels through it. Just like the car in the mud, this slowing down causes the light ray to bend towards the dense medium.

The opposite happens when light leaves the glass block and returns into the air. The light bends away from the dense medium.

This effect can also be seen when light travels from air to other mediums, such as water, plastic or diamond.

A line called the normal can be drawn at the point where light enters a glass block from air, as shown in Fig. 19.2.4. This gives us two angles:

1. The angle of incidence
2. The angle of refraction.

When light is refracted into a denser medium, the angle of refraction is smaller than the angle of incidence. The smaller the angle of refraction is compared to the angle of incidence, the better the dense medium is at refracting the light.

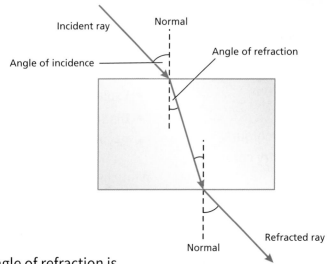

Fig. 19.2.4
Refraction of light travelling into and out of a glass block

Refracting ability

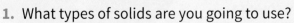

Plan, design, carry out and write up an investigation to compare the refraction that takes place when light passes through three different transparent solid blocks. Consider the following:

1. What types of solids are you going to use?
2. What are you going to measure? How are you going to measure it?
3. What way will you position the blocks to make this a fair test?
4. How many readings are you going to take?
5. How are you going to present your results in a way that clearly shows how well each block refracts light?

Seeing

When the light reflecting off an object passes into our eyes, we are able to see the object.

1. When we look at an object, the light reflected from it travels through an opening in the eye called the **pupil**. The size of the pupil is controlled by the **iris**.

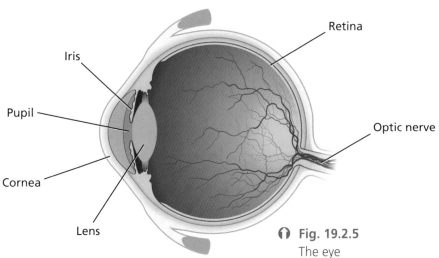

Fig. 19.2.5
The eye

2. The light is focused in the eye by the **cornea** and the **lens**.

3. The refracted rays of light form an image on the **retina**. The retina is a photosensitive layer of nerve cells at the back of the eye that sends impulses through the **optic nerve** to the brain.

335

Splitting Light

Key Words

Spectrum
Dispersion
Prism
Primary colours
Secondary colours
Cones
Rods
Filter

Learning Intentions

In this topic we are learning to:
- Explain the process of dispersion.
- Distinguish between primary and secondary colours.
- Review how we see coloured objects.

White light is made up of seven colours: **red**, **orange**, **yellow**, **green**, **blue**, **indigo** and **violet**. These colours are known as the **spectrum** of white light.

The splitting of white light into the seven colours that make it up is called **dispersion**.

These colours can be seen using a **prism**. Dispersion of white light can also be seen on the shiny surface of a DVD, in bubbles and in rainbows.

Fig. 19.3.1
White light dispersed using a prism

Colours

Red, green and blue are **primary colours**. Combining these three colours makes white light.

When two primary colours combine, they produce the **secondary colours** yellow, cyan and magenta.

In fact, all colours can be made from combining different quantities of the primary colours.

Fig. 19.3.2
Primary and secondary colours of white light

How We See Colours

Whatever colour is reflected from an object is the colour we see it as.

Objects absorb all the colours in white light except their own colour, which they reflect.

Fig. 19.3.3
White light dispersed on a DVD

Rainbows

With your lab partner, discuss what conditions must be present for a rainbow to occur.

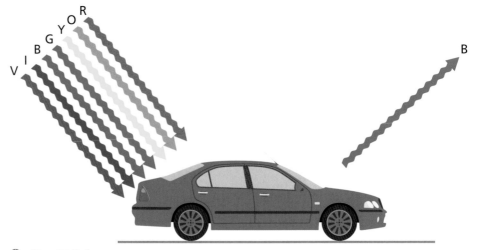

Fig. 19.3.4
A blue car absorbs every colour in white light except blue; it reflects the blue light

White objects absorb none of the colours in white light. Black objects absorb all of the colours and reflect no light.

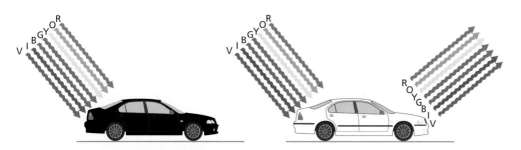

⟲ **Fig. 19.3.5**
White objects reflect all the colours of white light. Black objects absorb all of them and reflect none

We can see colours thanks to nerve cells in our eyes called **cones**. These are on the retina.

There are three types of cone – each one detects one of the primary colours. A person who lacks or has a faulty cone will be colour blind.

Cells called **rods** are also found in our eyes. Rods allow us to see in black and white.

Filters

Understanding how objects absorb and emit light can be used to create different colours of light.

A **filter** can be placed in front of white light to absorb all colours except its own. For example, a blue filter will allow blue light to pass through it and absorb all other colours.

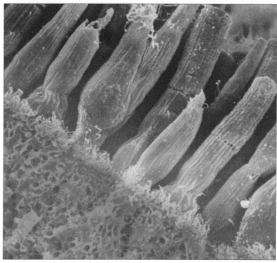

🎧 **Fig. 19.3.6**
A false-coloured scanning electron micrograph of the rods and cones in an eye

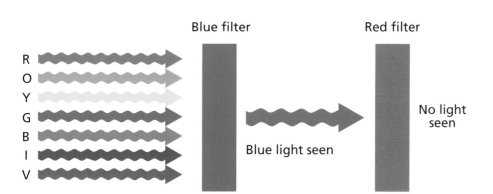

🎧 **Fig. 19.3.7**
A filter absorbs all colours except its own

Filters ⓐⓑⓒ

With your lab partner, discuss what light filters you would use to produce the following colours of light: green, cyan, red, magenta.

A career in light 🔍

Optics is the branch of physics that considers the properties of light. Between the years 2000 and 2012, a Nobel Prize was awarded almost every year for work in optics-related areas. Research the career of one optical scientist and draft an evidence-based report on the contributions this person has made to the study of optics.

Sound

Key Words

Vibrate
Speed of sound
Sound barrier
Frequency
Amplitude
Pitch
Loudness
Decibels

Sound insulation

Download a free sound-level meter. Use this meter to investigate the effect of changing the thickness of a material of your choice on the level of sound insulation that material provides.

Learning Intentions

In this topic we are learning to:

• Compare the speed of sound with the speed of light.

• Examine the factors that affect the pitch and loudness of a sound.

• Explore the importance of sound safety.

Sound is a form of energy that is transferred in waves.

To produce sound, we need to make something **vibrate**. For example, by plucking the strings of a guitar or vocal chords vibrating in our throats.

◑ **Fig. 19.4.1**
Sound is produced by vibrations

How Do We Hear?

1. When an object produces sound, it causes vibrations in the air molecules around it.

2. These vibrations produce a sound wave.

3. This wave passes through the air and makes the eardrum vibrate.

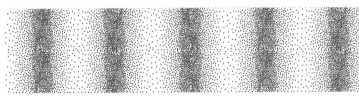

Sound wave

◑ **Fig. 19.4.2**
Sound vibrating an eardrum

Sound needs a medium to travel through. Without a medium, there would be nothing to pass on the sound waves.

Particles and sound

A student holds a clothes hanger from two pieces of string as shown in Fig. 19.4.3.

1. Their lab partner strikes the hanger gently with a wooden stick. Explain why a loud sound is not heard.

2. The student then puts the fingers holding the hanger in his ears. The hanger was again struck with the wood. Predict what happens to the loudness of the sound.

3. Try this out in class and discuss your findings with your lab partner.

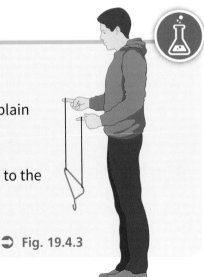

◑ Fig. 19.4.3

The effect of density on a ringtone

A student wanted to investigate how decreasing and increasing the density of a medium affected the volume of a mobile phone ringtone. She turned on the ringtone and placed the phone in a bell jar, as shown in Fig. 19.4.4.

⟳ Fig. 19.4.4

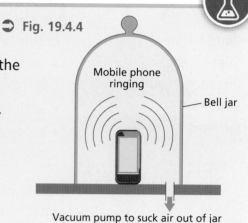

Mobile phone ringing

Bell jar

Vacuum pump to suck air out of jar

1. Predict what happens when the air is removed from the jar.
2. Set up this investigation in class and try it out. Record your observations.
3. Explain why your predictions did or did not match your observations.
4. Let the air back into the jar and note any changes.

Speed of Sound

The **speed of sound** is how fast vibrations pass through a medium. The speed of sound in air is around 340 m/s. It is possible to travel faster than sound in air. In doing so, you break the **sound barrier**. When an object breaks the sound barrier, it makes an explosive noise known as a 'sonic boom'.

Light travels nearly a million times faster than sound. This is why, during a thunderstorm, we see lightning before we hear the thunder.

What We Hear

Like all waves, sound waves have a **frequency** and an **amplitude**.

The frequency is how fast a sound wave is moving. The faster the sound wave moves, the higher **pitch** it will have, as shown in Fig. 19.4.6.

The amplitude of a sound wave determines its **loudness**. Loud sound waves have a large amplitude.

The human ear is very sensitive. We can hear a wide range of sounds, from quiet to very loud. Sound levels are measured in **decibels** (dB). Fig. 19.4.7 shows the levels of different sounds on the decibel scale.

🎧 Fig. 19.4.5
An aircraft dropping a sonic boom

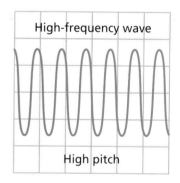

High-frequency wave

High pitch

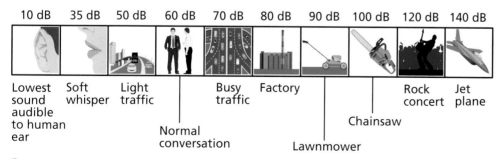

| 10 dB | 35 dB | 50 dB | 60 dB | 70 dB | 80 dB | 90 dB | 100 dB | 120 dB | 140 dB |

Lowest sound audible to human ear

Soft whisper

Light traffic

Normal conversation

Busy traffic

Factory

Lawnmower

Chainsaw

Rock concert

Jet plane

🎧 Fig. 19.4.7
The intensity of different sounds on the decibel scale

Exposure to sounds over 85 dB can cause ear damage. Ear damage can be permanent.

You should take precautions to protect your hearing, such as wearing earplugs at loud concerts.

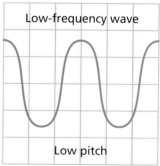

Low-frequency wave

Low pitch

🎧 Fig. 19.4.6
High-frequency and low-frequency waves

Heat Transfer

Learning Intentions

In this topic we are learning to:

- Investigate the ways in which heat moves through solids, liquids and gases.
- Distinguish between conductors and insulators of heat.
- Compare the colour of an object with its ability to absorb and emit radiated heat.

Heat is a form of energy. This energy transfers from a hot place to a cold place. It can do this in three ways:

1. Conduction
2. Convection
3. Radiation.

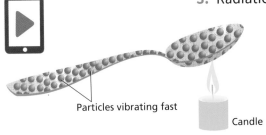

Fig. 19.5.1
A heated spoon conducts heat through fast-vibrating particles

Particles vibrating fast

Candle

Conduction

Solids transfer heat through **conduction**.

- When heat energy is transferred to a solid, it causes the particles of the solid to vibrate quickly.
- These vibrations pass through the rest of the solid, conducting the heat.

Conductors, such as metals, feel cold to the touch as they quickly draw heat away from your body.

Fast and slow melting

Plan, design, carry out and write up an investigation to determine the rate at which a cube of ice will melt when placed on top of the following substances:

a. Glass   b. Wood   c. Perspex   d. Aluminium   e. Styrofoam board   f. Copper

Consider the following:

1. How will you make this a fair test? What will you measure and how will you measure it?
2. Predict the rate at which the ice cube will melt when placed on top of each of the substances. Then explain why your observations did or did not match your predictions.

States of matter as conductors

Create a poster explaining why solids are generally the best conductors of heat, followed by liquids then gases. Use your knowledge of the particle theory to support your explanation.

Fun Fact

Baked Alaska is a dessert made of ice cream surrounded by meringue. The air in the meringue insulates the ice cream from the heat, stopping it from melting.

Fig. 19.5.2
Baked Alaska

Convection

Liquids and gases transfer heat by **convection**.

- When the particles of a liquid or gas are heated, they begin to rise. When they get to a certain point, they fall back down.
- If this process repeats, a **convection current** of moving particles is created.

Convection is the reason hot air and hot water rise.

Radiation

Radiation does not need a medium to transfer heat. Heat is transferred in the form of **infrared** waves.

- Hot bodies give out infrared radiation – the hotter the body, the greater the amount of infrared it radiates. This is how the Sun heats the air.

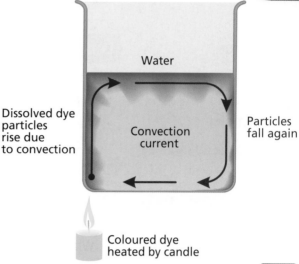

Water

Dissolved dye particles rise due to convection

Convection current

Particles fall again

Coloured dye heated by candle

🎧 **Fig. 19.5.3**
Convection currents in a liquid

GO Learn more about the Earth and the Sun in Earth and Space 23.1

- Dark surfaces absorb and radiate infrared heat faster than bright surfaces. For this reason, houses in hot climates can be painted white to keep the inside cool.

↻ **Fig. 19.5.4**
The infrared radiation from a hot body can be seen using a thermal imaging camera. What does this picture tell you about the heat radiated by spiders and humans?

Dark versus bright

A student set up the following apparatus to test the hypothesis: 'Dark surfaces absorb radiation better than bright surfaces.'

1. How did the student ensure that this was a fair test?

2. Predict what will happen and explain the reasons for your predictions.

3. Set up this apparatus in class and carry out the investigation. Write down the method followed and record your observations.

4. Explain why your predictions did or did not match your observations.

5. Comment on the original hypothesis in light of your results.

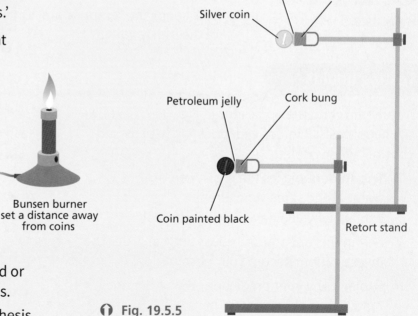

Petroleum jelly

Cork bung

Silver coin

Petroleum jelly

Cork bung

Coin painted black

Retort stand

Bunsen burner set a distance away from coins

🎧 **Fig. 19.5.5**

Retort stand

Effects of Heat

Learning Intentions

In this topic we are learning to:
- Investigate the expansion and contraction of substances with heat.
- Review examples of the expansion and contraction of solids in the real world.

Expansion and Contraction

Adding or removing heat from substances has different effects. In general:
- When a solid, liquid or gas is heated it expands.
- When a solid, liquid or gas is cooled it contracts.

Water is an exception, as it begins to expand below 4 °C.

We can see the **expansion** and **contraction** of substances in a number of places:
- There are expansion gaps on concrete roads. Expansion gaps are made of a soft substance, such as tar. When concrete slabs get hot, they expand and squeeze the soft material to stop the road from cracking. Steel railway lines also need expansion gaps.
- If metal bridges get hot, they can expand by up to one metre. They are built with expansion joints to stop this happening.
- The inside of an iron contains two strips of metal attached together. This is called a bimetallic strip. When these strips are heated, they expand at different rates and bend. This keeps the temperature of the iron regular.

🎧 **Fig. 19.6.1**
An expansion gap in a railway line

🎧 **Fig. 19.6.2**
Bridge expansion joints

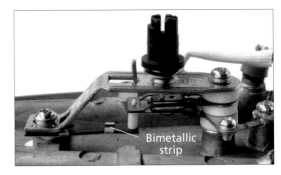
Bimetallic strip

🎧 **Fig. 19.6.3**
The bimetallic strip in a clothes iron

Testing liquids

A student set up the apparatus in Fig. 19.6.4 to test the hypothesis: 'Liquids expand when heated and contract when cooled.'

1. The student places the flasks into the hot water at the same time. Predict what happens. Explain why you have made this prediction.
2. Set up this apparatus in class and carry out the investigation. Record your observations.
3. Explain why your predictions did or did not match your observations.
4. What does this tell you about the expansion and contraction of the different liquids?

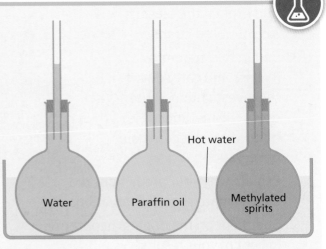
Hot water
Water
Paraffin oil
Methylated spirits

🎧 **Fig. 19.6.4**

Testing gases

Plan, design, carry out and write up an investigation to test the hypothesis: 'Gases expand when heated and contract when cooled.'

Passing through?

Fig. 19.6.5

A student was given the apparatus shown in Fig. 19.6.5 to test the hypothesis: 'Solids expand when heated and contract when cooled.'

The ball goes through the ring at room temperature. The student then heats the ball to over 100 °C. Predict what will happen when they try to pass the ball through the ring at this temperature. What will happen after it cools for 15 minutes?

Temperature

Changes in the quantity of heat energy added to or removed from an object can cause a change in the temperature of that object.

It is important to remember that heat and temperature are not the same:

- Heat is a form of energy.
- Temperature is a measure of how hot or cold an object is.

Heat or temperature?

A student wanted to investigate the difference between heat and temperature using hot water bottles. He filled one bottle to the top with water and filled the other halfway, as shown in Fig. 19.6.6.

He recorded the temperature of both bottles as 70 °C.

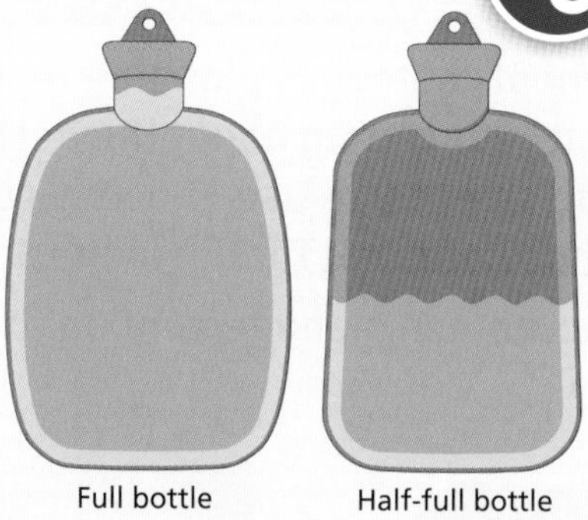

Full bottle   Half-full bottle

Fig. 19.6.6
Water bottles

1. With your lab partner, discuss:
    - Which bottle will stay hot for longer? Why?
    - Which bottle contains the least amount of heat energy? Why?

2. Come up with a statement explaining why this demonstrates the difference between heat and temperature.

Temperature is measured using a **thermometer**. The SI unit for temperature is the kelvin (K), but it is usually measured in degrees **Celsius** (°C).

The most common type of thermometer is the liquid-in-glass thermometer, which is based on the principle that liquids expand when heated and contract when cooled.

Football physics

Denis got a football for his birthday. Its mass was 19 g. When he pumped the ball full with air its new mass was 29 g. What was the mass of the air in the ball?

Denis left the ball outside overnight. When he came back in the morning the ball had gone soft, but there were no tears or rips in the ball. When he measured the mass of the ball in the morning, do you think it had changed or stayed the same? Explain your answer.

Fig. 19.6.7
A liquid-in-glass thermometer measuring °C

Chapter Summary

- Light, sound and heat are all forms of energy.
- We see objects because light reflects off them and travels into our eyes.
- Diffuse reflection happens when light bounces off a rough surface in all directions.
- Regular reflection happens when light bounces in one direction off a smooth surface.
- Refraction is the bending of light as it passes from one medium to another.
- The eye allows us to see objects by using a lens system to focus light onto the retina.
- White light can be split into a spectrum of seven colours using a prism. This is called dispersion.
- Red, green and blue are primary colours. Combined, they produce white light.
- Yellow, cyan and magenta are secondary colours. Each one is formed from combining two primary colours.
- Objects appear as certain colours because they absorb all the colours in white light except their own. This colour is reflected.

- Sound needs a medium to travel through, whereas light does not.
- Increasing the frequency of a sound wave increases the pitch of the sound.
- Increasing the amplitude of a sound wave increases the loudness of the sound.
- Conduction is the transfer of heat through the vibration of particles.
- Convection is the transfer of heat through liquids and gases by the movement of particles in convection currents.
- Radiation is the transfer of heat in the form of infrared waves. It does not require a medium to travel through.
- In general, when a substance is heated it expands and when it cools it contracts.
- Temperature is a measure of how hot or cold an object is. It is measured using a thermometer.

The BIG Challenge

The management of your school canteen is planning to introduce hot drinks to the menu, but it is uncertain about the best cups and accessories (such as lids and sleeves) to use. It needs cups that will keep soups, teas and hot chocolates hot for the longest period of time.

Create a leaflet advising the canteen management on the best types of cups and accessories to buy.

Your leaflet must be informed by the factors that affect the rate at which heat is lost.

Make sure your findings are communicated in a clear way.

Go to your Portfolio to check what you have learned in this chapter.

Take the chapter 19 quiz on educateplus.ie.

Questions

1. Copy and fill in the blanks:
   a. Unlike _____ waves, light can travel through a _____. It does not need a _____ to travel through.

   b. Refraction is the _____ of light as it passes from one _____ to another.

   c. The lens system of your eye consists of the _____ and the _____. This focuses light onto the _____ at the back of your eye. This sends a message through the _____ _____ to your brain, which interprets it as an image.

   d. The breaking up of white light into its seven colours is known as _____. This can be done using a _____.

   e. The primary colours are _____, _____ and _____. Combined, they make _____ light.

   f. The secondary colours are _____, _____ and _____. Each one is created from combining two _____ colours.

   g. Sounds can be created by _____. This forms sound waves in the air, which causes our _____ to vibrate, allowing us to hear the sounds.

   h. Heat transfer by vibration of particles is called _____. Heat transfer by the movement of particles in liquids and gases is called _____.

   i. Heat transfer in the form of infrared _____, without the need for a medium, is known as _____.

   j. In general, substances _____ when heated and _____ when cooled. Water is an exception, as it begins to _____ when cooled below 4 °C.

2. Explain why you cannot see an image of yourself in the bricks of the laboratory wall, but you can see a vague image of yourself in the glass of the window.

3. The speed of sound is 340 m/s. A student sees a flash of lightning and then hears the clap of thunder five seconds later. How far away is the lightning storm?

4. A student generated a sound wave and recorded it with a sound meter app. The following wave form was produced:

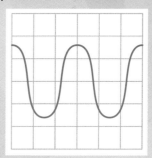

   Draw diagrams showing what the wave would look like if:
   a. The frequency was decreased.
   b. The amplitude was increased.

5. A student set up the following equipment:

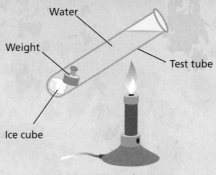

   a. Will the ice melt when the Bunsen burner is turned on? Explain the reason for your answer.
   b. Copy the diagram above and label the different types of heat transfers taking place.

6. Provide a scientific reason for the following:
   a. Rescue services can use a thermal imaging camera to locate people trapped under the rubble from an earthquake.
   b. The heating element of a kettle is at the bottom.
   c. A pot of hot water that is about to boil over can be stopped by placing a cold metal spoon into it.
   d. The heating wire of a toaster is able to toast bread without touching it.
   e. Fish can survive the winter at the bottom of a frozen pond.

7. Describe, with the aid of a labelled diagram, how convection heats the water when a kettle is boiled.

Working as a Scientist

Presenting and Analysing Data

Making a Thermometer

A thermometer measures changes in temperature. It has two important features:

1. A scale for measurement in °C or °F.

2. A thermometric property is something that can be changed with temperature. It can be measured.

   For example:

   - In a liquid-in-glass thermometer, it is the expansion and contraction of the liquid when heated or cooled.

   - In a digital thermometer, as the metal of the thermometer is heated, its resistance increases.

   - In a colour strip thermometer, the colour of the crystals in the strip change when it is heated.

🎧 **Fig. 19.8.1**
A digital thermometer

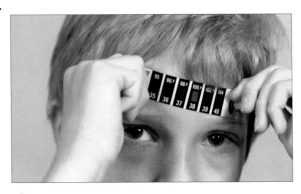

🎧 **Fig. 19.8.2**
A colour strip thermometer

Joe and Kelly set out to make a simple thermometer in class. They set up two different metals joined at the ends and connected to a sensitive voltmeter. This is called a thermocouple.

Junction A, the cold junction, was kept in ice at 0 °C for the duration of the investigation. Junction B, the hot junction, was placed in water and slowly heated using the Bunsen burner. As this happened, a small voltage was created between the hot and cold junctions and was recorded on the voltmeter.

After every 10 °C rise in temperature, the heat of the Bunsen burner (heat source) was temporarily removed for one minute and the voltage was recorded. The temperature was noted using a standard alcohol thermometer.

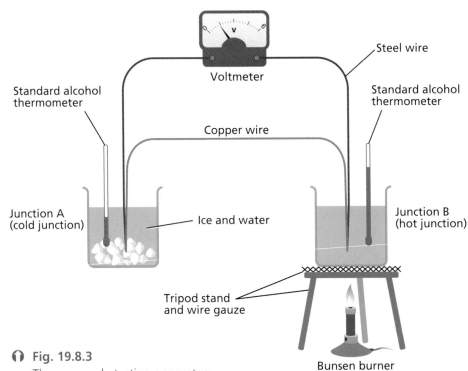

🎧 **Fig. 19.8.3**
Thermocouple testing apparatus

1 Using your knowledge of heat transfer by conduction, explain why a small voltage is created between the hot and cold junctions when the Bunsen burner is placed under junction B.

2 Describe all the forms of heat transfer occurring at junction B.

3 Why did Joe and Kelly remove the Bunsen burner and wait for a minute before recording the voltage?

The voltage generated between A and B is a thermometric property. Joe and Kelly wanted to use this property to develop a scale for the thermocouple and use it as a thermometer. They continued to heat junction B and recorded the temperature after every 10 °C rise in temperature. They collected a range of data and presented it in the following table:

Temperature (°C)	0	10	20	30	40	50	60	70	80	90
Voltage (mV)	0	0.4	0.8	1.2	1.61	2.02	2.44	3.0	3.27	3.68

4 Can you identify the outlier in the data? Why do you think this error may have occurred?

5 Can you suggest a way that Joe and Kelly might have got the reading for voltage at 0 °C? Why do you think this value is 0 mV?

6 Draw a suitable graph to show the relationship between temperature and voltage for the thermocouple. Describe this relationship.

Having completed the investigation, Joe and Kelly then placed the wires at junction B into two liquids of unknown temperatures, all the time keeping the wires at junction A in the cold ice and water. They recorded the following values for voltage:

- Voltage for liquid X = 2.25 mV
- Voltage for liquid Y = 1.5 mV

7 Use your graph to find out the temperatures of the liquids X and Y.

8 Advise Joe and Kelly on changes they could make to their thermocouple to make it more accurate.

In this task, the thermometric property of a thermometer was investigated and an accurate scale for that thermometer was created. When you have achieved this, it is known as **calibration**.

A calibrated thermocouple is a thermometer with a wide range of uses. Thermocouples can be used to record temperatures of up to 2,300 °C, allowing engineers to monitor temperatures during steel manufacture. They can also be used to monitor the temperature of lava flows in volcanoes.

9 Now try to make your own thermometer:

a. Think of other physical properties that change with temperature and write them down.

b. How could you go about testing these properties and calibrating them to make a thermometer?

c. What data would you collect? What thermometer would you use as a standard?

d. How would you go about presenting your data in a way that allows you to test unknown temperatures?

🎧 **Fig. 19.8.4**
Thermocouples can measure the temperature of lava flow

Chapter 20

The Modern Physical World

What you may already know:

- How to use mobile phones and the internet.
- Doctors can X-ray patients and check their temperature and heartbeat.
- CERN and the Large Hadron Collider have been in the news.

What you will learn in this chapter:

- How technology has developed.
- Certain medical devices allow us to monitor and treat the body.
- How particle accelerators work.

Think BIG

- What is a Higgs boson?
- How does social media work?

Puzzler

Can you identify this device?

(Hint: it is part of the largest machine ever built, which you will learn about in this chapter.)

The Information Age

Learning Intentions

In this topic we are learning to:

- Discuss the differences between analogue and digital signals.
- Describe how processors can store and transfer information.
- Explore the impact of modern technologies on our daily lives.

We live in the **information age**. This means that we access a large amount of digital information.

Mobile phones and the internet have become part of our daily lives. These tools allow us, at the touch of a button or screen, to speak face-to-face with a person in Australia quicker than we could call to a neighbour's house. Astronauts, such as former International Space Station commander Chris Hadfield, can even send tweets to Earth from outer space.

My modern life

Spend a day without using your mobile phone or the internet and write a diary entry about the experience.

Analogue to Digital

What happens when you make a phone call?

When you speak into the phone, a microphone detects the vibrations of the sound waves from your voice. Using a coil of wire and a magnet, these vibrations are converted into an electrical signal. This is known as an **analogue** signal.

An analogue signal is a signal that has varying values.

When an analogue signal is transmitted to a computer processor (such as those in a phone or laptop), it is converted into a **digital** signal.

A digital signal has two values only, 1 or 0.

Digital signals have two main advantages over analogue signals:

1. They can carry more information per second.
2. They have better quality over distances.

⌒ Fig. 20.1.1
One of Chris Hadfield's tweets from space: 'Don't tell my crew, but I brought them Easter eggs :)'

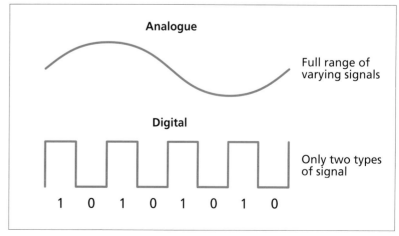

Analogue

Full range of varying signals

Digital

Only two types of signal

1   0   1   0   1   0   1   0

➲ Fig. 20.1.2
Analogue and digital signals

349

People and Science

Martin Cooper, an American inventor, developed the first handheld cellular phone in 1973. When asked why he invented it, he said, 'People want to talk to other people – not a house, or an office or a car. Given a choice, people will demand the freedom to communicate wherever they are, unfettered by the infamous copper wire. It is that freedom we sought to vividly demonstrate in 1973.'

⮕ Fig. 20.1.3
Martin Cooper with his 1973 prototype of the mobile phone

Bits to Bytes

The values that make up a digital signal are called **binary**.

- Each single number in binary (1 or 0) is known as a **bit**.
- Eight bits of information make up a **byte**.

Computers use binary to store data.

Fun Fact

It took 51 years to create a hard drive that could store 1 terabyte (1 TB) of information. It only took two more years to create a 2 TB hard drive.

Happy binary birthday!

Using the table below, convert your date of birth into binary code.

Binary number	Decimal number	Binary number	Decimal number
0000	0	0110	6
0001	1	0111	7
0010	2	1000	8
0011	3	1001	9
0100	4	1010	10
0101	5		

🎧 Fig. 20.1.4
Modern technology allows more information to be stored on smaller and smaller devices

There are different types of data storage. For example, hard drives in a computer or remote drives such as USB memory sticks or microSD cards.

The information stored on these drives is measured in gigabytes (GB). 1 gigabyte is 1000,000,000 bytes of information.

The following table shows byte measurement units:

Measure	Abbreviation	Scale
Kilo	k	Thousand (x 10^3)
Mega	M	Million (x 10^6)
Giga	G	Thousand million (x 10^9)
Tera	T	Million million (x 10^{12})

When you download a film or make a phone call, you transfer bits of information. These bits can be used to create analogue signals. Outputs, such as sound, motion and different-coloured lights, can be created by inputting these signals to components.

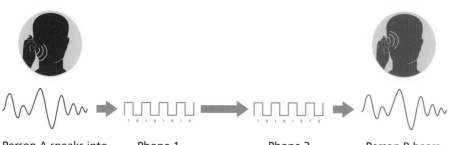

| Person A speaks into phone microphone | Phone 1 | Phone 2 | Person B hears person 1's voice through their phone speaker |

↻ Fig. 20.1.5
Microphone → phone → phone → speaker

Riding on the Wave of Modern Physics

Wireless technology has become very popular in the information age. When a device wants to communicate information without wires, it converts bits of information into different types of waves.

These types of waves are found on the **electromagnetic spectrum**. All waves on the electromagnetic spectrum travel at the speed of light.

- **Radio waves** are the lowest energy waves on the spectrum. Television, mobile phone and radio signals are transmitted using these waves.

- **Microwaves** are higher in energy than radio waves. Wi-Fi and Bluetooth signals are transmitted using microwaves.

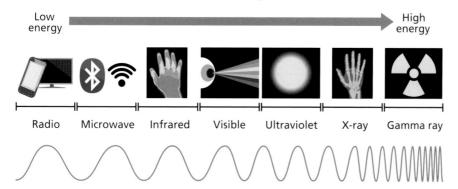

Low energy → High energy

Radio Microwave Infrared Visible Ultraviolet X-ray Gamma ray

Electromagnetic spectrum ⓐⓑⓒ

Research examples and uses of the other types of waves on the electromagnetic spectrum.

Give an example and use of each type of wave.

↻ Fig. 20.1.6
The electromagnetic spectrum

GO Learn more about waves in Earth and Space 26.3

The Internet

The internet is a globally interconnected group of computer networks.

The **World Wide Web** (WWW) allows us to use the internet to access and navigate between webpages. We access the web through browsers, such as Safari and Google Chrome.

People and Science

Sir **Tim Berners-Lee** is a British computer scientist. In 1989, while working at CERN in Switzerland, he developed a digital information management system and was the first person to make a hypertext transfer protocol (http) communication with the internet.

This protocol, along with URL and HTML, resulted in the creation of the World Wide Web.

◖ Fig. 20.1.7
Tim Berners-Lee

Physics and Health

Key Words

Vital signs

Thermistor

Defibrillator

Magnetic resonance imaging (MRI)

Electromagnets

Ultrasound

Endoscope

Optical fibres

Total internal reflection

Learning Intentions

In this topic we are learning to:

- Produce an electric circuit that can be used to monitor body temperature.
- Describe how ultrasound and MRI scanning work.

When a person is feeling unwell, two of the first things checked are their temperature and heart rate. These measures of general health are known as **vital signs**.

One device that can be used to measure vital signs is a thermistor.

Thermistors

A **thermistor** is a device whose resistance decreases when it is heated. When a thermistor is connected in a circuit and heated, it causes an increase in current.

A thermistor can be used as an electronic thermometer or as a temperature alarm.

🔊 **Fig. 20.2.1**
A thermistor

Look for the signs

There are five common vital signs that are measured to determine body function. Research what these are.

Thermistors in action

A thermistor is connected in series with a variable resistor and a buzzer all powered by a 6 V battery, as shown in Fig. 20.2.2.

At the outset, the thermistor is at room temperature and the buzzer is not sounding.

1. Predict what will happen when the thermistor is heated with a hairdryer. Explain the reasons for your predictions.

2. Set up this circuit and heat the resistor with a hairdryer. Record your observations.

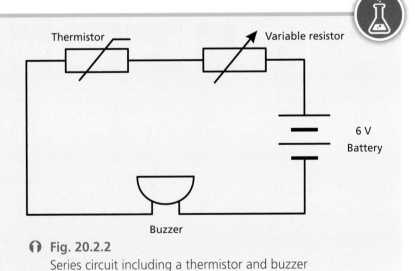

🔊 **Fig. 20.2.2**
Series circuit including a thermistor and buzzer

3. Explain why your predictions did or did not match your observations.

Adjusting the variable resistor changes the overall resistance of the circuit. A student would like to be able to adjust the circuit so that the thermistor will sound the buzzer when the temperature goes above 38 °C. At this body temperature, a person would have a fever.

4. Plan, design, carry out and write up the investigation you would conduct to achieve this task.

Defibrillators

If a person has a heart attack, their heart rhythm can become irregular.

A **defibrillator** is a device that sends a large voltage across the chest and heart muscle. This 'kick-starts' the heart into beating at a normal rhythm again.

If a person is having problems with their

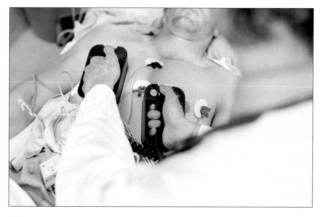

⌒ Fig. 20.2.3
A doctor using a defibrillator to 'shock' a patient

⌒ Fig. 20.2.4
A pacemaker

heartbeat rhythm, they can be fitted with a pacemaker. A pacemaker is a device 3–4 cm long and is placed in the chest. It provides a regular voltage to help the heart beat in rhythm. Some pacemakers have defibrillators in them, so if a person has a heart attack they can receive a shock to make their heart beat normally.

There are a number of other devices that can be used to diagnose patients. These include MRI scanners, ultrasound scanners and endoscopes.

GO Learn more about how the heart functions in Biological World 8.3

Magnetic Resonance Imaging

Magnetic resonance imaging, or MRI, uses a very strong magnetic field to create an image of the inside of the body.

The magnetic field in an MRI scanner is generated by **electromagnets**.

A simple electromagnet is made by winding a loop of wire around an iron core.

Iron is easily magnetised and demagnetised. This means that electromagnets can be turned on and off.

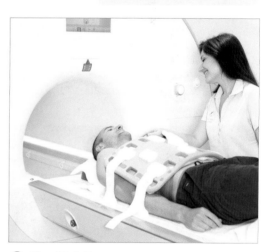

⌒ Fig. 20.2.5
A patient about to be scanned in an MRI machine

Make your own electromagnet

1. Using some insulated wires, an iron nail and a battery, make your own electromagnet and test its performance.

2. Plan, design, carry out and write up an investigation to look at the factors that would improve the performance of your electromagnet.
   - Remember to change only one factor at a time and to come up with a valid way of comparing the different performances.
   - It might be helpful to take pictures of your work in progress so you can track how the design of your electromagnet changes.

⌒ Fig. 20.2.6
A simple electromagnet

Ultrasound

An **ultrasound** scan, also called a sonogram, uses high-frequency sound waves to create an image of the inside of the body.

A transmitter sends ultrasound waves into the body. The waves are then reflected back from organs and the spaces between them. These reflections (echoes) are detected by a receiver, which creates the image.

Ultrasound is a safe way of monitoring babies during pregnancy. It can also be used to view other organs such as the liver, heart and kidneys.

Fun Fact

Ships use ultrasound to calculate sea depths. A beam of ultrasound is sent through the water. Its echo is detected by a receiver. Knowing the time it took to detect the echo and the speed of the ultrasound wave, the crew can calculate the depth of the water.

◯ Fig. 20.2.7
A doctor performing an ultrasound on a pregnant woman

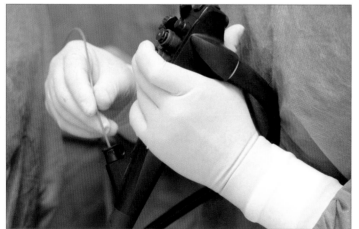

◯ Fig. 20.2.8
An endoscopic operation

Endoscopy

Surgeons can use an **endoscope** to look inside the body without having to make large cuts.

An endoscope is made up of wires of flexible glass called **optical fibres**. Light is shone through one of the fibres to light up the inside of the body. This light is then passed through a lens in the endoscope and back up to a computer screen, creating a clear image of the inside of the body.

High-speed internet

Optical fibres can also be used to transmit an internet broadband feed. Research the advantages of fibre-optic broadband over traditional broadband transmitted through metal wires.

The body has many twists and turns. However, we know that light travels in straight lines. For this reason, the light in an endoscope is made to 'bend' through the optical fibres.

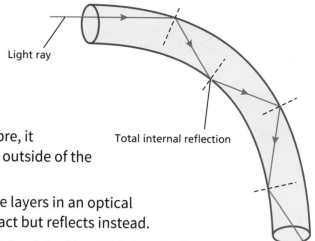

1. When light passes through optical fibre, it begins to refract. This is because the outside of the fibre is less dense than the middle.

2. If the light strikes the boundary of the layers in an optical fibre at a large angle, it does not refract but reflects instead.

3. This light then bounces along the inside of the fibre. This is called **total internal reflection**.

🎧 **Fig. 20.2.9**
Total internal reflection in an optical fibre

Bending light

The following set-up demonstrates how an optical fibre 'bends' light:

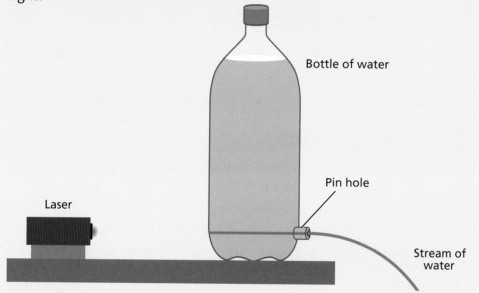

🎧 **Fig. 20.2.10**

1. Predict what will happen when the laser is turned on and shone through the bottle.

2. Using your knowledge of total internal reflection, explain why you have made this prediction.

3. Your teacher can demonstrate this investigation in the school laboratory. Record your observations.

4. Explain why your predictions did or did not match your observations.

Safety note: never look directly into the beam of light emitted from a laser as it could seriously damage your sight.

Medical technology: good or bad?

While it is clear that medical technology has led to us living longer, there may be some negatives. In groups of four, prepare a debate about the statement 'Medical technology: good or bad?'

Fast Physics

Key Words

Particle accelerator
Electron beam
X-rays
Large Hadron Collider

Learning Intentions

In this topic we are learning to:

- Model the collision of particles in a particle accelerator.
- Research the work being done at CERN.

Particle Accelerators

A **particle accelerator** is a device that uses large electrostatic forces to accelerate charged particles to very high speeds. These fast-moving particles collide with specially designed surfaces or with each other and their kinetic energy is converted into different forms.

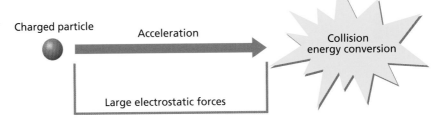

⊃ **Fig. 20.3.1**
The physics of particle accelerators

There are many types of particle accelerators with different levels of energy, including:

- Cathode ray tubes
- X-ray tubes
- Particle smashers

Cathode Ray Tubes

Cathode ray tubes, or CRTs, contain a vacuum in which a beam of electrons is accelerated. This **electron beam** strikes a powder-covered screen, converting its kinetic energy into visible light.

Old televisions and computer monitors used CRTs. This technology has largely been replaced by slimmer devices, such as plasma screens.

🎧 **Fig. 20.3.2**
A cathode ray tube from an old television

X-Ray Tube

An X-ray tube works in a similar way to a CRT but uses higher energies. The electrons in an X-ray tube move at higher speeds and strike a tungsten metal target.

The kinetic energy of the electrons is converted into **X-rays**. These are high-energy electromagnetic waves capable of penetrating through various substances. X-rays can pass through less dense tissue, such as muscle, but not through denser tissue, such as bone, making them useful for seeing the bones of the body.

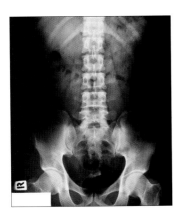

🎧 **Fig. 20.3.3**
An X-ray of a pelvis and spinal column

Particle Smashers

For the last century, scientists have been colliding particles with each other to see what is produced. New and higher-energy particle accelerators have been providing answers about what matter is made up of and how it is made.

The **Large Hadron Collider** at CERN in Geneva, Switzerland, is one of the most advanced particle accelerators in the world.

1. This machine uses huge electrostatic forces to accelerate particles close to the speed of light in a circular loop. The particles are kept moving in a circle by high-powered electromagnets.

2. These particles then collide with each other. When these collisions happen, the particles' kinetic energy is converted into matter.

3. This creates a huge number of new particles to be studied. These pass at high speed through detectors that record the mass, charge, velocity and energy of the particles.

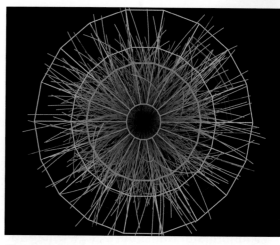

Fig. 20.3.4
A computer-generated image of a particle collision

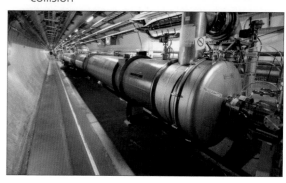

Fig. 20.3.5
The Large Hadron Collider, CERN

Fun Fact

CERN needs to be able to cool its electromagnets very quickly if they are shut off in an emergency. Its cooling rooms are one of the coldest environments in the universe, with operating temperatures of 1.9 K (−271 °C), almost absolute zero.

One of the most recent particles discovered at CERN was the Higgs boson. It is thought that this particle was responsible for the transforming of energy into matter at the dawn of time.

The Higgs boson also provides the missing piece in the standard model theory that explains how particles interact.

 Learn more about the origins of the universe in Earth and Space 21.1

Fields and particles

Research the Higgs boson and the standard particle model.

People and Science

Born in Dungarvan, County Waterford, **Ernest Walton** is the only Irish scientist to win the Nobel Prize in Physics. He shared this honour with John Cockroft in 1951 for their development of the first linear particle accelerator. This accelerator collided protons with lithium metal, causing the lithium atoms to break down into two helium nuclei. This was commonly called 'splitting the atom'.

Fig. 20.3.6
Ernest Walton

Chapter Summary

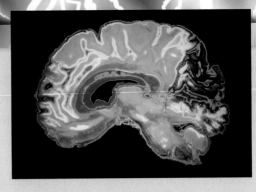

- We live in the information age. This means that we access a large amount of digital information.

- All waves on the electromagnetic spectrum travel at the speed of light.

- Radio waves and microwaves are used for different forms of wireless communication.

- A thermistor is a device whose resistance decreases when it is heated. It can be used in an electric circuit to monitor body temperature.

- A defibrillator transmits a large voltage across the heart to make it beat with a normal rhythm.

- Magnetic resonance imaging (MRI) uses a very strong magnetic field to create an image of the inside of the body. The magnetic fields are generated by electromagnets. Electromagnets can be turned on and off.

- Ultrasound treatment involves high-frequency sound waves passed into the body and reflected to a receiver. It can be used as a safe way to view babies during pregnancy.

- An endoscope contains optical fibres. Light is totally internally reflected along the fibres to allow you to see an image of the inside of the body.

- A particle accelerator is a device that uses large electrostatic forces to accelerate charged particles to very high speeds. These particles then collide with specially designed surfaces or with each other, converting their kinetic energy into different forms.

- A cathode ray tube (CRT) uses large electrostatic forces to accelerate electron beams. These strike a screen and release light.

- An X-ray tube uses large electrostatic forces to produce high-speed electrons that strike a tungsten metal target. This produces X-rays that can be used to take images of bones.

- The Large Hadron Collider (LHC) at CERN in Geneva uses huge electrostatic forces and high-powered electromagnets to collide particles into each other.

- When particles collide in the LHC, their energy is converted into matter in the form of new particles. This is providing answers about what matter is made up of and how it is made.

The BIG Challenge

CERN is a European-wide nuclear research organisation. It has 22 member states that donate millions of euro every year to fund their ongoing work. What are the benefits of being a member state of CERN? Are there any drawbacks?

1. Research this topic in groups of three and create an evidence-based summary of the pros and cons of being a member state of CERN. What discoveries are being made at CERN about the nature of existence? Why is this important to know about? What other research goes on at CERN? What inventions have come out of CERN? What has their impact on humankind been?

2. Use your group work findings to either support or reject the following motion for a class debate: 'Ireland should become a member state of CERN.'

Go to your Portfolio to check what you have learned in this chapter.

Take the chapter 20 quiz on educateplus.ie.

Questions

1. Copy and fill in the blanks:

a. An _____ signal is one that has many varying values. A _____ signal only has two values.

b. All waves on the _____ spectrum travel at the _____ of _____.

c. The _____ is a globally interconnected group of _____ _____.

d. A thermistor is a device whose _____ _____ when it is heated. It can be used to monitor _____.

e. A defibrillator is a device that transmits a large _____ across the chest and heart muscle. This kick-starts the heart into a normal _____ again.

f. MRI scanners use a very strong _____ field to see inside the body. This is created by _____.

g. A particle accelerator is a device that uses large _____ _____ to accelerate charged particles to very high speeds. These particles are then collided with specially designed surfaces or with each other, converting their _____ energy into different forms.

h. When electrons strike a tungsten metal target, they produce _____. These can be used to take images of _____.

i. When particles collide in the _____ _____ _____, their energy is converted into _____ in the form of new particles. This is providing answers about what matter is made up of and how it is made.

2. Identify waves A–D on the electromagnetic spectrum.

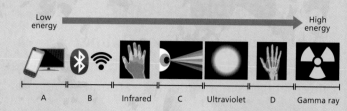

3. Describe the analogue and digital exchanges that take place when you make a video call over the internet. Use a diagram to support your answer and mention the components involved that convert the analogue signal.

4. 'The internet has made our lives better.' Write an evidence-based argument either defending or rejecting this statement.

5. Create a poster detailing the similarities and differences between a cathode ray tube, an X-ray tube, an MRI scanner and the Large Hadron Collider.

6. Describe, with the aid of diagrams, how an endoscope allows us to see an image of the inside of the body.

7. Make a list of three items that you use in everyday life that involve the conversion of analogue to digital signals. In each case, state the input and output of the device.

8. Compare radio waves and X-rays in terms of speed, energy and uses.

Working as a Scientist

Responsible Science

Are We Living Our Lives Online?

Internet use in Ireland is very high. In 2012, it was estimated that there were over 3.5 million internet users in the country – around 80 per cent of the population.

At different points over the last 12 years, data has been collected about Irish internet use. Statistics – the science of collecting and analysing numerical data in large quantities – can allow us to identify trends and patterns in a population.

According to national statistics, Ireland's internet use from 2000 to 2012 has increased, as outlined in the following table:

Year	Number of internet users	Irish population
2000	784,000	3,755,300
2002	1,319,608	3,780,600
2008	2,060,000	4,156,119
2010	3,042,600	4,622,917
2012	3,627,462	4,722,028

1 **Calculate the percentage of the Irish population using the internet in each year.**

2 **Present the percentages of Irish internet users from 2000 to 2012 on an appropriate graph and identify any trends.**

Social networking and use of social media is very popular among young people. In a recent study, the statistics shown in Fig. 20.5.1 were collected for users of social media in Ireland.

3 **Are there any social networks missing from this list?**

You are going to generate evidence to represent the ways students in your school use social media. This needs to be in a form that can be understood by people in this age bracket and their parents.

4 **As a class, design and carry out a survey to ask the people in your year group about their use of social media. In your groups, consider the following points when designing your survey:**

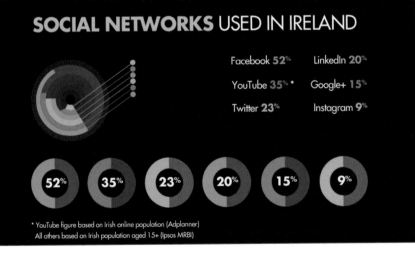

🎧 **Fig. 20.5.1**
Social network use in Ireland

  a. What are the types of social media being used?

  b. What are the types of activities that students can engage in on the different forms of social media?

c. How will you gather data on the quantity of time people are spending on these different social media sites?

d. How will you gather data on the ways people are using the different forms of social media?

e. How are you going to group the students? According to age? Gender? Class groups? Interests?

f. How many students will you include to get a large enough sample to represent the overall population?

It is important to collect this data anonymously, meaning that you cannot know the identity of the people filling out the surveys. Also, if you are planning to hand out surveys, you may need to get permission from your teacher and the school principal first.

5 **Once you have collected the data:**

a. Will you separate all the different types of social media or combine them?

b. Will you break down the use of social media per day, week, month or year? It might be useful to use statistics such as percentages of students in the entire school population.

c. How will you present this data in a form that is clear to understand? It might be useful to use tables of results or graphs.

🎧 Fig. 20.5.2

6 **Review your findings. In doing so, consider the following questions:**

a. Does the data you collected reflect the national statistics for social media use? Why do you think this is the case?

b. How did you lay out your survey? In what ways is it similar or different to the other groups' surveys?

c. Have any potential concerns come from your study about students' use of social media? What are these issues?

d. Can you suggest any ideas for follow-on studies?

e. What parts of your findings do you think parents would be interested in hearing? How would you present them?

f. What differences, if any, would you anticipate if you repeated this survey with (i) parents (ii) students in rural Africa?

7 **What role do statistics play in informing the public about issues such as social media use?**

Earth and Space

Since humans first walked on the Moon in 1969, we have made many more leaps into the universe. Recently, the *Voyager* spacecraft travelled further into space than anyone or anything in history. And there is still so much of our universe to explore.

In Earth and Space we will think about how our universe began. We will learn about the planets, suns, moons and stars in our galaxy, the Milky Way.

The way we live can damage our planet. We will look at how we can protect Earth for future generations by making different choices about the types of energy we use, how we look after the land, how we trade and how we get rid of our rubbish.

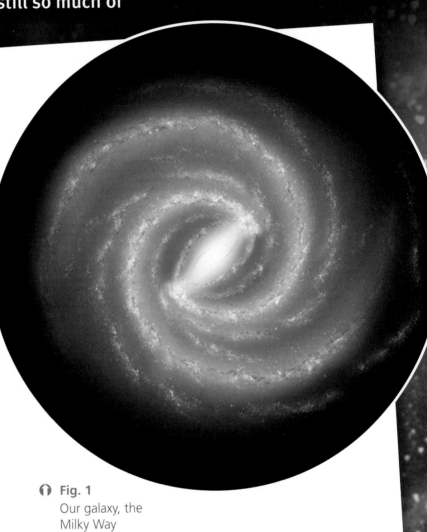

🎧 **Fig. 1**
Our galaxy, the Milky Way

What you may already know:

- There are many planets in outer space. Some of these planets have moons, including Earth.
- There are ideas about how the universe began, such as the Big Bang theory.
- Humankind has made many advances in space travel, such as landing on the Moon and putting machines on Mars.
- Human activities, such as burning fossil fuels, have negative environmental effects.

- How big is the universe?
- What is a light-year?
- How can we use our understanding of science to care for the Earth?

Code Breaker

Can you solve this code?

It reveals a quote from one of the twentieth century's most famous people, astronaut Neil Armstrong.

a	b	c	d	e	f	g	h	i	j	k	l	m	n	o	p	q	r	s	t	u	v	w	x	y	z
z	y	x	w	v	u	t	s	r	q	p	o	n	m	l	k	j	i	h	g	f	e	d	c	b	a

G s z g ' h   l m v   h n z o o   h g v k   u l i   n z m ,

l m v   t r z m g   o v z k   u l i   n z m p r m w .

In Earth and Space you will learn about:

Chapter 21   Celestial bodies and the origins of the universe.

Chapter 22   Rocks and nutrient cycles, the water cycle and the atmosphere.

Chapter 23   Seasons, lunar phases and eclipses.

Chapter 24   Sources of energy, how our current energy needs are being met and how they may be met in the future.

Chapter 25   Sustainability, human influence on the biosphere and conservation.

Chapter 26   How new ideas and inventions have allowed us to see and travel deeper into outer space.

Space

What you may already know:

- The Earth is surrounded by a vast area called space.
- The universe began with a big bang.
- Astronauts have walked on the Moon.

What you will learn in this chapter:

- How to tell the difference between types of celestial bodies.
- Some theories about how the universe began.
- How the Earth compares with other planets.

Think BIG

- Why is Pluto no longer considered a planet?
- What would happen if the Sun did not exist?

Puzzler

Can you crack this code?

The first letter of each image spells out a key word that you will come across in this chapter. Use the hints provided if you need to, or revisit the Puzzler after you finish this chapter.

1.

Planet between Jupiter and Uranus

2.

Used for viewing the solar system

3.

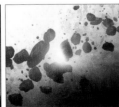

Lumps of rock that were left over after the formation of the solar system

4.

The machine that propels itself across the surface of Mars

1. _____ 2. _____ 3. _____ 4. _____

Origins of the Universe

Key Words

Astronomy
Geocentric
Heliocentric
Universe
Big Bang
Galaxy
Antimatter

Learning Intentions

In this topic we are learning to:

- Outline how our understanding of the universe has changed over time.
- Explore a scientific model to illustrate the origin of the universe.
- Describe the different types of celestial bodies that exist.

The study of the universe and everything in it is called **astronomy**. The scientists who study in this area are called astronomers.

Thousands of years ago, people believed that the Earth was flat. In India, people thought that the flat Earth was held up by 12 pillars. They believed these pillars would collapse if humankind did not make sacrifices to the gods.

By 300 BC, most people believed that the Earth was, in fact, a sphere.

The following timeline shows how humanity's understanding of the Earth changed over time.

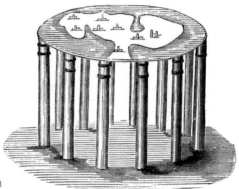

⊃ **Fig. 21.1.1**
The flat Earth

DATE	WHO	IDEA
350 BC	**Plato and Aristotle** (*Greek philosophers*)	The **geocentric** model: the Sun, Moon, planets and stars all orbit (move around) the Earth, which does not move.
200 BC	**Aristarchus** (*Greek astronomer*)	The **heliocentric** model: planets orbit the Sun instead of the Earth.
150 AD	**Ptolemy** (*Greco-Egyptian writer*)	Agreed with the geocentric model. His calculations could be used to predict planetary movements.
1543 AD	**Copernicus** (*Royal Prussian mathematician and astronomer*)	Agreed with the heliocentric model. His theory placed the Sun, rather than the Earth, at the centre of the solar system.
1603 AD	**Kepler** (*German mathematician and astronomer*)	Proved that Copernicus's theory was correct. Kepler also proved that the planets' orbits were elliptical (oval).
1609 AD	**Galileo** (*Italian astronomer*)	Galileo invented the telescope and saw objects in orbit around Jupiter. This proved that not everything was in orbit around the Earth. In 1632 he published his findings that proved the Sun is at the centre of the solar system.
1687 AD	**Newton** (*English physicist and mathematician*)	Published a book to explain why planets orbit the Sun rather than the Earth. As the Sun is 100 times heavier than all of the planets put together, its gravity (pull) is the strongest and planets orbit it.
1851 AD	**Foucault** (*French physicist*)	Used a pendulum to prove that the Earth is spinning on its own axis. It explained why the Sun, Moon and stars seem to move across the sky.

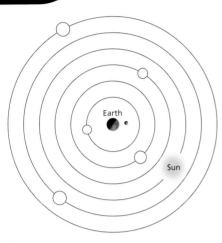

🎧 **Fig. 21.1.2**
Ptolemy's geocentric model

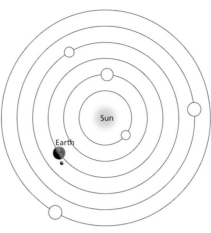

🎧 **Fig. 21.1.3**
Copernicus's heliocentric model

As new technologies develop, our view of the universe continues to change.

'Geocentric' and 'heliocentric'

Geo means 'Earth' in Greek, so 'geocentric' means that the Earth is at the centre. *Helio* means 'Sun', so heliocentric means the Sun is at the centre.

The Big Bang Theory

The **universe** is made up of everything that exists, including planets, stars, galaxies and all forms of matter and energy.

The **Big Bang** theory is an idea that scientists use to explain how our universe was formed. This idea best explains what scientists already know about matter, light and energy.

The Big Bang theory suggests that billions of years ago all space and matter in the universe was together in a single mass.

Most scientists believe that about 14 billion years ago the single mass of matter exploded – the Big Bang.

This Big Bang created space and matter that moved apart. As the universe expanded, atomic matter formed. Gravity then caused atoms to form galaxies and solar systems.

Since the Big Bang

- The Sun and all the planets that orbit it were formed five billion years ago.
- The first forms of life on Earth started four billion years ago.
- Dinosaurs lived on Earth between 200 million and 65 million years ago.
- Humans have existed for less than a quarter of a million years.

Galaxies

The first stars started to appear 150 million years after the Big Bang. Next, galaxies began to form.

A **galaxy** is a large group of stars, dust, gas and dark matter held together by gravity.

Galaxies vary in size. Some contain millions of stars, while others could contain as many as a trillion. They can also form in different shapes, such as elliptical galaxies and spiral galaxies.

Bazinga!

The Big Bang Theory is a popular TV comedy series. Listen to the theme tune in full online and examine the scientific accuracy of the lyrics.

↻ **Fig. 21.1.4**

Planet Earth and our solar system are part of a galaxy called the Milky Way. Our solar system is in one of the spiral arms of this galaxy.

Using telescopes, astronomers have found billions of other galaxies in the universe.

Antimatter

We know that matter is anything that takes up space and has a mass.

Antimatter is the mirror image of matter. Every particle of matter has a corresponding particle of antimatter.

When particles of matter and antimatter meet, they destroy each other and are changed into pure energy.

It is believed that equal amounts of matter and antimatter were formed in the Big Bang. By investigating antimatter, scientists hope to find out how the universe we live in, which is made entirely of matter, can exist.

 Learn more about matter in Chemical World 9.1

The Expanding Universe

In 1982, Edwin Hubble discovered that galaxies are moving apart. This shows that the universe is getting bigger. This discovery is key to the Big Bang theory.

At the beginning, the universe was very small. By measuring the rate it is growing at, astronomers can calculate that the Big Bang happened almost 14 billion years ago.

○ Fig. 21.1.5
The Milky Way

We are here

Modelling the Big Bang and the expanding universe

1. Draw dots on a balloon to represent the different galaxies. (Hint: it is best to start with a slightly inflated balloon.)
2. Predict what will happen to the dots when you blow into the balloon.
3. Blow into the balloon.
4. Explain how this model can be used to describe the expansion of the universe.

⊃ Fig. 21.1.7

Celestial Bodies

Learning Intentions

In this topic we are learning to:
- Distinguish between celestial bodies and give examples.
- Interpret data to compare various celestial bodies.

Our **solar system** includes the Sun and all the objects that orbit it due to its gravity, including the Earth.

A **celestial body** is any natural body outside of the Earth's atmosphere. There are various celestial bodies, including planets, stars, moons, comets and asteroids.

Planets

A **planet** is an object that:
- Is in orbit around a star.
- Has enough mass to have a nearly round shape.
- Has enough gravity to clear the space debris (waste) in its orbit.

Moons

A **moon** is a natural satellite which orbits a planet.

The Earth's moon is simply called the Moon. The moons of other planets in the solar system have been given names. For example, Titan is a moon of Saturn.

Fig. 21.2.1
Titan, one of Saturn's moons

The table below shows the features of some moons compared to the Earth.

Object	Type of object	Relative mass	Relative radius	Relative surface gravity	Composition of atmosphere
Earth	Planet	1	1	1	Nitrogen and oxygen
Ganymede	Moon of Jupiter	0.0248	0.413	0.15	Oxygen
Titan	Moon of Saturn	0.0225	0.404	0.14	Nitrogen and methane
Callisto	Moon of Jupiter	0.0180	0.378	0.126	Carbon dioxide
Io	Moon of Jupiter	0.0150	0.286	0.183	Sulfur dioxide
Moon	Moon of Earth	0.0123	0.273	0.166	No atmosphere
Europa	Moon of Jupiter	0.00803	0.245	0.134	Oxygen
Triton	Moon of Neptune	0.00359	0.212	0.0797	No atmosphere

Stars

A **star** is a ball of heat-radiating gas that is held together by gravity. Stars contain mostly hydrogen, as well as helium and smaller amounts of other elements.

Nuclear fusion releases large amounts of energy and fuels stars. Nuclear fusion involves two small nuclei (usually hydrogen) joining together to form a larger nucleus. We will learn more about nuclear fusion later.

The life cycle of a small to medium-sized star is as follows:

1. A nebula is a cloud of gas and dust in outer space. Stars form in a nebula when dust and gas from space are pulled together by gravity. Friction between these particles produces heat and the nuclei of hydrogen join together. A star is now formed. It is called a yellow dwarf.

2. The star remains stable for millions of years. When the star runs out of hydrogen fuel, fusion slows down.

3. The temperature decreases and the star expands to form a red giant.

4. Eventually the inner core of the star collapses under gravity to form a very hot and dense white dwarf.

5. The white dwarf fades out as fusion reactions stop. The star goes cold and becomes a black dwarf.

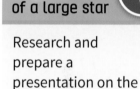

The life cycle of a large star

Research and prepare a presentation on the life cycle of a large star.

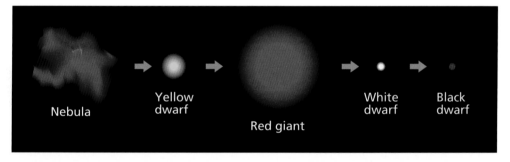

Nebula — Yellow dwarf — Red giant — White dwarf — Black dwarf

↻ **Fig. 21.2.2**
The life cycle of a small star

The **Sun** is the closest star to Earth. It is the biggest object in our solar system. It burns brightly in the centre of the solar system as planets and other objects orbit it.

The Sun has a diameter 110 times bigger than the Earth's diameter. It is around 150 million kilometres away from Earth.

What is a light-year?

When you see a star in the night sky, you see the star as it was when the light left it. You are in fact seeing something that happened in the past. As a result, distances in space are measured in **light-years**.

A light-year is the distance that light travels in one year. Light-years are often used in astronomy to describe the distance to faraway stars and galaxies.

The star Alpha Centauri is one of the closest stars to the Earth. It is 4.3 light-years away. This means that the light we see coming from Alpha Centauri left the star 4.3 years ago.

Light from the Sun takes eight minutes to reach the Earth.

🎧 **Fig. 21.2.3**
Alpha Centauri

⋔ Fig. 21.2.4

Asteroids

Asteroids are lumps of rock that orbit the Sun. They are too small to be classified as planets. They range in size from less that 1 km to 1,000 km in diameter.

Asteroids are thought to have been left over from the formation of the universe. The asteroid belt lies between the orbits of Mars and Jupiter. It contains a large amount of irregular-shaped asteroids that vary in size and what they are made of.

Investigating asteroids

Investigate one of the following well-known asteroids: Apophis, Ceres, Chiron, Eros or Vesta.

Write a report describing the asteroid using the following headings: diameter, composition and date of discovery.

Also include any interesting facts you found out about this asteroid.

⋔ Fig. 21.2.5
The asteroid belt between Mars and Jupiter

There are three types of asteroids:

- C-type asteroids are made up of carbon compounds.
- S-type asteroids are made up of stony material.
- M-type asteroids are mostly made of metals, such as iron.

The words 'meteor', 'meteorite' and 'meteoroid' look and sound very similar to each other. Research the difference between these three types of celestial bodies. Using a labelled diagram, describe what they are and how they differ.

Comets

A **comet** is a small lump of ice and dirt that orbits the Sun. Comets are made up of a nucleus, a coma and one or more tails.

- The nucleus of a comet is made up of dust and ice.
- The coma, which is a fuzzy outline or atmosphere caused by the Sun's radiation, is made up of carbon dioxide, dust and water vapour.
- The tail is made up of gas and dust produced by the nucleus.

Comets can only be seen when they travel near the Sun, as they reflect the Sun's light.

When a comet travels towards the Sun, its tail travels behind it as it is being blown away from the Sun by solar winds. As a comet travels away from the Sun, the tail is in front of the comet.

Comets are found in the Kuiper Belt or the Oort Cloud. The Kuiper Belt is found beyond Neptune. The Oort Cloud is found at the edge of our solar system.

Halley's Comet is the most well-known comet in the solar system. It orbits the Sun and can be seen with the naked eye from Earth approximately every 75 years. It is due to return again in 2061.

↺ Fig. 21.2.6
A comet

What age will I be? 1 2 3

Calculate what age you will be the next time Halley's Comet will be visible with the naked eye from Earth.

On 12 November 2014, as part of the Rosetta mission, the *Philae* lander became the first spacecraft to land on a comet nucleus. *Philae* was able to take images of the comet's surface, letting us see a comet in a way that had never been possible before.

Philae Lander a b c

Write a short report outlining some of the findings of the Rosetta mission. Outline some difficulties the mission encountered.

⊃ Fig. 21.2.7
A comet's surface, photographed by *Philae*

The Planets in Our Solar System

Key Words

Terrestrial planets
Gas giants
Gravity
Force field

Learning Intentions

In this topic we are learning to:

- List the planets in the solar system.
- Compare the Earth with other planets in terms of mass, gravity, size and composition.
- Appreciate that gravity is a force that binds the universe together.

'Terra' **abc**

The Latin word *terra* means 'land' or 'earth'.

Our solar system contains four inner planets and four outer planets.

The four inner planets are called **terrestrial planets** because they are made up of rock, like the Earth.

They are:

- Mercury
- Venus
- Earth
- Mars

Fig. 21.3.1
The planets in our solar system

Fun Fact

Up until 2006, Pluto was also considered a planet. Since then it has been reclassified as a dwarf planet or planetoid.

The outer planets are called **gas giants** because they are mainly made of gases hydrogen and helium.

They are:

- Jupiter
- Saturn
- Uranus
- Neptune

MVEMJSUN

Come up with a mnemonic to help you remember the names of the planets in the solar system.

The eight planets in our solar system are very different from each other.

Mercury

- Mercury is small for a planet and roughly the same size as our moon.
- It has no atmosphere and is covered in craters.
- The side of the planet facing the Sun is very hot (approximately 430 °C).

Venus

- Venus is similar in size to Earth.
- It is covered in clouds of sulfuric acid and has an atmosphere made up of carbon dioxide.
- It is even hotter on Venus than it is on Mercury.
- Venus spins in the opposite direction to all the other planets in the solar system.

Earth

- Earth is the fifth largest planet in the solar system.
- It is the only planet with liquid water, oxygen and living things.
- It is at the right distance from the Sun and has the right chemicals to support life.

Mars

- Mars is also called the Red Planet.
- Iron oxide gives Mars its reddish colour.
- It has a dusty, rocky surface, calm conditions and a thin atmosphere of carbon dioxide.
- It is rocky, with mountains and valleys.
- The asteroid belt is between Mars and Jupiter.

Jupiter

- Jupiter is the largest planet in our solar system.
- It has no solid surface and is mainly made of hydrogen and helium.
- It has many moons, some of which have volcanoes.
- It has a giant storm system, three times the size of the Earth, called the Red Spot.

Saturn

- Saturn is the second largest planet in our solar system.
- It has an impressive system of rings. The rings are not solid, but are made up of billions of tiny particles of ice.

Uranus

- Uranus is the third largest planet in the solar system.
- It has an atmosphere of hydrogen and helium. It looks blue-green and has very faint rings.
- Its axis is tilted so that it is lying on its side as it rotates the Sun.

Neptune

- Neptune is nearly four times the size of Earth.
- It has strong winds and violent weather.
- It is blue in colour due to a thick atmosphere of cold methane gas.
- It has a Great Dark Spot, which is a storm.

Planet data

1 2 3

Look at the table below and then answer the questions that follow.

Planet	Diameter (km)	Distance from the Sun (million km)	Time for one orbit (planet's year)	Time for one spin (planet's day)	Average temperature on the sunny side (°C)	No. of moons
Mercury	5,000	60	88 days	1400 hours	+430	0
Venus	12,0000	110	225 days	5800 hours	+470	0
Earth	12,800	150	365.25 days	24 hours	+20	1
Mars	7,000	230	2 years*	25 hours	−20	2
Jupiter	140,000	780	12 years*	10 hours	−150	67
Saturn	120,000	1,400	30 years*	10 hours	−180	62
Uranus	52,000	2,900	84 years*	17 hours	−210	27
Neptune	50,000	4,500	160 years*	16 hours	−220	14

Year = 365.5 days

1. Use a chart or a graph to explain three trends you notice from this data set.

2. Explain why Venus has such a high surface temperature.

3. Which planet is most like the Earth?

My Mercury age

1 2 3

If you celebrated your birthday every time the planet you are on orbits the Sun, how old would you be on Mercury?

GO Learn more about non-contact forces in Physical World 17.3

Gravity

Imagine a golf ball travelling through the air. The Earth attracts the ball downwards even though it is not touching the golf ball. The force that pulls the golf ball back to Earth is **gravity**.

Gravity is a very useful force – it holds everything together. It keeps us on the Earth, and keeps the Earth and the other planets orbiting the Sun. Without it everything would float around.

Gravity is a non-contact force of attraction between objects.

Scientists know that:

- There is a gravitational pull between all masses.

- Larger masses give a stronger pull. The Moon is not as heavy as the Earth, and so gravity is much weaker there. In fact, it is only about one-sixth of the gravity on Earth.

- The closer things are to each other, the greater the force of gravity between them. The Earth and the Moon have a stronger pull on each other than the Earth and Jupiter because the Earth and Moon are closer to each other.

Gravitational Force Fields

A **force field** is a region in space where an object feels a force.

A gravitational force field is a region in space where an object that has mass feels the force of gravity. It is responsible for the weight of every object on the surface of the Earth. This is the force that pulls you down towards the Earth.

The strength of this force field is approximately 10 N/kg on Earth. This means that gravity places a 10 N force on every kilogram of matter on Earth. It is also known as 'acceleration due to gravity'.

Calculating Gravity

Using our knowledge of force fields, we can calculate the weight of an object by multiplying the mass of that object (kg) by the gravity in that location (g).

Weight (N) = mass (kg) x gravity (N/kg)

For example, if your mass was 60 kg, then your weight on Earth would be 600 N:

W = 60 x 10 = 600 N

On the Moon, the only thing that would change is your weight (the size of the force pulling you towards the Moon).

Your mass will be the same no matter where you are in the universe.

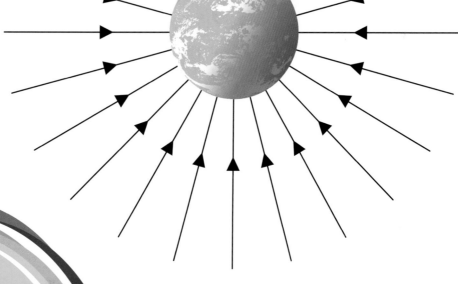

Fun Fact

Spending a long period of time in outer space can have strange effects on the body. Away from the large gravitational ('g') force on Earth, the spine begins to straighten out. Your internal organs shift upwards inside your torso, reducing your waist measurements by several inches. The forces you apply with your leg muscles shifts your blood upwards, creating a condition that NASA calls 'chicken legs'. All these effects wear off once you return to Earth.

🎧 **Fig. 21.3.2**
Earth's gravitational force field

School in space 123

Use the table below to calculate the weight of your schoolbag on the following planets:

Planet	Size of g (N/kg)
Mercury	3.8
Jupiter	25
Neptune	13.8
Saturn	10.2

Chapter Summary

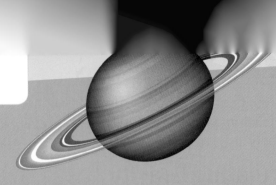

- The study of the universe and everything in it is called astronomy. The scientists who study in this area are called astronomers.

- Our understanding of the universe has evolved over time and is still changing.

- The universe is made up of everything that exists, including planets, stars, galaxies and all forms of matter and energy.

- The Big Bang theory is used to explain how the universe was formed. It states that the universe began with an explosion called the Big Bang. It also states that the universe is expanding.

- A galaxy is a large group of stars, dust, gas and dark matter held together by gravity. The galaxy that the Earth belongs to is called the Milky Way.

- Our solar system includes the Sun and all the objects that orbit it.

- Celestial bodies include planets, moons, stars, comets and asteroids.

- Our solar system contains four inner planets and four outer planets.

- The four inner planets – Mercury, Venus, Earth and Mars – are called terrestrial planets as they are made up of rock.

- The four outer planets – Jupiter, Saturn, Uranus and Neptune – are called gas giants as they are mainly made of gases such as hydrogen and helium.

- Gravity is a non-contact force of attraction that acts between two masses.

- The gravitational force field is responsible for your weight.

Weight (N) = mass (kg) x gravity (N/kg)

The BIG Challenge

The year is 2050 and your job is running a travel website. Choose one of the planets in our solar system (not Earth) and make up an advertising slogan to attract tourism to the planet. Create a brochure and make sure you include a list of things visitors may need to bring with them on their trip and for how long they will be away from home.

Go to your Portfolio to check what you have learned in this chapter.

Take the chapter 21 quiz on educateplus.ie.

Questions

1. Copy and fill in the blanks.

   a. The _____ model of the solar system has the Earth at the _____ of the universe.

   b. The _____ model of the solar system states that all the planets _____ the _____.

   c. The _____ _____ _____ is a theory to explain the _____ of the _____.

   d. The Moon is an example of a natural _____.

   e. There are _____ inner and _____ outer _____ in our solar system.

   f. The band of dust and rocks between Jupiter and Mars is called the _____ _____.

   g. The coldest planet is _____. This is because it is the _____ from the _____.

   h. The Sun is an example of a _____.

   i. _____ is the force of attraction between two objects that are not in _____.

   j. _____ is equal to mass in _____ multiplied by the gravitational force.

2. Describe what is meant by the Big Bang theory.

3. Put the following in order of size (smallest first): the Sun, the Moon, the galaxy, Earth, Halley's Comet. Write a sentence about each to explain what it is.

4. State one similarity and one difference between the inner and outer planets.

5. Define the word 'planet' in such a way that it includes objects such as the Earth, Mars and Jupiter but does not include objects such as Pluto or the Sun.

6. Give three reasons why life has developed on Earth and not on other planets.

7. Create a poster, as a revision tool, that explains the difference between various celestial bodies.

8. Copy and complete the crossword.

   Across
   2. The 'red planet' (4)
   4. Planet with an atmosphere that mainly consists of nitrogen and oxygen (5)
   5. Largest planet in our solar system (7)
   6. Planet closest to the Sun (7)

   Down
   1. Separates the inner planets from the outer planets (8, 4)
   2. Name of the Earth's natural satellite (4)
   3. Number of moons orbiting Venus (4)

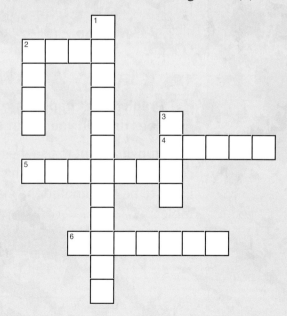

Working as a Scientist

Asking Questions and Making Predictions

Gravitational Force and Celestial Bodies

A group of students has been asked to develop a model to represent the gravitational force and to compare the size of gravity among different celestial bodies.

Before developing an idea or a model, it is useful to make a note of all the information you already know. This will help you to make predictions about how the model will work to simply demonstrate an idea or process.

1 **Make notes about everything you know about gravity. What is it? What is its range? Does it vary for different celestial bodies? If so, in what ways?**

The students develop their model using a tightly stretched rubber sheet. The rubber sheet represents the gravitational field in that region of space.

⊃ **Fig. 21.5.1**

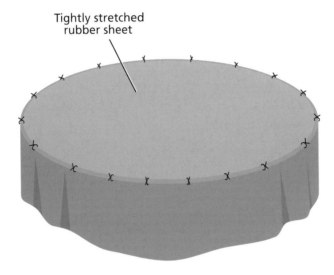

Tightly stretched rubber sheet

2 **Predict what happens when a weight is added to the rubber sheet. What does this tell you about the effect a large mass has on the gravitational field?**

The students want to use the model to compare the gravitational force around four celestial bodies: Earth, Earth's moon, Venus and Pluto. They took the relative mass of Earth to be 1 and noted the mass of the other bodies compared to this in the following table.

Celestial body	Relative mass
Earth	1
Venus	0.815
Earth's moon	0.0123
Pluto	0.0022

The students use a mass of 500 g to represent the mass of the Earth.

3 **How would you work out the amount of weights the students should put on the rubber sheet to represent the mass of the other celestial bodies?**

They continue with their task as follows:

- They place a marble at the point A while the sheet is flat and pulled tightly.
- They record the time it takes for the marble to move to position B when the weight is added to the centre of the sheet.
- The test is repeated for each celestial body listed in the table.

4 **What does the movement of the marble represent in this model?**

5 **Predict in order of the fastest to slowest the time it will take for the marble to move from A to B for the different runs of this test. Explain the reasons for your prediction.**

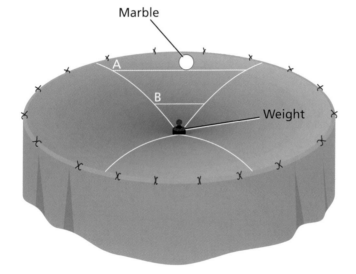

↻ Fig. 21.5.2

> **What makes a planet a planet?**
>
> Remember that a defining feature of a planet is that it can clear the space debris in its orbit. This means that it has become gravitationally dominant.

6 **Does this model help to explain why the Earth and Venus are classified as planets but the Moon and Pluto are not? Why?**

7 **Remember that a model should help to explain natural phenomena in a simpler way. Is this a good model for representing the nature of the gravitational field around celestial bodies of different masses? In what way? What improvements could you make to this model to represent the nature of the gravitational field?**

Set up this model in class. Collect relevant data for the time it takes for the marble to move from A to B and present the data in a clear way. Record your trials and use video evidence to back up your reported findings.

Earth

What you may already know:

- The Earth is a large rock orbiting the Sun.
- Water is key to the survival of life on Earth.

What you will learn in this chapter:

- The Earth is made up of three layers: core, mantle and crust.
- The atmosphere is a layer of gases that blankets the Earth's crust.
- How matter cycles through living and non-living things.
- The water cycle describes the changes that water goes through as it passes through the Earth.

Think BIG

- What is the Earth made from?
- Why is the Earth suitable for life?
- How are key nutrients cycled through the Earth?

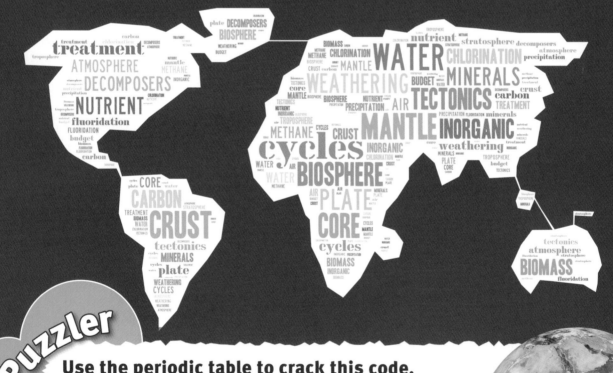

Puzzler

Use the periodic table to crack this code.

Your answer should rank the elements by their abundance in the Earth's crust. (Hint: look at the atomic numbers.)

8	14	13	26	20	11	19	12	22	1

Which element is there most of?

The Structure of the Earth

Key Words

Crust
Mantle
Magma
Core
Plate tectonics
Seismology
Igneous
Sedimentary
Metamorphic

Learning Intentions

In this topic we are learning to:

- Name the three layers that make up the Earth.
- Describe plate tectonics and seismology.
- Identify the three types of rock that the Earth's crust is composed of: igneous, sedimentary and metamorphic.

The Earth is a huge rock that orbits the Sun. It was formed approximately 4,600 million years ago in molten (liquid) form. Over time, it cooled to become the Earth we live on today.

The Layers of the Earth

The Earth is made up of three layers:

1. The crust
2. The mantle
3. The core.

1. The Crust

The outside layer of the Earth is the **crust**. The oceans and continents lie on top of the crust.

Along with the atmosphere, the crust is the part of Earth that can support life. This is the called the biosphere.

2. The Mantle

Beneath the Earth's crust is the **mantle**.

The mantle is mostly made up of solid rock, except for the upper mantle, which is made of liquid called **magma**. Magma is a mixture of hot molten or semi-molten rock.

3. The Core

The centre of the Earth is the **core**. It is the hottest part of the planet.

The core is made up of two layers:

- The outer core is a thick liquid made up of molten iron and nickel.
- The inner core is also made up of iron and nickel, but here they are in a solid state because of the very high pressure.

As the core is mostly made up of metal, the Earth has its own magnetic field. This magnetic field has a big influence on natural processes and is one of the reasons life has survived on Earth.

Crust
Mantle
Inner core
Outer core

◠ Fig. 22.1.1
The structure of the Earth

GO Learn more about the Earth's magnetic field in Physical World 18.1

Fig. 22.1.2
Damage caused by the earthquake in Christchurch, New Zealand, in 2011

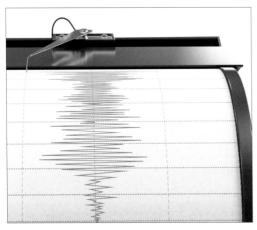

Fig. 22.1.3
A seismograph recording the movement of the ground during an earthquake

Fig. 22.1.4
Granite is an igneous rock

Plate Tectonics

The Earth's crust is broken up into large chunks called plates. These plates float because of convection currents in the magma of the upper mantle.

 Learn more about convection currents in Physical World 19.5

The movement of the Earth's crust is called **plate tectonics**. This movement can cause volcanoes and earthquakes.

Seismology

Seismology is the study of volcanoes and earthquakes.

After an earthquake or a volcano, the ground moves because of seismic waves passing through the Earth's crust. The more energy carried by seismic waves, the more movement there will be in the Earth's crust.

Scientists measure the movement of the ground using a seismograph. The Richter scale describes the magnitude (size) of an earthquake in numbers from 0 to approximately 9.

The Richter scale is not a linear number scale. It is a logarithmic scale. This means that an earthquake that measures 2 on the Richter scale is 10 times bigger than an earthquake that measures 1.

Logarithmic scale

1. What are the advantages of using a logarithmic scale?
2. What other physical quantities or natural phenomena are reported using a logarithmic scale?

Rock

The Earth's crust is made up of three main types of rock:

1. Igneous rocks
2. Sedimentary rocks
3. Metamorphic rocks.

1. Igneous rocks

Igneous rocks form when magma breaks through the surface of the Earth's crust during a volcano. When it cools, the magma becomes solid.

Granite and basalt are examples of igneous rocks.

2. Sedimentary Rocks

Sedimentary rocks are formed by layers of rock particles and dead plant and animal material building up over millions of years.

Limestone and sandstone are examples of sedimentary rocks.

3. Metamorphic Rocks

Metamorphic rocks are formed when igneous and sedimentary rocks are changed into harder rocks by high temperatures and pressure.

Quartzite, slate and marble are examples of metamorphic rocks.

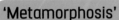
'Metamorphosis'

'Metamorphosis' means to change from one thing to another, such as igneous or sedimentary rocks changing form. In the biological world, it refers to an animal changing into its mature form, such as a caterpillar turning into a butterfly.

⌒ **Fig. 22.1.5**
Limestone is a sedimentary rock

⌒ **Fig. 22.1.6**
Quartzite is a metamorphic rock

Testing rocks for the presence of carbon

Geologists are scientists who study the rocks that make up the Earth. Geologists often use an acid test to find out if rocks are made up of carbon compounds.

1. Collect some small pebbles and rocks and bring them to school. Your teacher will give you a small quantity of hydrochloric acid (five to ten per cent concentration). Be extremely careful with this acid as it is corrosive.

2. Place a small drop of acid on each pebble or rock. Prepare a data collection sheet and a scale to note 'fizziness'. Consider the following:

   - Why do some of the rocks fizz? Research the chemical reaction online.

   - What may you conclude from the 'fizziness' of the reaction?

   - What type of data are you recording when you are noting 'fizziness'? How accurate do you think this data is?

⌒ **Fig. 22.1.7**
A selection of rocks

The Cycling of Matter

Learning Intentions

In this topic we are learning to:

- Consider the cycling of matter through the living and non-living parts of the Earth.
- Review models for the cycling of carbon and nitrogen.

Unlike energy, which constantly flows from the Sun to the Earth, the quantity of matter on Earth stays the same.

The Rock Cycle

Most of the matter in the Earth's crust is found in igneous, sedimentary and metamorphic rocks.

These rocks are changed by weathering, erosion, heat and pressure. The **rock cycle** describes how and why these changes take place.

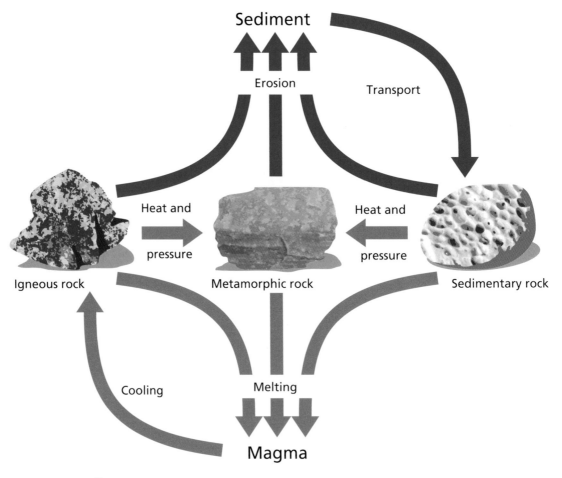

↻ **Fig. 22.2.1**
The rock cycle shows how and why rocks change

As rocks are changed, they break down to release minerals. These minerals formed the building blocks for the first life on Earth.

Nutrient Cycles

The cycling of matter and minerals through the living and non-living parts of the Earth are described by **nutrient cycles**.

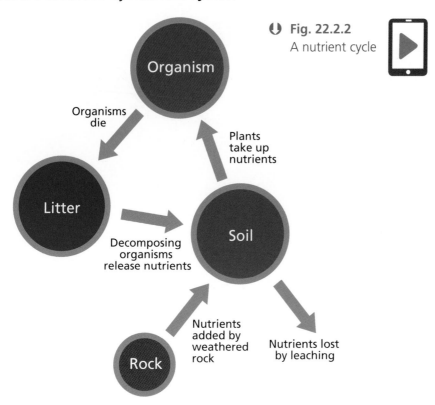

Fig. 22.2.2
A nutrient cycle

1. The nutrients released into the soil when rocks are broken down are taken up by organisms.

2. When an organism dies it becomes known as 'litter' and it returns nutrients to the soil as it decomposes (breaks down).

3. Some nutrients are lost from the soil due to high rainfall or irrigation. This is known as leaching.

The Carbon Cycle

Carbon is present in all living things. When the organisms die, carbon is recycled by decomposers as part of the **carbon cycle**.

The carbon cycle explains how carbon is recycled through the Earth.

- Anything that takes carbon out of the atmosphere is known as a **carbon sink**. For example, plants take carbon out of the atmosphere as carbon dioxide during photosynthesis.

GO Learn more about photosynthesis in Biological World 3.2

- Anything that releases carbon into the atmosphere is known as a **carbon source**. For example, all living things release carbon into the atmosphere as carbon dioxide during respiration.

GO Learn more about respiration in Biological World 3.3

GO Learn more about combustion in Chemical World 14.1

The combustion of fuels also releases carbon to the atmosphere in the form of carbon dioxide. Increased levels of carbon dioxide in the atmosphere causes air pollution and global warming.

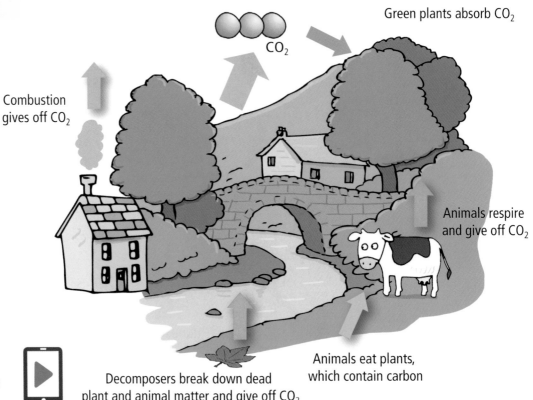

Green plants absorb CO_2

CO_2

Combustion gives off CO_2

Animals respire and give off CO_2

Animals eat plants, which contain carbon

Decomposers break down dead plant and animal matter and give off CO_2

⮑ **Fig. 22.2.3**
The cycling of carbon in the atmosphere

Carbon in the news

⦾ **Fig. 22.2.4**
Carbon footprint

The terms 'carbon budget' and 'carbon footprint' are often used by the media to report on the causes and effects of changing carbon levels in our atmosphere.

Research simple definitions for each of these terms and give one example of their use in a news headline.

The Nitrogen Cycle

Nitrogen is another important element for living organisms. It is an important part of many proteins and other structures in cells. Nitrogen is also important for the building of DNA.

Like carbon, nitrogen is released from the rocks of the Earth's crust very slowly.

The **nitrogen cycle** explains how nitrogen is recycled through the Earth.

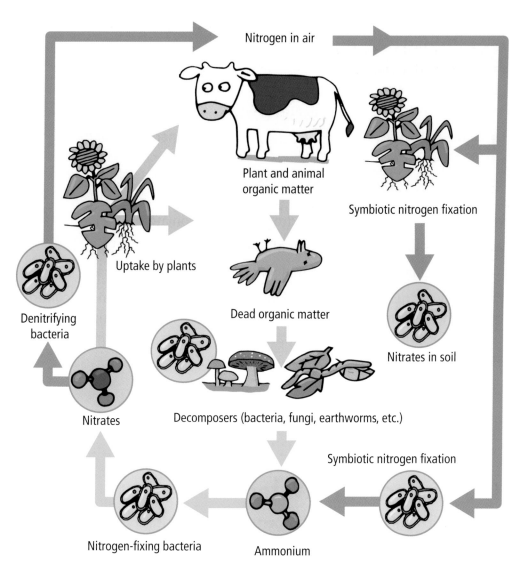

↻ **Fig. 22.2.5**
The nitrogen cycle

1. Approximately 80 per cent of the air is nitrogen gas. However, most of this nitrogen is not available to animals and plants.

2. Certain bacteria, known as nitrogen-fixing bacteria, can change the nitrogen in the atmosphere into nitrates. These nitrates can then be taken up from the soil by plants.

3. The plant supplies the bacteria with food (sugars) and water.

4. The plant uses nitrogen to form protein. Animals get their protein by eating plants or other animals.

5. Decomposers such as bacteria, fungi and earthworms return nitrogen to the soil as ammonium by breaking down dead organic matter.

6. Denitrifying bacteria in the soil break down nitrates, returning nitrogen to the air.

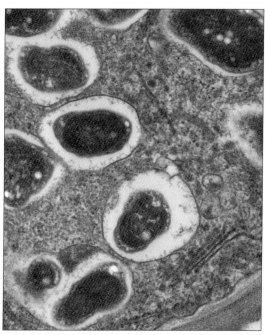

↥ **Fig. 22.2.6**
Nitrogen-fixing bacteria in a soybean

Water

Key Words

Water cycle
Water treatment
Screening
Settling
Filtration
Chlorination
Fluoridation
Electrolysis
Electrolyte
Electrode

Learning Intentions

In this topic we are learning to:

- Examine the properties and roles of water.
- Outline how water cycles through the living and non-living parts of the Earth.
- Investigate the electrolysis of water.

Water (H_2O) is a compound of hydrogen and oxygen atoms.

Water covers just over 70 per cent of the Earth's surface.

A supply of clean water is essential for all humans.

Day to day, we need water for drinking, cooking and washing. In agriculture, water is needed for crops and livestock. Water is also used in industry for cooling machinery and as a raw material for products such as medicines and paint.

Water exists in three states:

- Solid (ice)
- Liquid (water)
- Gas (vapour or steam).

The Properties of Water

Water has a number of special properties that make it very useful.

- The freezing point of pure water is 0 °C and its boiling point is 100 °C. This means that water typically exists as a liquid on Earth, which is ideal for supporting life.
- Water expands as it freezes. Most other compounds contract as they freeze. This is why pipes can burst if the water in them freezes.
- The density of water is 1.0 g/cm³. At 0.92 g/cm³, ice is less dense than water. This means that ice floats on water.
- Water is an excellent solvent. Many substances dissolve in water. This makes it difficult to find pure water.
- Adhesion. Water clings to and climbs up through xylem vessels to deliver water and mineral nutrients from the soil to leaves.
- Surface tension. Molecules of water are attracted to one another so it appears as if there is a thin skin on the surface. This allows some small insects to walk on water and also helps water move through the xylem tissue of a plant.

○ Fig. 22.3.1
Humans need to drink around two litres of water a day

GO Learn more about the test for water in Biological World 2.1

GO Learn more about transport in plants in Biological World 7.2

○ Fig. 22.3.2
Surface tension allows some insects to walk on water

The Water Cycle

The **water cycle** describes all of the changes that water undergoes as it moves through the Earth.

The water cycle is powered by energy from the Sun.

The steps in the water cycle are:

1. Evaporation: the Sun heats water on the Earth's surface (in soil, rivers, lakes and seas). Liquid water turns into water vapour, which rises upwards.

2. Condensation: the water vapour cools and changes back into liquid water, forming clouds.

3. Precipitation: as water adds to the clouds, they get heavier (more dense) and eventually water falls back to the Earth as rain or snow.

4. Water flow: liquid water collects in soil, rivers, lakes and seas and the cycle begins again.

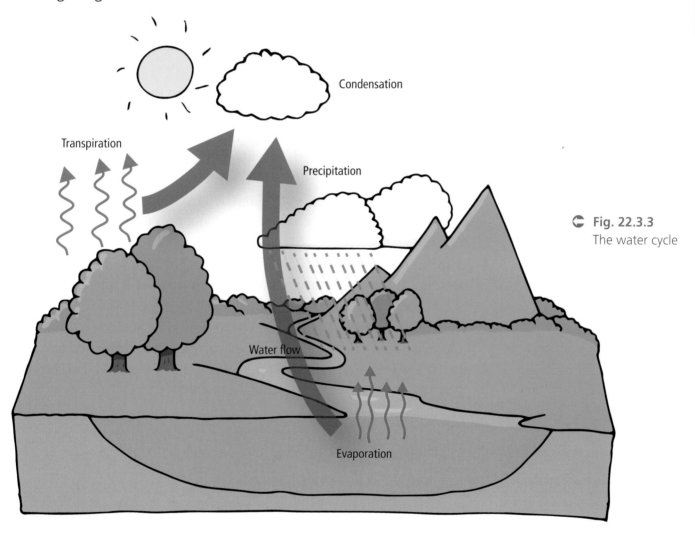

↻ **Fig. 22.3.3**
The water cycle

Water Treatment

Approximately 80 per cent of diseases in developing countries are caused by water that has not been treated to make it safe for drinking. Common diseases caused by untreated water are cholera and typhus.

⊃ **Fig. 22.3.4**
A water treatment plant

The main stages of **water treatment** are:

1. **Screening**: water from lakes or rivers is passed through a wire mesh to remove floating material, such as rubbish and branches.

2. **Settling**: the water flows into large tanks, where a chemical called aluminium sulfate is added. This helps small particles clump together and settle to the bottom of the tanks.

3. **Filtration**: the water passes through beds of sand and gravel. Any remaining particles are removed. The water now looks clear but may still contain bacteria.

4. **Chlorination**: chlorine is added to the water to kill any harmful bacteria. A very small amount of chlorine is needed. It must be enough to kill bacteria but not enough that we can smell or taste it.

5. **Fluoridation**: flourine is added in some countries (including Ireland) to prevent tooth decay. Finally, the pH of the water is checked to make sure it is within an acceptable range (pH 7–8). Treated water is stored in reservoirs or water towers until it is needed.

GO Learn more about testing pH in Chemical World 13.2

Water charges in Ireland

The introduction of water charges in Ireland in 2014 caused a lot of debate.

1. List three reasons why some people are against water charges.

2. Ireland was one of the last countries in Europe to charge for water. List at least three reasons why most European governments think it is necessary to charge for water.

⊃ **Fig. 22.3.5**
Water charges were introduced in Ireland

Electrolysis

Electrolysis is splitting up a compound by passing electricity through it.

An **electrolyte** is a substance that will conduct electricity when molten or dissolved in water.

Electrodes are two rods that dip into an electrolyte and complete the electrical circuit. There is a positive and a negative electrode.

Fun Fact

Electrolytes are important for cells to function properly. When you exercise heavily, you lose electrolytes in your sweat, in particular sodium and potassium. These electrolytes must be replaced. Many sports drinks have sodium chloride or potassium chloride added to them for this reason.

GO Learn more about electrodes in Physical World 18.6

Electrolysis in action

Using a Hofmann voltameter, carry out the electrolysis of water in the school laboratory. Record your observations.

Splitting Water

In 1781, English scientist Henry Cavendish showed that water was produced through the combustion of hydrogen and oxygen. This proved that water is in fact a compound and not an element.

Water can also be split into hydrogen and oxygen by passing an electric current through it. This is known as the electrolysis of water.

The piece of equipment used in the electrolysis of water is a Hofmann voltameter.

The battery supplies the electrical energy for the reaction. The electrolyte in the reaction is water and some dilute sulfuric acid. The electrodes can be made of either platinum or carbon.

The word equation for the splitting of water is:

> Water → hydrogen + oxygen

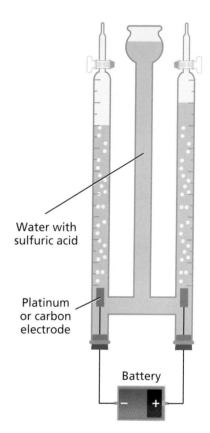

Water with sulfuric acid

Platinum or carbon electrode

Battery

○ **Fig. 22.3.6**
A Hofmann voltameter

Electrolysis of water

During the electrolysis of water, twice as much of one gas is produced as another. Look at Fig. 22.3.6.

1. Which gas has twice the volume of the other?

2. Explain this observation.

3. How would you test each gas to make sure you were correct?

The Atmosphere

Key Words

Atmosphere
Troposphere
Stratosphere
Ozone
Mesosphere
Thermosphere
Exosphere
Meteorologist

Learning Intentions

In this topic we are learning to:

- Recognise that the atmosphere is a mixture of gases that blanket the Earth.
- Evaluate how living organisms contribute to changes in our atmosphere.
- Appreciate that changes in atmospheric pressure affect weather.

The **atmosphere** is the layer of gases that blanket the Earth. The atmosphere is commonly known as air.

Gravity holds the atmosphere close to the Earth's surface.

⮕ Fig. 22.4.1
The Earth's atmosphere, as seen from space

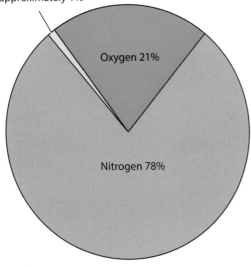

Argon, carbon dioxide and water vapour approximately 1%

Oxygen 21%

Nitrogen 78%

◖ Fig. 22.4.2
The gases that make up air

Composition of the Air

The air in our atmosphere is a mixture of gases including nitrogen, oxygen, carbon dioxide, argon, water vapour and other gases.

As air is a mixture, the percentages of the gases it is made up of can change.

For example, humans and plants in a sealed room will change the composition of the air through respiration and photosynthesis. This is because these processes change the amounts of oxygen, carbon dioxide and water in the air.

GO Learn more about photosynthesis in Biological World 3.2

GO Learn more about respiration in Biological World 3.3

Uses of Oxygen and Carbon Dioxide

The table below shows the properties and uses of oxygen and carbon dioxide in the air.

Gas	Properties	Uses	Test
Oxygen	• Colourless, odourless, tasteless • Only slightly soluble in water • Slightly more dense than air • Supports combustion • Reacts with many elements to form oxides	• Respiration • Combustion • Medicine (ventilation and resuscitation) • Diving and mountain climbing gear • Welding and cutting metals • Steel manufacture • Launching rockets	• Relights a glowing splint • No effect on litmus
Carbon dioxide	• Colourless, odourless, tasteless • Only slightly soluble in water • Slightly more dense than air • Does not support combustion	• Photosynthesis • Fire extinguishers • Refrigeration and food packaging • Carbonation (fizzy drinks) • Special effects (dry ice)	• Changes limewater from colourless to milky • Dissolves in water to form carbonic acid, which turns blue litmus red

↻ **Fig. 22.4.3**
An oxygen tank used for diving

GO Learn more about testing for oxygen in Chemical World 12.5

Testing for gases

Using the information in the table above, plan, design, carry out and write up an investigation to test for the presence of oxygen, carbon dioxide and hydrogen in the air.

Fun Fact

Nitrogen is such an unreactive gas that food-packaging companies often remove the air surrounding their product and replace it with nitrogen. The gas in a bag of crisps is actually nitrogen gas.

The Layers of the Atmosphere

The atmosphere is made up of five layers:

1. The troposphere
2. The stratosphere
3. The mesosphere
4. The thermosphere
5. The exosphere.

The composition of gases in each layer is very different.

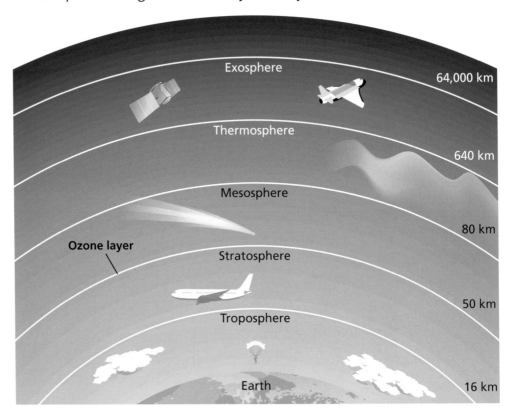

⤷ **Fig. 22.4.4**
The layers of the
atmosphere

1. **Troposphere**: clouds and weather systems form up to 16 km above the Earth. Above only 6 km, the air becomes so thin that mountain climbers have to carry special equipment to help them breathe. Some military planes can fly above this height, but most planes stay within the troposphere.

GO Learn more about UV rays in Biological World 4.3

2. **Stratosphere**: the **ozone** layer is found in this layer of the atmosphere. Ozone gas protects the Earth from harmful UV rays from the Sun.

3. **Mesosphere**: this layer makes up less than five per cent of the atmosphere. Space debris burns up as it enters this layer and shooting stars can be seen here. The coldest place on Earth is at the top of the mesosphere.

4. **Thermosphere**: this layer is only a tiny fraction of the Earth's atmosphere but it absorbs a lot of solar radiation and temperatures can get very hot here. The charged particles in this layer are influenced by the Earth's magnetic field and sometimes produce beautiful aurorae.

GO Learn more about aurorae in Physical World 18.1

5. **Exosphere**: this uppermost layer is where the Earth's atmosphere merges with space.

Weather

How the gases in our atmosphere behave is affected by:

- Temperature
- Altitude
- Pressure

GO Learn more about atmospheric pressure in Physical World 17.6

As a result, changes in atmospheric pressure have a big effect on our weather.

A scientist who studies the atmosphere is called a **meteorologist**. They can use changes in atmospheric pressure to predict the weather.

A barometer is used to measure atmospheric pressure.

Air moves from high to low pressure. This movement of air causes changes in our weather.

- Low atmospheric pressure usually brings wet and windy weather.
- High atmospheric pressure usually brings calm and dry weather.

⋒ Fig. 22.4.5
A barometer

Weather Charts

Lines on a weather chart that join areas of equal pressure are called isobars.

The closer the isobars are together on a weather chart, the stronger the wind will be.

The boundary between two different air masses is called a front.

- Warm fronts form where warm air rises over cold air. This causes cloudy weather. On a weather chart, a warm front is shown as a red line with red semicircles.
- Cold fronts form where cold air replaces warmer air. This causes rain. On a weather chart, a cold front is shown as a blue line with blue triangles.
- Where a cold front overtakes a warm front, an occluded front forms. An occluded front causes changeable weather. On a weather chart, an occluded front is shown as a purple line with purple triangles and semicircles (a mix of the warm and cold front lines).

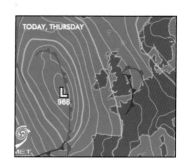

⋒ Fig. 22.4.6
What weather conditions is Ireland experiencing in this picture?

Chapter Summary

- The Earth is made up of three layers: crust, mantle and core.
- There are three main types of rock: igneous, sedimentary and metamorphic. The rock cycle describes how rocks change over time due to weathering and erosion.
- Anything that takes carbon out of the atmosphere is known as a carbon sink. For example, plants take carbon out of the atmosphere as carbon dioxide during photosynthesis.
- The carbon cycle explains how carbon is recycled through the Earth.
- Anything that releases carbon into the atmosphere is known as a carbon source. For example, respiring organisms release carbon dioxide.
- Nitrogen and oxygen also cycle through the living and non-living parts of the Earth.
- Water has special properties that make it very useful.
- The water cycle describes all of the changes that water undergoes as it moves through the Earth.
- Water exists in three states: solid (ice), liquid (water) and gas (vapour or steam).
- Electrolysis is splitting up a compound by passing electricity through it.
- Water can be split into hydrogen and oxygen by electrolysis.
- Water goes through a series of treatment steps before it is safe for humans to drink: screening, settling, filtration, chlorination and fluoridation.
- The positive test for oxygen is that it relights a glowing splint. The positive test for carbon dioxide is that limewater turns from colourless to milky.
- The Earth's atmosphere is a mixture of gases that blanket the Earth's surface.
- The Earth's atmosphere is separated into five layers: troposphere, stratosphere, mesosphere, thermosphere and exosphere.
- Atmospheric pressure describes the pressure placed on the surface of the Earth by the gases in the atmosphere. Atmospheric pressure has a big effect on weather.

The BIG Challenge

Your task is to model atmospheric pressure using just a glass of water and a sturdy piece of card. You should then explain the method to one of your classmates using Twitter (140 characters maximum per tweet). You are not allowed to send images. Agree on a time that suits both of you.

Write five tweets that explain to your partner how to carry out this activity at home. The five tweets should have the following hashtags and be sent in order:

1. #equipment, 2. #method (including safety), 3. #observations, 4. #conclusion, 5. #explanation (of atmospheric pressure).

Fig. 22.5.1
Use Twitter to help conduct a demonstration of atmospheric pressure

Go to your Portfolio to check what you have learned in this chapter.

Take the chapter 22 quiz on educateplus.ie.

Questions

1. Copy and fill in the blanks.

   a. The three layers of the Earth are the crust, the _____ and the core.

   b. The three main types of rock are _____, sedimentary and _____.

   c. The _____ is a mixture of gases that blanket the Earth's surface.

   d. Anything that takes carbon out of the atmosphere is known as a _____ _____. Anything that releases carbon into the atmosphere is known as a _____ _____.

   e. The _____ _____ describes all of the processes and changes that water undergoes as it moves through the Earth.

   f. Electrolysis is splitting up a compound by passing _____ through it.

   g. A _____ _____ is the piece of equipment used to split water into _____ and _____.

   h. The positive test for carbon dioxide is that it turns limewater _____.

   i. The five stages in the treatment of water are screening, _____, filtration, chlorination and _____.

   j. The five layers of the atmosphere are the troposphere, _____, mesosphere, _____ and exosphere.

2. Produce a table to compare oxygen, carbon dioxide and water under the following headings:

   a. Physical properties (x 3)

   b. Chemical properties (x 3)

   c. Uses (x 5)

   d. Test

3. Draw a labelled sketch of the carbon cycle. Identify all key processes and label each item as a 'carbon source' or 'carbon sink'.

4. Draw a flowchart to describe the order of the different stages in the treatment of water. At each point in your flowchart, explain the specific purpose of each treatment step.

5. Consider the following statement: 'The introduction of water charges is a necessary evil.' Do you agree or disagree with this statement? Prepare a short report to explain your opinion. You must justify your position with reference to at least three economic and scientific reasons.

6. The following diagram shows the electrolysis of water.

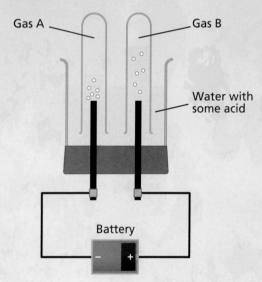

   a. Why is some acid added to the water?

   b. Give a test for gas A.

   c. The volume of gas A is twice that of gas B. What does this tell us about the composition of water?

7. Outline the role of atmospheric pressure in determining weather conditions. In particular, refer to:

   a. Wind speed

   b. Cloud cover

   c. Precipitation

   d. Temperature

   e. Humidity

Working as a Scientist

Investigation Design

Hard Water

We use water every day to wash our clothes. In some areas, it is difficult for water to lather with soap or detergents. This type of water is called hard water.

Hard water contains a high concentration of calcium (Ca^{2+}) and magnesium (Mg^{2+}) ions. These ions enter the water as it flows over certain types of rock.

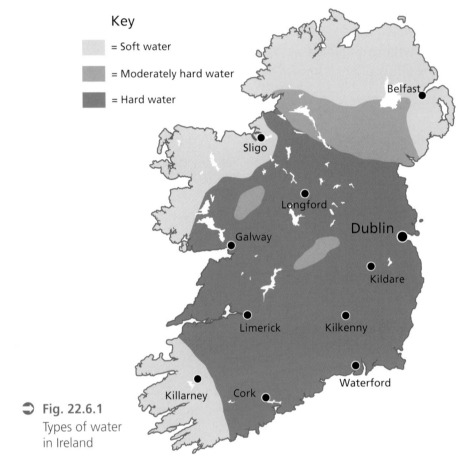

Key
- = Soft water
- = Moderately hard water
- = Hard water

⮑ **Fig. 22.6.1**
Types of water in Ireland

Instead of forming a lather with soap, hard water produces a dirty scum that settles on the surface of the water.

Adding soap to water and monitoring the lather (or scum) that is formed is a simple test for the degree of hardness in water samples.

1 Compare the above map to a geological map of Ireland. Which rock type do you think causes the hardness in Irish water?

The presence of calcium hydrogencarbonate and magnesium hydrogencarbonate in water is responsible for temporary hardness. Temporary hardness may be removed by heating the water, as shown by the limescale that builds up on the elements of kettles and washing machines.

2 Research the difference between temporary hardness and permanent hardness in water. Write a short report and present it to your classmates.

You have been asked to carry out an investigation to test the following hypothesis: 'The hotter the water, the more temporary hardness that will be removed.' Gather the following equipment for use during your investigation:

- 500 cm^3 of hard water
- 500 cm^3 of soft water
- Graduated cylinder
- Beaker(s)
- Soap flakes
- Mass balance
- Spatula
- Tripod and gauze
- Bunsen burner
- Digital thermometer

3 **Draw a labelled diagram of the set-up you will use. Write a step-by-step method.**

Consider the following as you plan and carry out your investigation:

4 **Identify the:**
  a. **Independent variable.**
  b. **Dependent variable.**
  c. **Controlled (fixed) variables.**

5 **What would be a suitable control for this investigation?**

6 **How much time will you need and what protective equipment will you need to wear?**

7 **Produce a suitable data collection sheet and comment on any trends that you see in your table of data. Construct an appropriate chart or graph to present your data.**

8 **Do your results indicate that your original hypothesis is false or not false? Do you need to change your hypothesis in light of the new information you gathered during this investigation?**

9 **Consider all sources of error and recommend potential adjustments to your method.**

10 **How do your results compare with those of your classmates? Is there evidence of trends within the class data set? How do your results compare with similar investigations online?**

11 **How might the results of your investigation be used to inform people living in hard water areas?**

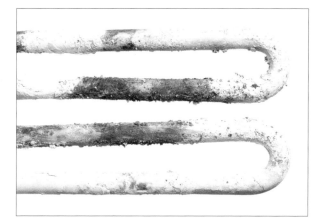

🎧 Fig. 22.6.2
Limescale on a kettle element

12 **What other physical, chemical and biological properties of water should local authorities consider monitoring before water is delivered to homes for human use?**

The Interaction Between Earth and Space

What you may already know:

- There are four seasons: winter, spring, summer and autumn.
- The rotation of the Earth on its axis causes day and night.

What you will learn in this chapter:

- Lunar phases.
- How lunar and solar eclipses happen.
- How to develop a model of the Earth, Sun and Moon and use it to explain seasons.

Think BIG

- What are the seasons?
- Why can we not see stars during the day?

Puzzler

Can you crack this code?
The first letter of each image spells out a key word that you will come across in this chapter. Use the hints provided if you need to, or revisit the Puzzler after you finish this chapter.

1.	2.	3.	4.	5.

Everything that exists	Natural satellite of the Earth	Second man to walk on the Moon	Term used to describe light bouncing off an object	The imaginary line that the Earth spins around on

1. _____ 2. _____ 3. _____ 4. _____ 5. _____

The Earth and the Sun

Key Words

Luminous
Non-luminous
Transparent
Translucent
Opaque
Shadow
Season

The Sun is the closest star to the Earth. The temperature at the centre of the Sun is approximately 14 million °C. Reactions in the Sun change nuclear energy into light and heat energy that falls onto the Earth.

Light

The light energy we get from the Sun is useful as it is changed into other forms of energy. For example, plants convert energy from the Sun into chemical energy during photosynthesis.

A **luminous** object transforms and emits its own light, such as stars, a light bulb or a candle. An object is luminous only when it is transforming and giving out light. For example, when a light bulb is turned off it is non-luminous.

Non-luminous objects reflect light from other sources. You can read the words on this page because light from another source is reflecting off the book and entering your eyes.

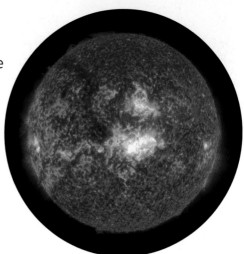

🔵 Fig. 23.1.1
The Sun

GO Learn more about bouncing light and how we see objects in Physical World 19.2

Materials can be described in three ways in relation to light:

1. **Transparent**: allows light to pass through with no shadows formed. For example, a clear window.

2. **Translucent**: allows only some light to go through (not all) and forms a shadow that is very light. For example, a stained-glass window.

3. **Opaque**: allows no light to pass through and forms a shadow. For example, a table, chair or a human.

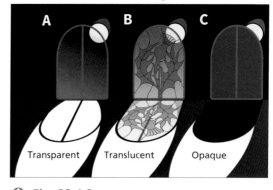

🔵 Fig. 23.1.2
Materials in relation to light

How does light travel?

1. Set up the investigation in Fig. 23.1.3. Predict what will happen when the student moves card B to the left.

2. Carry out the investigation. What happens? Why does this happen?

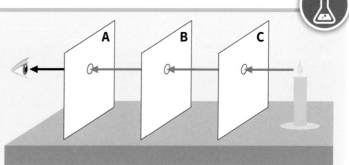

⮑ Fig. 23.1.3

🎧 Fig. 23.1.4
Shadows

Shadows

On a bright day you can see your own **shadow** on the ground. Shadows are formed because:

- Light travels in straight lines.
- Light cannot pass through opaque material, such as a person.

The Spinning Earth

The Earth's axis is an imaginary line that links the North and South poles. The Earth is tilted at an angle of 23.5° on its axis.

When the Earth spins, half the Earth is facing the Sun and in the light and half is facing away from the Sun and in the dark. This is what gives us day and night.

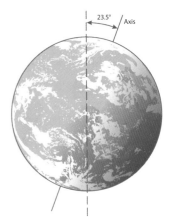

🎧 Fig. 23.1.5
The Earth's axis

The Earth takes 24 hours to complete one full spin. The Sun appears in the east each morning, it reaches its highest point in the sky at noon and then disappears from view in the west in the evening.

It is important to remember that the Sun is not moving; the Earth is moving.

The Orbiting Earth

The Earth moves round the Sun in an elliptical (oval) orbit. The Earth is pulled into this orbit by the gravitational force that exists between the mass of the Sun and the mass of the Earth.

The Earth moves around the Sun once each year, in an anticlockwise direction. The Earth takes 365.25 days to orbit the Sun. This is why we need a leap year every four years. A leap year contains one extra day.

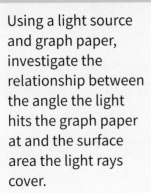

Investigating shadows

Using a small ball, a light source and a white screen, plan, design, carry out and write up an investigation to find out the factors that affect the size and shape of a shadow.

Looking at angles

Using a light source and graph paper, investigate the relationship between the angle the light hits the graph paper at and the surface area the light rays cover.

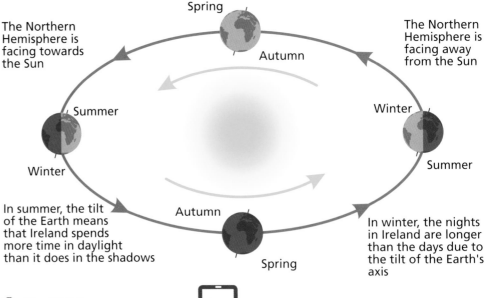

🎧 Fig. 23.1.6
How the seasons change due to the tilt of the Earth's axis

Seasons

A **season** is a division of the year. It is marked by changes in the weather and by the number of hours of daylight.

Seasons change on or around the 21 March, June, September and December.

Differences in seasons are caused by the tilt of the Earth on its axis (23.5°). The Earth holds this axis as it moves around the Sun. The seasons in the Northern and Southern Hemispheres are opposite.

Winter

In the winter, the Northern Hemisphere is tilted away from the Sun. The Sun's rays strike the Earth at a lower angle, as shown in Fig. 23.1.8. This means that the energy from the Sun is spread out over a larger area, which reduces its effectiveness at heating that location on Earth.

Along with shorter daylight hours, the temperatures are cooler in winter. In the Northern Hemisphere, winter begins in December.

Summer

In the summer, the Northern Hemisphere tilts toward the Sun. It is warmer because there are more hours of daylight, providing us with more heat energy. As shown in Fig. 23.1.8, the midday sun shines more directly on the location, increasing the amount of solar energy the Earth receives. In the Northern Hemisphere, summer begins in June.

The seasons in the Northern and Southern Hemispheres are opposite.

At the equator, the Sun's rays are always direct. As a result, temperatures at the equator are always high and constant.

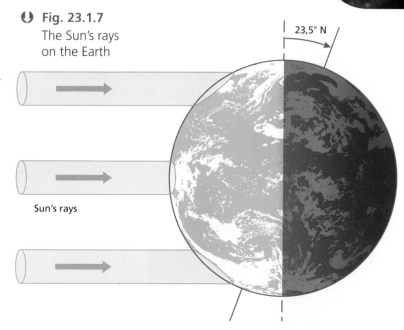

◔ Fig. 23.1.7
The Sun's rays on the Earth

Sun's rays

23,5° N

Winter

Summer

◑ Fig. 23.1.8
The angles the Sun's rays hit Ireland at in midwinter and midsummer

What season is it in the North Pole?

Using Fig 23.1.6, work out the time of year in the North Pole when it is:
   a. Daylight for 24 hours.   b. Night-time for 24 hours.

Explaining the seasons

Design a model of the Sun and the Earth that can be used to explain how seasons happen.

Use this model to explain why temperatures and number of daylight hours differ in summer and winter.

The Earth and the Moon

Key Words

Lunar phases
Eclipse
Solar eclipse
Lunar eclipse
Umbra
Penumbra

Learning Intentions

In this topic we are learning to:
- Outline the phases of the Moon.
- Describe how eclipses occur.
- Distinguish between solar and lunar eclipses.

🔊 **Fig. 23.2.1**
The surface of the Moon

The Moon orbits the Earth once every 27 days. It also rotates on its own axis once every 27 days.

The Moon is smaller than the Earth, so its gravitational field is less. Its gravity is one-sixth that of the Earth's gravity.

As the gravity on the Moon is less, all gas particles have escaped. This means that the Moon does not have an atmosphere.

The Moon is covered in craters that are believed to have been caused by large rocks from space crashing onto its surface.

It is important to remember:
- Planets orbit stars. The Sun is a star.
- Moons orbit planets.
- Moons, planets and stars all rotate around their axes.

Examining craters

Plan, design, carry out and write up an investigation to find out what factors change the size and shape of a crater formed when an object, for example a rock or a ball, falls onto a surface such as sand or flour.

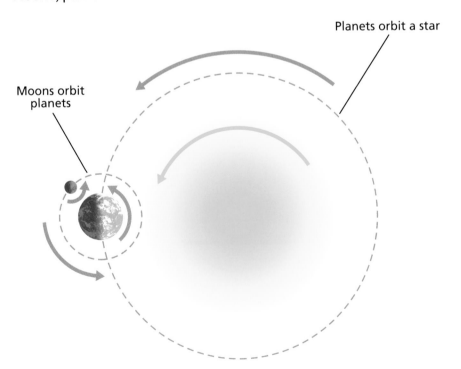

Planets orbit a star

Moons orbit planets

🔊 **Fig. 23.2.2**
How the Earth, Sun and Moon orbit and rotate

Phases of the Moon

The Moon is non-luminous. We can see the Moon because sunlight reflects off its surface towards us.

The same side of the Moon faces us all the time, but it is not always lit by sunlight.

On Earth it looks like the Moon is changing shape, but the Moon orbits the Earth and this changes the amount of reflected light that we see. These changes are known as **lunar phases**.

A lunar phase is the shape of the illuminated part of the Moon as seen on Earth.

Lunar phases repeat over a period of time, which allows us to predict the type of moon we will see.

> ### Fun Fact
>
> The Sea of Tranquility is on the Moon. But it is not a sea as we know it. It is, in fact, a lunar mare. This is a large, dark area that was formed by ancient volcanic eruptions. These areas were called a mare (Latin for 'sea') by early astronomers who mistook them for seas.

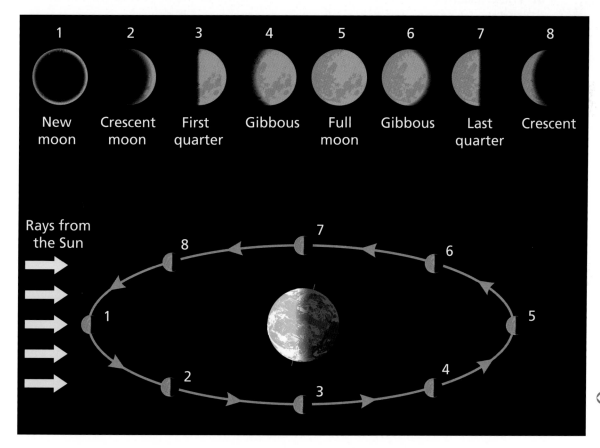

↻ Fig. 23.2.3
The phases of the Moon

1. At new moon, the Moon is lined up between the Earth and the Sun. We see the side of the Moon that is not being lit by the Sun.

2. As the Moon moves eastwards away from the Sun, we see a bit more of the sunlit side of the Moon each night on Earth. A few days after a new moon, we see a thin crescent in the sky.

3. The crescent moon waxes. This means it appears to grow each night. When half of the Moon's disc is illuminated, we call it the first quarter moon. This name comes from the fact that the Moon is now one-quarter of the way through the lunar month.

4. The Moon continues to wax. As soon as more than half of the disc is illuminated, its shape is referred to as gibbous. The gibbous moon appears to grow each night until we see the full sunlit face of the Moon.

5. When the Moon is on the far side of the Earth, the side of the Moon we see is totally lit up. This is known as a full moon.

6. During the second half of the lunar month, the Moon grows thinner each night. This is called waning. Its shape is still gibbous at this point, but grows a little thinner each night.

7. As it approaches a new moon again, the Moon is a waning quarter.

8. The crescent wanes until we can again see none of the lit part of the Moon and the phase starts again with a new moon.

The phases of the Moon are usually included on calendars.

> **Fun Fact**
>
> A 'blue' moon happens when there are two full moons in one calendar month. It happens about once every three years.

Eclipses

An **eclipse** happens when the light of the Sun is blocked by the Moon or the Earth.

A **solar eclipse** happens when the Moon comes between the Sun and the Earth and causes a shadow to fall on the Earth's surface. At the time of total eclipse, only the flames of the outer edge of the Sun can be seen.

➲ **Fig. 23.2.4**
How a solar eclipse happens

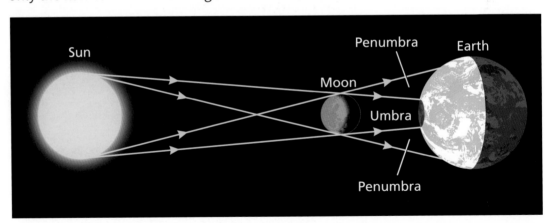

A **lunar eclipse** happens when the Earth's shadow falls on the Moon.

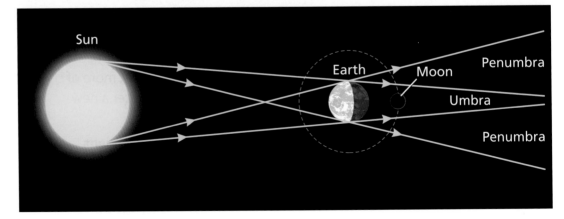

➲ **Fig. 23.2.5**
How a lunar eclipse happens

There are two types of shadows during an eclipse: an **umbra** and a **penumbra**.

The umbra is the darkest part of the shadow. If you are standing in the umbra, the source of light is completely blocked by the object causing the shadow.

A penumbra occurs when the light source is only partly blocked and there is a partial shadow.

Eclipses do not occur every month because the Earth, Moon and Sun do not always line up exactly. Lunar eclipses can be seen much more often than solar eclipses.

Fun Fact

The Ancient Chinese thought a solar eclipse was a demon eating the Sun.

When will the next solar and lunar eclipses happen?

Find out the dates that the next lunar and solar eclipses can be seen from where you live.

Observing Eclipses

We must never look directly at the Sun. When observing an eclipse, we need to protect our eyes. Sunglasses will not provide sufficient protection during an eclipse.

The Sun's ultraviolet (UV) radiation can burn the retinas in our eyes, leading to permanent damage or even blindness. This can happen even if your eyes are exposed to direct sunlight for a few seconds.

GO Learn more about UV radiation in Biological World 4.3

⟴ **Fig. 23.2.6**
A solar eclipse

Looking at solar eclipses safely

Investigate how solar eclipses can be viewed safely. List three precautions that should be taken when viewing a solar eclipse. Ensure the information you use is from a reliable source.

Chapter Summary

- Light is a form of energy that we get from the Sun.
- A luminous object transforms and gives out its own light.
- Light travels in straight lines. This is how shadows are caused.
- Transparent means that light can pass through with no shadows formed.
- Translucent means only some light is allowed to pass through and forms a very light shadow.
- Opaque means that no light can pass through and shadows are formed.
- Day and night are caused by the Earth spinning on its own axis.
- A season is a division of the year. It is marked by changes in the weather and by the number of hours of daylight.
- The different seasons occur because the Earth is tilted at an angle of 23.5°.
- The Earth revolves around the Sun and the North Pole always points in the same direction.
- The Moon is smaller than the Earth, so its gravitational field is less.

- The Moon orbits the Earth once every 27 days. It also rotates on its own axis once every 27 days.
- The Moon does not give off its own light. We see the Moon because sunlight reflects off its surface towards us.
- A lunar phase is the shape of the illuminated part of the Moon as seen on Earth.
- An eclipse can happen when the light of the Sun becomes blocked by the Moon or Earth.
- A solar eclipse happens when the Moon comes between the Sun and the Earth and causes a shadow to fall on the Earth's surface.
- A lunar eclipse happens when the Earth's shadow falls on the Moon.
- The umbra is the darkest part of the shadow.
- A penumbra happens when the light source is only partly blocked and there is a partial shadow.

The BIG Challenge

Keep a logbook of the lunar phases you observe. This report should contain the following information: date, observation and a sketch or picture of what the Moon looks like.

You should:

- Start this project at the beginning of the lunar phase (i.e. the new moon). Find out when the next new moon is.
- Go outside every night at the same time to look at the Moon. Take pictures of what you observe.
- Keep a log for 29 nights so that you can see the entire cycle of the Moon. You will most likely miss a few nights due to cloud cover – keep notes on how the weather changes what the Moon looks like or if it makes it disappear altogether.

Go to your Portfolio to check what you have learned in this chapter.

Take the chapter 23 quiz on educateplus.ie.

Questions

1. Copy and fill in the blanks.

    a. The Sun is the _____ around which the Earth _____. A star is _____ as it makes and gives out its own _____.

    b. Light travels in _____ lines. _____ are evidence that light travels in _____ lines.

    c. An object is described as _____ if light cannot pass through it.

    d. An _____ is an imaginary line on which the Earth _____.

    e. The effect of _____ is less on the Moon than on the Earth.

    f. The Moon does not give off its own _____. The Moon can be seen as _____ is _____ off it.

    g. A solar eclipse happens when the _____ comes between the _____ and the _____.

    h. A lunar eclipse happens when the _____ comes between the _____ and the _____.

    i. The darkest part of a shadow is called the _____.

    j. _____ eclipses can be seen much more often than _____ eclipses.

2. Copy and complete the sentences using a time from the following list: 12 hours, 24 hours, one week, 27 days, six months, one year.

    a. The Moon moves around the Earth once every _____.

    b. The Earth spins on its own axis once every _____.

    c. The Earth moves around the Sun once every _____.

3. How would the Earth's seasons differ if:

    a. The Earth was not tilted?

    b. The Earth turned more slowly on its axis?

4. The shadows created during the summer and the winter differ from each other. Explain this difference using diagrams.

5. In relation to lunar phases, explain the terms waxing and waning.

6. Using a diagram or a model, explain the difference between a lunar and a solar eclipse.

7. During an eclipse, it is dangerous to look at the Sun directly. Create a safety information brochure for the general public that could be handed out before the next eclipse.

8. Copy and complete the crossword.

Across

    4. Imaginary line around which the Earth rotates (4)

    5. Term used to describe something that makes and gives out its own light (8)

    6. Light cannot pass through an object (6)

    7. Location of the Sea of Tranquillity (4)

    8. The nearest star to the Earth (3)

    9. Occurs when the Earth's shadow falls on the Moon (5, 7)

   12. Time taken for the Earth to orbit the Sun (4)

Down

    1. The lunar phase when none of the illuminated side of the Moon can be seen (3, 4)

    2. Something that the Moon does not have (10)

    3. Winter, spring, summer and autumn (7)

   10. The darkest part of a shadow (5)

   11. Time taken for the Earth to rotate once on its own axis (3)

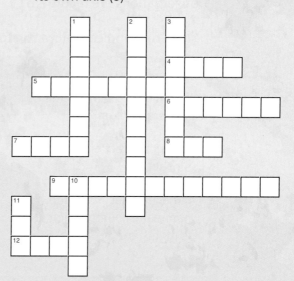

Working as a Scientist

Making and Recording Observations

Modelling the Earth, Sun and Moon

Develop a model of the Earth, Sun and Moon using a light bulb, a small globe and a golf ball and use the model to carry out the investigations that follow. During the investigations make and record observations that would explain different occurrences that happen on Earth, such as the seasons.

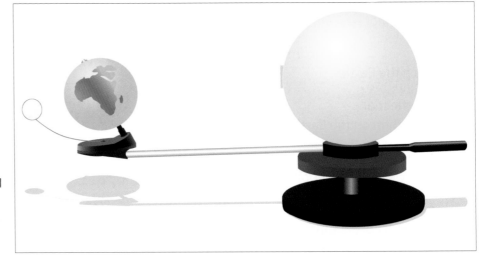

⬤ Fig. 23.4.1
Model of
the Moon,
Earth and
Sun

When constructing your model, remember:

- The Earth orbits the Sun in an anticlockwise direction.
- The Moon orbits the Earth in an anticlockwise direction.
- The Earth, Sun and Moon all rotate on their own axes.
- The Earth is tilted on its axis by approximately 23.5°. (Hint: the Earth rotates on its own axis in an anticlockwise direction.)

Night and Day

Use your model to explain night and day. Use Ireland as the point from where observations are recorded.

1 **Copy and complete the following table.**

Question	Observation	Conclusion
Which direction does the Sun appear from?		
In which direction does the Sun set?		
If it is daytime in Ireland, name one country where it is night-time		

Seasons

Use the model to gather information about the seasons. It is important to remember:

- It takes the Earth 365.25 days to orbit the Sun.
- The Earth rotates on its own axis every 24 hours.
- The North Pole always stays in the same position.

2 Copy and complete the following table.

Question	Observation	Conclusion
Name a country experiencing summer if Ireland is experiencing winter		
Use the model to find out if days are longer or shorter in the summer		
At what time of the year is there 24 hours of daylight at the North Pole?		

3 Use your model to explain why the equator has a similar climate all year round. How did the model explain this? Sketch your answer.

4 Provide an answer for each question in the following table based on what you have observed using the model.

Question	Observation	Conclusion
How would the Earth's seasons differ if the Earth was not tilted?		
How would the Earth's seasons differ if the Earth was closer to the Sun?		

Eclipses

Using this model, or one that you have created yourself, explore what an eclipse is. Remember:

- A solar eclipse occurs when the Moon comes between the Sun and the Earth.
- A lunar eclipse occurs when the Earth comes between the Sun and the Moon.

5 Copy and complete the following table.

Question	Observation
During a solar eclipse, what is observed from Earth?	
During a lunar eclipse, what is observed from Earth?	
During a lunar eclipse, what is observed from the Moon?	

Sources of Energy

What you may already know:

- There are wind farms in Ireland.
- At present, there are no nuclear power stations in Ireland.
- Calculators and even some cars can run on solar power.

What you will learn in this chapter:

- How fossil fuels generate energy.
- Renewable energy sources.
- Nuclear power is a possible energy source for the future.
- Future technology and materials.

Think BIG

- Will we ever run out of energy?
- Why don't people live in Chernobyl any more?

Puzzler

Can you crack the code?

Can you crack this code to reveal a quote by a famous figure in global energy.

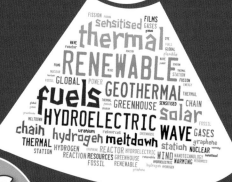

a	e	w	r	s
#	!	?	@	&

I think th! co&t of !n!@gy ?ill com! do?n ?h!n ?!

___ ___ ___ __ _____ ____ ____ ____ ___

m#k! thi& t@#n&ition to @!n!?#bl! !n!@gy

_____ ____ _____ __ _____ _____ #l Go@!

__ ____

Our Current Energy Needs

Fossil Fuels

We know that energy comes from a chemical reaction and that any substance that burns in oxygen to produce heat is a fuel.

We use energy for many things – to heat our homes, cook our food and run our cars. The energy for these things mostly comes from the chemical energy stored in fossil fuels.

Fossil fuels were formed millions of years ago from the remains of plants and animals.

Fossil fuels are **non-renewable** sources of energy. This means that they will eventually run out.

Coal, oil and natural gas are fossil fuels.

Powering with Fossil Fuels

Power stations can burn coal, oil or gas to generate electricity. We will look at how a coal-fired power station works.

1. When the coal burns, it heats water. This produces steam.

2. The steam is forced through pipes and has a large amount of kinetic energy. It transfers the kinetic energy to a turbine, which in turn spins a generator.

3. The generator converts the kinetic energy into electricity. This electricity is sent to homes via power lines.

4. Once the steam has been used to turn the turbines, it loses energy and turns back into water. It is then recycled back to the start to be reheated.

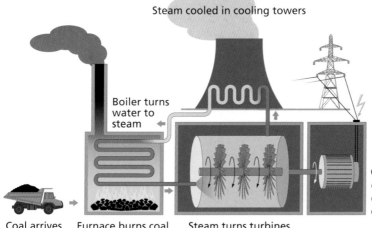

Steam cooled in cooling towers

Boiler turns water to steam

Generator converts kinetic energy to electrical energy

Coal arrives Furnace burns coal Steam turns turbines

Key Words

Fossil fuels
Non-renewable
Renewable
Wind
Solar
Hydroelectric
Geothermal
Wave
Biofuels

From Moneypoint to your home $1 2^3$

⬤ Fig. 24.1.1
Moneypoint power station

Moneypoint in County Clare is a coal-fired power station. It is the largest electricity generation station in Ireland.

Using what you learned in Physical World 16.2, draw an energy transfer diagram to show the useful energy transfers between the coal that powers Moneypoint and a hairdryer plugged in at your home.

↺ Fig. 24.1.2
A coal-fired power station

413

Renewable Energy

Renewable energy sources are sources that will not run out. As fossil fuels decline, it is important that we research and use alternative energy sources.

The following table describes renewable sources and the energy change that takes place when they are used.

	Renewable source	Method	Energy change
Fig. 24.1.3 A wind farm uses the kinetic energy from wind to turn turbines and generate electricity	Wind energy	Wind turbines turn generators to produce electricity	Kinetic → electricity
Fig. 24.1.4 Solar power plants can use mirrored panels to track the Sun's movement, maximising the amount of light converted to electricity	Solar energy	Solar cells generate electricity from sunlight	Light → electricity
Fig. 24.1.5 Hoover Dam in Arizona, USA, converts the kinetic energy of the water into electricity	Hydroelectric power	A body of water is held behind a dam. When the dam is opened, the water transfers its potential energy to kinetic energy as it falls through openings in the wall of the dam. This turns turbines and generates electricity	Potential → kinetic → electricity

Fig. 24.1.6 A geothermal power station takes heat from the Earth's core to heat steam and turn turbines	**Geothermal** energy	Pipes are placed into the ground to absorb the heat from the rocks in the Earth. This heat is used to generate steam to turn turbines	Heat → kinetic → electricity
Fig. 24.1.7 A Pelamis is a device that converts the energy from ocean waves into electricity	**Wave** energy	When ocean waves crash against a machine called a Pelamis, their kinetic energy is converted to electricity	Kinetic → electricity
Fig. 24.1.8 Miscanthus, also known as elephant grass, being grown as a biofuel	Biomass	Plants are burned as a fuel source in power stations. Cars may run on the **biofuels** created from such plants; for example, biodiesel and bioethanol. These fuels can also be produced from other biological materials, including algae and faeces	Chemical → heat → kinetic → electricity

Although the energies listed in the table above are renewable, they are not entirely free of carbon emissions. The energy needed to build these devices and plant biomass crops produce a certain amount of carbon dioxide.

 GO Learn more about types of energy in Physical World 16.1

Debating renewable energy

Renewable energy sources make us less dependent on fossil fuels. However, these energy sources can also have an impact on the environment.

1. In groups, create posters on the environmental impact of one of the following:
   - Wind farms in Ireland.
   - River damming in China.
   - Building solar cells.
2. Present your findings to the class.

Nuclear Energy

Key Words

Energy crisis
Nuclear power
Uranium
Fission
Nuclear reactor
Radioactive
Chain reaction
Fusion
Hydrogen

Learning Intentions

In this topic we are learning to:

- Evaluate the global energy crisis.
- Distinguish between nuclear fission and fusion.

Our world is facing a shortage in energy supply. This is known as an **energy crisis**. A growing global population and new technology mean that we rely on electricity even more.

Energy and impacts

Research and discuss some of the social and economic effects of society's growing energy demands.

Nuclear Power

One alternative source of energy is **nuclear power**. Nuclear power has a number of advantages over fossil fuels and renewable sources:

- It does not add to climate change or air pollution.
- Nuclear power sources last for a very long time and contain a huge amount of nuclear energy. They currently produce far more energy than any renewable sources or fossil fuels.
- The quantity of waste generated from nuclear power plants is small. However, the disposal of this small quantity of waste causes concerns.

Nuclear power comes from releasing the energy that binds particles together in the nucleus of an atom. There are two ways of producing energy from the nucleus:

1. Nuclear fission
2. Nuclear fusion.

Nuclear Fission

A fuel source for nuclear power is an isotope of the element **uranium**.

When the large nucleus of the uranium atom is bombarded with neutrons, it splits into two almost equal parts. This splitting is called **fission**.

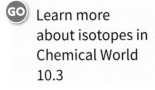

GO Learn more about isotopes in Chemical World 10.3

⊃ **Fig. 24.2.1** Nuclear fission

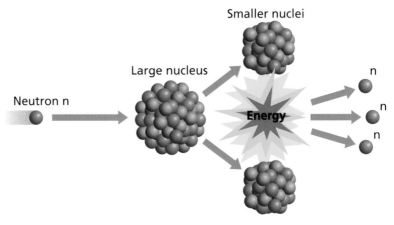

Smaller nuclei

Large nucleus

Neutron n

Energy

n

n

n

Nuclear fission converts its nuclear energy into huge quantities of heat energy. A **nuclear reactor** uses this heat to make steam. The steam then turns turbines to generate electricity.

Problems with Nuclear Fission

- Uranium needs to be mined from the ground as an ore. This activity is expensive and dangerous.
- The waste from uranium is **radioactive**. Radiation can cause mutations in DNA.

GO Learn more about mutation and radiation in Biological World 4.3

- Radioactive material decays very slowly. This means it can continue to cause harm for thousands of years.
- The splitting of a uranium isotope causes the release of more neutrons, which can cause further fission. This type of reaction is known as a **chain reaction**. If a nuclear chain reaction gets out of control, it can cause a large explosion. An uncontrolled chain reaction is the source of energy for an atomic bomb.

◖ Fig. 24.2.2
Uranium, the fuel for nuclear fission

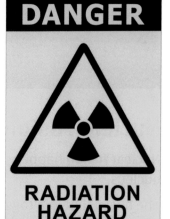

DANGER

RADIATION HAZARD

◖ Fig. 24.2.3
Radioactive hazard symbol

People and Science

In 1938, German scientists **Fritz Strassman** and **Otto Hahn** discovered nuclear fission by firing neutrons at uranium nuclei. They were the first people to realise that the atom could be split into smaller parts.

Lise Meitner, an Austrian physicist, was also part of this team. Her part in the discovery was overlooked because she was Jewish. Although she had no hand in the making of it, she became known as 'the mother of the atomic bomb'.

◖ Fig. 24.2.4
Lise Meitner and Otto Hahn in the laboratory

Isotope versus element **1 2 3**

The isotope of uranium used for nuclear fission has a mass number of 235 and an atomic number of 92. Calculate how many neutrons are contained in a nucleus of this isotope. Compare this number with the number of neutrons in a nucleus of the most common isotope of uranium on the periodic table.

⬅ **Fig. 24.2.5**
A mushroom cloud produced by an atomic bomb

Nuclear Fusion

Nuclear **fusion** happens when two smaller nuclei combine to form a large nucleus.

The nuclei that join together are isotopes of the element **hydrogen**. When they fuse, they create a new nucleus and release a very large quantity of energy.

Fun Fact

The Sun is powered by a nuclear fusion reaction taking place in its core.

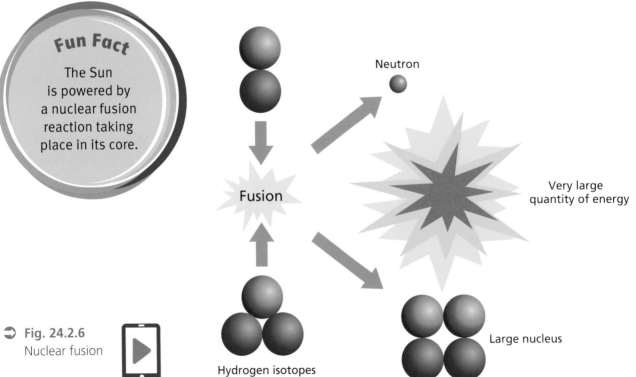

Neutron

Very large quantity of energy

Fusion

Large nucleus

Hydrogen isotopes

⬅ **Fig. 24.2.6**
Nuclear fusion

Advantages of Nuclear Fusion

Fusion has a number of advantages over fission as a source of nuclear power:

- There is more energy produced in a fusion reaction than is produced in a fission reaction.
- The hydrogen isotopes can be sourced easily from the ocean. They are not harmful. The nuclei created by fusion are not harmful.
- There is no possibility of an uncontrolled chain reaction.

Hydrogen isotopes need to be heated to a very high temperature to cause them to fuse. For this reason it has not yet been possible to develop a fusion reactor that can be used on a wide scale. If this technology can be developed, nuclear fusion could be the answer to our energy crisis.

Fun Fact

The International Thermonuclear Experimental Reactor (ITER) project began in 2007 with the aim of building the world's largest experimental fusion reactor in Cadarache, France. It is expected to begin fully functioning fusion reactions in 2027. So far it has cost over $50 billion to develop.

Everyday meaning

Find out the everyday meaning of the words fission and fusion. See if you can identify a link between their everyday meaning and their use in physics.

Hydrogen

1. The isotopes of hydrogen that are used for nuclear fusion have mass numbers of 2 and 3. Calculate how many neutrons are contained in the nuclei of these isotopes. Compare this with the number of neutrons in a nucleus of the most common isotope of hydrogen on the periodic table.

2. When the two isotopes of hydrogen involved in fusion react, they combine to create one large nucleus. Work out the number of protons and neutrons in this new nucleus. Using the periodic table, name this newly produced nucleus.

Nuclear or not?

Imagine you are an adviser to the Irish government. Write a summary for the Taoiseach with the title 'The pros and cons of building a nuclear power plant in Ireland'.

Smart Technologies

Key Words

Flexible films
Dye-sensitised
  material
Nanotechnology
Graphene

Learning Intentions

In this topic we are learning to:
- Consider future sources of renewable energy.

Although renewable energy works in harmony with the planet, it is not very cost-effective and currently only meets a small amount of our energy needs.

Scientists are coming up with new and exciting ways of making renewable energy more productive.

Improved Solar Power

Solar power is energy from the Sun. Solar cells convert light energy into electrical energy.

You have probably seen solar cells on the roofs of houses and even on top of some parking meters, road signs and bus shelters. Small solar cells can be found on calculators, while huge solar cells are used to power some satellites that orbit Earth.

Scientists have now made solar cells that are thinner and more flexible than the rigid, black solar cells you may have seen.

These new cells are developed on **flexible films** and contain **dye-sensitised material**.

Advantages of the new cells:
- They are 30 per cent more efficient than typical solar cells.
- They can be easily placed on curved surfaces. In the future they may be placed on cars, on the windows of curved buildings and even on clothing.

Today, almost one-fifth of the world's solar power is generated by these new solar cells.

Scientists are researching other ways to use solar energy, such as solar-powered road panels and solar power plants in space.

Fig. 24.3.1
A typical solar cell

Fig. 24.3.2
New flexible solar cells

Fig. 24.3.3
Objects on the nanoscale

Nanotechnology

Nanotechnology is the science of the very small. The nanoscale accounts for anything that is smaller than 1 nanometre (one-thousandth millionth of a metre).

Nanotechnology is one of the most exciting areas of scientific research. It may be possible to use nanotechnology to:
- Make batteries and solar cells more efficient.
- Build more sturdy, corrosion-proof and lightweight devices. For example, stronger and lighter wind turbine blades.

Strand of DNA
= 2.5 nanometres

Diameter of a red blood cell
= 6,000–8,000 nanometres

Head of a pin
= 1,000,000 nanometres

- Produce new devices that cost less to make and need less energy. Matter at the nanoscale displays new properties. For example, carbon can be broken down into a sheet that is one atom thick, known as **graphene**. This material is very strong, ultra-thin and can conduct large electric currents. Clear plastic coated in graphene can conduct electricity and still remain transparent. This could be used for touchscreen devices.

↻ **Fig. 24.3.4**
Transparent phones may be possible in the future thanks to graphene

Fun Fact

Your fingernails grow a nanometre every second. How long would it take your fingernails to grow 1 cm?

People and Science

In 2010, **Andre Geim** and **Konstantin Novoselov**, scientists at the University of Manchester, were awarded the Nobel Prize in Physics for isolating graphene from the same material as found in the lead of a pencil. They used normal sticky tape to pull the thin layers from a piece of graphite. They repeated this method on the thin sheets of graphite until they had a single sheet of graphene.

🎧 **Fig. 24.3.5**
Konstantin Novoselov and Andre Geim in their laboratory

Creating graphene

Using your own pencils and sticky tape, how thin a piece of graphite can you collect? Maybe you can get to the Nobel level of graphene!

Nano – good or bad?

While nanotechnology clearly has benefits, there are concerns about its impact on living things. This is partly because the nanoparticles involved are so small they could pass into cells and cause damage to health.

Research and create an evidence-based presentation on the pros and cons of nanotechnology. Present your findings to your classmates.

Chapter Summary

- A coal-fired power station burns fossil fuels to produce electricity.

- Our energy needs are mostly being met by fossil fuels such as coal, oil and gas. These are non-renewable. This means that they will eventually run out.

- Renewable energy sources will not run out. Examples of renewable energy sources include wind, solar, hydroelectric, geothermal, biomass and wave energy.

- Nuclear power comes from releasing the energy that binds particles together in the nucleus of an atom. There are two ways of producing energy from the nucleus: nuclear fission and nuclear fusion.

- Nuclear fission is the splitting of a large nucleus into two smaller nuclei with the release of a large quantity of energy. This is used in a nuclear power station to generate electricity.

- Nuclear fusion occurs when two smaller nuclei combine to form a single larger nucleus, releasing a very large quantity of energy.

- Nanotechnology is the science of the very small.

- Graphene is a material that is very strong, ultra-thin and can conduct large electric currents.

The **BIG** Challenge

There is an ongoing 'food versus fuel' debate. Should land be used to grow biofuel crops instead of being used to grow food crops that could feed people in underdeveloped parts of the world?

Research this issue and prepare a speech for your classmates titled 'My views on the "food versus fuel" debate'.

Go to your Portfolio to check what you have learned in this chapter.

Take the chapter 24 quiz on educateplus.ie.

Questions

1. Copy and fill in the blanks:

    a. Energy sources that are ▭ ▭ will eventually run out.

    b. Fossil fuels include ▭, ▭ and ▭.

    c. A ▭ energy source is one that will never run out.

    d. Due to a growing global ▭ and new ▭, the world faces an ▭ crisis.

    e. Plants burned as an energy source are called ▭.

    f. Hydroelectric power converts the ▭ energy of the water behind a dam into ▭ energy. This turns a ▭, which generates electricity.

    g. ▭ power comes from releasing the ▭ that binds particles together in the nucleus of an atom.

    h. Nuclear ▭ is when a ▭ splits into two smaller ▭ and releases energy. This is used in a nuclear power station to generate electricity.

    i. Nuclear ▭ is when two smaller ▭ combine into a large ▭, releasing very large amounts of energy.

    j. ▭ is the science of the very small.

2. Draw a renewable energy sources mind map. Include the types of energy sources involved and the energy conversions taking place.

3. Compare the generation of electricity in a nuclear power station with the generation of electricity in a coal-fired power station. Use diagrams to illustrate your answer.

4. Copy and complete the following table:

Energy type	Original source	Advantages	Disadvantages
Hydroelectric			
Solar			
Geothermal			
Wind			
Wave			

5. At which times of the year in Ireland are our demands for energy greatest? Why?

6. The following pie chart shows the electricity demands for a country using different energy resources.

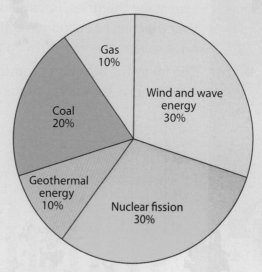

    a. What is the percentage of electricity generated from wind and wave energy?

    b. What percentage of the overall energy is being met by renewable resources?

    c. What is the percentage of electricity generated using a source that produces nuclear waste?

    d. What is the percentage of electricity generated by sources that directly use kinetic energy?

7. Compare fission and fusion as nuclear power sources under the headings: Inputs, Outputs, Energy produced and Hazards.

8. Research the nuclear disasters of Chernobyl in 1986 and Fukushima in 2011. Note the causes of the disaster, what the immediate and after effects were and what the long-term effects were or may be. Write an evidence-based report.

Working as a Scientist

Presenting and Analysing Data

Our Past and Future Energy Needs

Like many countries, Ireland has seen a big increase in its energy demands in recent years. Increased economic activity, a growing population and greater urbanisation have caused this growth in energy use.

The following bar chart produced by the Sustainable Energy Authority of Ireland (SEAI) shows the energy requirements in Ireland by fuel type from 1990 to 2013.

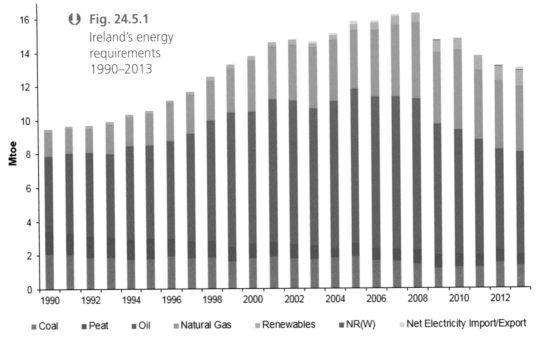

ⓘ Fig. 24.5.1 Ireland's energy requirements 1990–2013

■ Coal   ■ Peat   ■ Oil   ■ Natural Gas   ■ Renewables   ■ NR(W)   ■ Net Electricity Import/Export

NR(W) = Non-renewable energy from wastes

An important part of analysing data is to recognise patterns and relationships. In this case, the data is presented in a bar chart and shows energy requirements from different sources against time. The energy use is measured in millions of tonnes of oil equivalent (Mtoe) and the time is displayed in years. When we identify trends, we aim to represent them using simple statements called 'evidence-based statements'.

1 State whether or not the following statements are justified by this data.

   a. The quantity of energy generated from renewable fuels has increased from 1990 to 2013.

   b. Oil and natural gas make up the largest proportion of the energy requirement.

   c. Coal provided a larger proportion of Ireland's energy requirement in 2013 than it did in 1990.

   d. The energy generated from peat has declined steadily from 1990 to 2013.

2 Calculate the difference in Ireland's total energy demand between 1990 and 2013.

3 Suggest why there might be such a large difference in energy demands.

4 Which fuel type seems to be showing the biggest growth in demand from 2000 onwards? Suggest why this may be the case.

5 The quantity of energy generated by peat has declined steadily. Suggest two reasons to explain this trend.

The bar chart in Fig. 24.5.1 is based on data that was collected between 1990 and 2013. This is known as baseline data. This data provides a basis for comparison with projections of future energy requirements.

The SEAI have collected further data that predicts our future energy demand and the sources that will meet it. The table below shows their projections for the period 2009–2020.

Fuel	Total primary energy supply (million tonnes of oil equivalent)		
	2009	**2016**	**2020**
Coal	1.214	1.397	1.256
Oil	7.745	7.984	8.245
Gas	4.309	4.394	5.243
Peat	0.856	0.723	0.507
Renewables	0.665	1.184	1.196
Electricity imports	0.066	−0.098	−0.298
Total	**14.855**	**15.584**	**16.149**

6 Based on this data:

    a. Which fuel will show the biggest growth in energy supply from 2009 to 2020?

    b. Which fuel will show the biggest decrease in growth over this period?

    c. Which fossil fuel will show the biggest increase in growth over this period?

    d. Calculate the average percentage growth per year for each of the fuels.

A manufacturing company is considering relocating its business to Ireland. It is part of company policy to invest in renewable energies. As a team, you and your classmates have been tasked with advising them on the advantages and disadvantages of relocating to Ireland.

7 Produce a summary for this company, based on the data, to include the following:

    a. The story of Ireland and its energy demand from 1990 onwards.

    b. Data presented in an appropriate way that shows the major trends in the use of different energy sources over this period.

    c. The future of energy supplies in Ireland. Identify current and future trends for energy supply from the different sources.

It might be helpful to compare the data from 1990 to 2020 on one bar chart and to draw trend lines along the data. It might also be helpful to produce a number of evidence-based statements about the use of renewables compared with the other energy sources during this time period.

8 Would you advise the company to relocate? Write a concluding paragraph in your report, identifying at least two evidence-based statements why the company should or should not relocate to Ireland.

A Sustainable World

What you may already know:

- The Earth is home to many different species that all need energy and raw materials.
- Humans influence the Earth in many ways, both positive and negative.

What you will learn in this chapter:

- How some human behaviours negatively affect the Earth.
- What we can do to protect the planet's resources and species.

Think BIG

- Will the human species ever become extinct?
- How can we make sure that the needs of today's society are met without risking the survival of future generations?

Puzzler

Can you solve this puzzle?

Use the pictures to work out a key term that you will come across in this chapter.

The Growth of the Human Population

Learning Intentions

In this topic we are learning to:

- Recognise that humans are a relatively new species.
- Appreciate the significance of the huge explosion in the human population over the last 300 years.

Key Words

Human population

Scientists believe humans have lived on Earth for 200,000 years. Given that the first organisms appeared on Earth 3,800 million years ago, humans are quite a new species.

For many years, the number of humans stayed low and fairly constant. Within the last 300 years there has been a huge increase in the **human population**. This is because we have better access to food, clean water, medicine and energy sources.

Billions of people

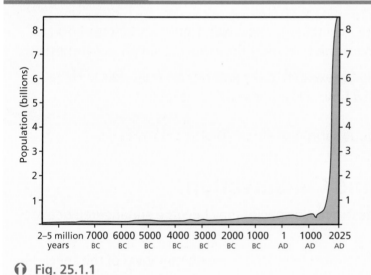

○ **Fig. 25.1.1**
The growth of the human population

1. Using Fig. 25.1.1, estimate:
   a. How long it took the human population to reach one billion.
   b. After reaching one billion, estimate how long it took for the human population to increase to two billion, then three billion and so on.

2. Research today's global population. Cite your source clearly.

3. What do these figures suggest about the rate of growth of the human species?

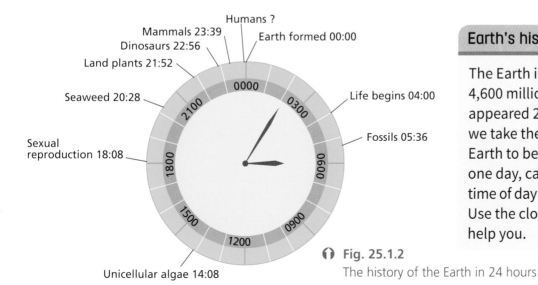

○ **Fig. 25.1.2**
The history of the Earth in 24 hours

Earth's history in 24 hours

The Earth is approximately 4,600 million years old. Humans appeared 200,000 years ago. If we take the entire history of the Earth to be represented by just one day, can you estimate the time of day that humans evolved? Use the clock in Fig. 25.1.2 to help you.

Human Impact on the Earth

Key Words

Deforestation
Extinct
Conservation
Pollution
Desertification
Enrichment
Littering
Greenhouse gases
Greenhouse effect
Global warming
Climate change
Acid rain

Learning Intentions

In this topic we are learning to:

• Describe human behaviours that damage the Earth.

• Consider pollution from agricultural, industrial and domestic sources.

The fast growth of the human population has affected the Earth in many ways.

Deforestation

Deforestation is when large areas of forest are destroyed to make way for non-forest use, such as farmland, housing and roads.

For example, in the Amazon rainforest a huge number of trees are being cut down to make way for housing, farmland and for the export of timber. When trees are cut down, species that live in the area lose their habitat.

Deforestation has a number of negative effects:

• Overgrazing with sheep, cattle or goats leads to an increased rate of soil erosion.

• After trees are removed, there are fewer producers to return oxygen to the atmosphere and remove carbon dioxide via photosynthesis.

• The opportunity to research many natural raw materials and the potential for new products and medicines is lost.

○ Fig. 25.2.1
A large field to grow crops cut out of the Amazon rainforest

GO Learn more about habitat studies in Biological World 6.5

Extinction and Conservation

When a habitat is destroyed, a species may become endangered or even **extinct**.

An animal or plant is extinct when there are no members of the species left alive.

Endangered animals and plants are under threat of extinction. In Ireland, otters, the lesser horseshoe bat and cornflowers are among the most endangered species.

○ Fig. 25.2.2
Otters are under threat of extinction in Ireland

As dead as a dodo

The dodo was a large flightless bird that nested on the ground and lived in Mauritius in the Indian Ocean. The dodo had no natural wariness of humans and was easy prey for the sailors that visited Mauritius in the sixteenth century. By the mid- to late-seventeenth century the dodo was extinct.

The dodo is often used as an example of extinction because it became extinct in recent history as a direct result of human activity. The phrase 'as dead as a dodo' is often used to refer to something that is definitely dead.

○ Fig. 25.2.3

Methods of preventing species extinctions include:

- Nature reserves.
- Zoo breeding programmes.
- Seed banks (the storage of seeds to protect biodiversity).

The careful management of the Earth's natural resources to prevent species from becoming extinct is called **conservation**.

Human population and species extinction

In maths, two factors are said to be 'correlated' if the changes in both factors are related. Correlation can be positive or negative. As scientists, it is important to remember that correlation does not always mean causation.

1. Consider the following statements. Which statement has merit?
   - 'I am good at basketball because I am tall.'
   - 'I am tall because I am good at basketball.'
2. Research the relationship between the growth of the human population and species extinctions. Is there a correlation? Is it a causal relationship? Explain your answer.

Pollution

Pollution happens when harmful substances are added to the environment.

The three main sources of pollution are:

1. Agricultural   2. Industrial   3. Domestic

All three sources can pollute air, water and soil.

1. Agricultural Pollution

As the human population grows, more food is needed. This causes a number of problems.

Growing too many crops can damage the soil. This can lead to **desertification**.

Desertification means that the land becomes more arid (dry) and the species that once lived there are lost.

Fertilisers are used to boost the growth of crops. The spreading of fertilisers on farmland can lead to the pollution of soil and water. Fertilisers may also contain chemicals that can poison organisms.

If too much fertiliser is spread, nutrients can be washed off the soil and into nearby rivers and lakes. This is known as **enrichment**.

Enrichment causes a sudden rise in algae (algal bloom):

- The algae stop light entering the water and aquatic plants cannot photosynthesise.
- When the algae die, decomposing bacteria use up the oxygen in the water. As a result, fish and other aquatic plants and animals cannot respire and so die.

○ Fig. 25.2.4
Desertification

○ Fig. 25.2.5
Algal bloom

2. Industrial Pollution

Industry relies very heavily on fossil fuels, such as oil and natural gas.

The burning of fossil fuels releases large quantities of smoke and dust, carbon dioxide, carbon monoxide and lead, which pollute the air. If fossil fuels are not fully burned, smoke particles are released into the air. These particles can combine with fog to form smog over cities.

3. Domestic Pollution

The large quantities of waste produced in highly populated areas is a problem.

Littering is the careless disposal of rubbish. Litter causes a number of problems:

- It can be a health hazard.
- Animals may get caught in it and die.
- It is unsightly.

Waste that flows into rivers and lakes as raw sewage can pollute the water and lead to the death of fish.

The Greenhouse Effect

Greenhouse gases, such as carbon dioxide and methane, act like a blanket, trapping heat from the Sun near the Earth's surface. This is called the **greenhouse effect**.

The carbon dioxide in our atmosphere is increasing. This is mainly caused by the burning of fossil fuels.

The increased greenhouse effect is causing the Earth to become warmer. There is a 0.2–0.5 °C rise in temperature each decade. This is known as **global warming**.

Global warming has a number of effects:

- Earth's weather patterns will change. A change in rainfall will have a bad effect on food production. Wind strength is also expected to increase, leading to more extreme weather. These changing weather patterns are called **climate change**.
- Sea levels will rise due to the melting of ice and the expansion of the oceans as the Earth warms up. This will lead to floods and the loss of farming land.
- The loss of polar ice caps will threaten the existence of species such as polar bears.
- The range of disease-carrying insects may increase, causing major health problems. For example, the mosquito that transmits malaria appears to be moving into new territories.

Less heat escapes into space

The sun heats the earth

Greenhouse gases

🎧 **Fig. 25.2.6**
The greenhouse effect

Rising sea levels

Scientists often use models to help them see patterns and predict the outcome of a situation.

Research the data that scientists would need to collect so they can build models to predict future changes in sea levels.

Discuss how these models could help the government come up with ways to care for our environment.

Acid Rain

Unpolluted rain is slightly acidic (pH 5.5) due to the presence of dissolved carbon dioxide. Some rain is far more acidic (pH 4–5). Rainwater with a pH of less than 5.5 is called **acid rain**.

GO Learn more about the pH scale in Chemical World 13.2

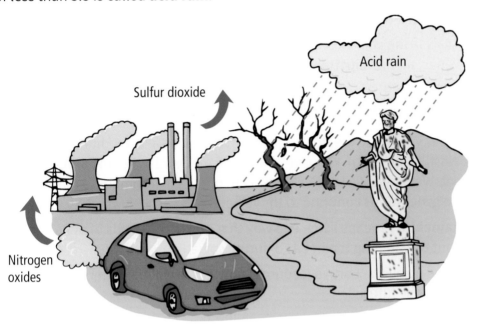

↻ Fig. 25.2.7
How acid rain forms

The burning of fossil fuels, particularly coal, releases sulfur dioxide (SO_2). The burning of fuels in cars releases nitrogen oxides (NO_x) into the air.

These gases dissolve in the air's moisture to form sulfuric acid and nitric acid. This falls back to Earth as acid rain.

Effects of Acid Rain

The main effects of acid rain are:

- It washes minerals such as aluminium out of soil and into lakes and streams, which kills fish.
- It damages buildings and statues, especially those made of limestone.
- It harms leaves, which means trees and plants cannot photosynthesise.

∩ Fig. 25.2.8
A limestone statue worn away by acid rain

Reducing the Effects of Global Warming and Acid Rain

The effects of global warming and acid rain can be reduced in the following ways:

- Use less fossil fuels and use more renewable energy sources, such as solar, wind or hydroelectric energy.
- Reduce the sulfur in fuels such as coal, oil and gas.
- Drive hybrid electric vehicles and install catalytic converters in cars to decrease the harmful emissions from exhaust fumes.
- Plant more trees to return oxygen to the atmosphere and remove carbon dioxide via photosynthesis.

GO Learn more about catalysts in Chemical World 12.4

Meeting the Challenges Facing the Earth

Learning Intentions

In this topic we are learning to:
- Analyse the challenges facing the Earth.
- Reflect on the importance of conserving the Earth's natural resources.
- Demonstrate an awareness that each person and every society must promote sustainability.

Our ability to think, create and problem solve has allowed humans to live successfully on Earth. We have also made many mistakes in caring for our planet. We now have to take better care of the environment to make sure future generations continue to thrive here.

Sustainability means living in a way that meets the needs of our society without threatening the needs of future societies.

If we use up all the Earth's resources now, there will be nothing left for people in the future.

We all have a role to play in sustainability.

◉ **Fig. 25.3.1**
We all have a role to play in looking after the Earth

Waste Management

Waste is any material that has no further use or commercial value. Ireland produces around two million tonnes of waste every year – an average of 0.5 tonnes per person. It is important that we manage this waste carefully to prevent further damage to the environment.

The way that society deals with waste is known as **waste management**.

There are a number of ways of dealing with our waste:

1. Landfill sites
2. Incineration
3. Waste minimisation.

1. Landfill

Ninety per cent of Ireland's domestic waste is dumped in **landfill** sites. Landfill sites are big holes in the ground where waste is buried.

This method of waste disposal creates a number of problems:

- Landfill sites are unsightly and smelly and attract gulls and rats. This can reduce the value of nearby houses.
- Poisonous substances from the waste can leak into the soil and pollute nearby water supplies.
- The rotting rubbish produces methane gas. If pockets of this gas form underground, it can cause an explosion.

◉ **Fig. 25.3.2**
A landfill site

2. Incineration

Incineration is the burning of waste. This method quickly reduces the volume of waste that is sent to landfill sites. However, the burning of materials releases poisonous gases into the air.

3. Waste minimisation

Waste minimisation involves reducing waste at the source. It is often described by the three Rs: reduce, reuse, recycle.

- Reduce the packaging on goods – the government levy on plastic bags is a good example of this. **Composting** reduces the amount of organic waste, such as vegetable peelings, fruit and teabags, sent to landfill.

- Reuse materials when possible. For example, by using glass jars for a different purpose or using 'bags for life'. In industry, sawmills use waste timber to produce materials such as chipboard and plywood.

- Recycle glass, aluminium cans, paper and cardboard.

Fig. 25.3.3
Plywood is made of waste timber

Evaluating impact

Using the description of the various methods of waste disposal, make a list of advantages and disadvantages associated with each method.

Fig. 25.3.4
It is important to recycle our waste

The Waste Management Pyramid

The waste management pyramid illustrates the least favoured to most favoured approaches to waste management.

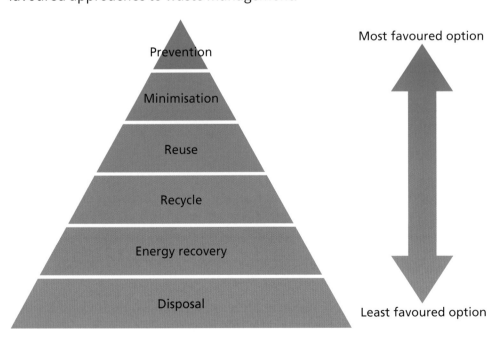

Prevention
Minimisation
Reuse
Recycle
Energy recovery
Disposal

Most favoured option

Least favoured option

Fig. 25.3.5
The waste management pyramid

GO Learn more about the disposal of waste and recycling in Chemical World 9.4

Bioremediation

Microorganisms play an important role in waste management and pollution control by breaking down organic matter in compost bins, landfills and sewage treatment plants.

Bacteria are also used to break down harmful substances in damaged habitats, such as oil spill sites. This process is called **bioremediation**.

GO Learn more about bacteria in Biological World 5.2

Fig. 25.3.6
A gardener putting organic waste into a compost bin

What We Can Do

A big part of living sustainably is changing people's habits. This can be done in a number of ways:

1. Having laws and government bodies in place to protect the environment. For example, the Environmental Protection Agency (EPA) regularly monitor air, water and soil quality.

2. Raising awareness of environmental issues. For example, the Sustainable Energy Authority of Ireland (SEAI) promotes energy efficiency through their 'Power of One' and 'One Good Idea' campaigns.

3. Research alternatives. For example, the decline in fossil fuels has led to research into the development of renewable energies.

Sustainable Agriculture

Agriculture (farming) supplies our food, as well as the fibres to make fabrics and the crops for biofuels. As the Earth's population grows, the demand for these things will increase.

Sustainable agriculture means meeting this demand while making sure that habitats are not destroyed.

Sustainable agricultural methods include:

Fig. 25.3.7
Water is monitored for pollution

- Crop rotation: growing the same crop on a piece of land takes the nutrients out of the soil. By planting different crops in a sequence, the nutrients that are taken from the soil by one crop can be returned by the crop that follows it, and so on.

- The use of organic fertilisers, such as slurry and manure, instead of inorganic fertilisers.

- Reforestation: replacing trees in an area where they have been removed or destroyed (a 'tree for a tree').

Biotechnology may also help meet our growing food demands. For example, genetically modified (GM) plants and animals. However, this is a controversial topic.

Fairtrade

Fairtrade means that local producers are paid a fair price for their products. Common Fairtrade goods include coffee, chocolate, tea and fruit.

Fairtrade is sustainable because producers can be sure of how much they will be paid and grow crops accordingly.

Many Irish companies support Fairtrade and many consumers seek out products that have been fairly traded. You can look for Fairtrade certification marks on goods when you are shopping.

® **FAIRTRADE**

🎧 **Fig. 25.3.8**
Look for the Fairtrade.ie certification mark when you are shopping

🎧 **Fig. 25.3.9**
Coffee is a common Fairtrade product

Fun Fact

In 2008, Electric Picnic, held in Stradbally, County Laois, became the world's first Fairtrade arts and music festival.

Since then, all the tea, coffee, hot chocolate, sugar and bananas sold on the festival site each year have been Fairtrade certified.

Chapter Summary

- The human population has increased hugely in the last 300 years.

- Humans have caused destruction of habitats, leading to a loss of biodiversity and, in some cases, the extinction of entire species.

- Conservation is the careful management of the Earth's natural resources to prevent species from becoming extinct.

- Pollution happens when harmful substances are added to the environment. The three main sources of pollution are agricultural, industrial and domestic.

- The burning of fossil fuels causes air pollution, such as smog and acid rain.

- The burning of fossil fuels has led to an increased greenhouse effect. This has led to global warming.

- Global warming is causing climate change. Some of the effects of climate change include rising sea levels, a threat to food production, more extreme weather events and the spread of diseases.

- Sustainability means living in a way that meets the needs of today's society without threatening the needs of future societies.

- Landfill sites, incineration and waste minimisation are methods of waste management.

- Waste minimisation is the favoured approach: reduce, reuse, recycle.

- The research into and development of renewable energies is ongoing. There is also a greater awareness of energy efficiency and fairly traded products.

- All of us have a role to play in conservation and sustainability.

The BIG Challenge

Imagine your school wants to apply for the Green Flag that is awarded by An Taisce to schools that demonstrate commitment to caring for our environment.

Your task is to make a poster about your school's carbon footprint.

Your poster must:

- Educate teachers and students about their carbon footprint.
- Explain simple steps they can take in school to reduce their carbon footprint.

Go to your Portfolio to check what you have learned in this chapter.

Take the chapter 25 quiz on educateplus.ie.

Questions

1. Copy and fill in the blanks:
   a. _____ is caused by any harmful addition to the environment that affects the environment's ability to support life.
   b. The three main sources of pollution are _____, _____ and industrial.
   c. The dodo is an example of an _____ species.
   d. Carbon dioxide and methane are both examples of _____ _____ that cause global warming and lead to _____ change.
   e. _____ is the careful management of the Earth's natural resources.
   f. Ninety per cent of domestic waste produced in Ireland is dumped in _____ sites.
   g. The most favoured waste management approach is waste _____, better known as reduce, _____, _____.
   h. Smog and _____ rain are types of air pollution.
   i. Microorganisms are also used to break down pollutants in damaged habitats, such as oil spill sites. This process is called _____.
   j. _____ means living in a way that meets the needs of today's society without threatening the needs of future societies.

2. Consider the greenhouse effect.
   a. Explain how the build-up of carbon dioxide and other gases is contributing to the greenhouse effect.
   b. Identify five consequences of global warming and climate change.
   c. Identify five ways that humans are trying to slow and reverse the effects of climate change.

3. Consider waste management.
   a. List three environmental problems caused by landfills.
   b. Identify ten items of household waste that can be recycled.
   c. If more rubbish was recycled, how would this affect (i) our supply of raw materials, (ii) our energy needs and (iii) the area of land needed for landfills?

4. Explain what conservation is and identify three conservation strategies.

5. Consider the role of each of the following strategies in promoting conservation and sustainability:
   a. The introduction of water charges.
   b. Breeding programmes in zoos.
   c. A levy on plastic shopping bags.
   d. The introduction of fishing quotas.
   e. The promotion of Fairtrade goods.
   f. The planting of trees and shrubs along the sides of motorways.

6. Explain the term 'enrichment'. Identify one common cause of enrichment and explain how it kills aquatic plants and animals.

7. Complete the following paragraph in 100 words: 'If I was elected Minister of the Department of Environment, Community and Local Government, I would …'

8. Using the descriptions of the various waste management methods in this chapter, research and develop arguments for or against the following:
   a. Landfill
   b. Recycling
   c. Composting
   d. Incineration
   Organise a class debate.

Working as a Scientist

Communicating Science

Climate Change

The media portrayal of climate change is often affected by misinformation and bias. Read these two extracts from reports on climate change and answer the questions that follow.

Source 1: 'Climate Change: How Do We Know?', NASA

The Earth's climate has changed throughout history… Most of these climate changes are attributed to very small variations in Earth's orbit that change the amount of solar energy our planet receives.

The current warming trend is of particular significance because most of it is very likely human-induced and proceeding at a rate that is unprecedented in the past 1,300 years…

Ice cores drawn from Greenland, Antarctica, and tropical mountain glaciers show that the Earth's climate responds to changes in solar output, in the Earth's orbit, and in greenhouse gas levels. They also show that in the past, large changes in climate have happened very quickly, geologically speaking: in tens of years, not in millions or even thousands.

The evidence for rapid climate change is compelling:

- *Sea level rise*
- *Global temperature rise: all three major global surface temperature reconstructions show that Earth has warmed since 1880*
- *Warming oceans*
- *Shrinking ice sheets*
- *Declining Arctic sea ice*
- *Glacial retreat*
- *Extreme events*
- *Ocean acidification*
- *Decreased snow cover*

Source 2: 'No Need to Panic About Global Warming', *The Wall Street Journal*

There's no compelling scientific argument for drastic action to 'decarbonize' the world's economy.

Although the number of publicly dissenting scientists is growing, many young scientists furtively say that while they also have serious doubts about the global-warming message, they are afraid to speak up for fear of not being promoted – or worse…

Why is there so much passion about global warming, and why has the issue become so vexing?… Alarmism over climate is of great benefit to many, providing government funding for academic research and a reason for government bureaucracies to grow. Alarmism also offers an excuse for governments to raise taxes, taxpayer-funded subsidies for businesses that understand how to work the political system, and a lure for big donations to charitable foundations promising to save the planet…

→

Speaking for many scientists and engineers who have looked carefully and independently at the science of climate, we have a message to any candidate for public office: There is no compelling scientific argument for drastic action to 'decarbonize' the world's economy. Even if one accepts the inflated climate forecasts of the IPCC [Intergovernmental Panel on Climate Change], aggressive greenhouse-gas control policies are not justified economically.

1 Consider the different sources of these articles. The first is a report from a scientific organisation and the second is an opinion piece from a financial newspaper. How do they differ?

2 What evidence does each source offer to support its argument?

   a. **Source 1** – Global climate is changing now.

   b. **Source 2** – There is no need to reduce our production of carbon dioxide.

3 The following note was added to *The Wall Street Journal* article: 'Editor's note: The following has been signed by the 16 scientists listed at the end of the article.' Why do you think this note was added?

4 Why does so much of our current energy generation produce carbon dioxide?

5 Research the Kyoto Protocol. Prepare a short summary for your classmates that includes the following points:

   a. A brief history of the protocol. Why was it required? What countries signed up? What targets did member countries originally set? Did Ireland sign up?

   b. Identify the strategies in the protocol to lower greenhouse gas emissions.

   c. The current status of the protocol. Are countries meeting their targets? What are some of the big issues surrounding the protocol?

   d. What other plans have been put in place since the Kyoto Protocol to reduce greenhouse gas emissions?

6 Complete the following sentence. 'If I could make just one change to stop global warming it would be…'

Space Travel

What you may already know:

- You can look at space through a telescope.
- Humans have travelled to the Moon. A rover landed on Mars.
- Sometimes the International Space Station can be seen crossing the night sky.
- Satellites orbit the Earth.

What you will learn in this chapter:

- How we can see further and deeper into the night sky.
- The history and future of space flight.
- Humankind's attempts to move further into the cosmos and to understand the nature of the universe, including the search for alien life.

Think BIG

- Will we ever live on other planets?
- Do aliens exist?

Puzzler

Can you identify this object?
(Hint: it provides detailed information about weather systems on Earth.)

Space Flight

Learning Intentions

In this topic we are learning to:
- Research the history of human space flight.
- Investigate how a rocket works.

After World War II, Russia (formerly the USSR) and the USA started to think about using rockets for space flight rather than for military purposes. In 1955, this started a competition between the two nations that became known as the **Space Race**.

The following timeline marks the major milestones in the Space Race.

USA

1958
NASA founded

1969
Astronaut Neil Armstrong is the first person to walk on the Moon

1972
Astronaut Gene Cernan is the most recent person to walk on the Moon

Russia

1957
Russia launch the first satellite, *Sputnik 1*, into space

1961
Cosmonaut Yuri Gagarin is the first person to fly into space

Astronaut or cosmonaut?

These words mean the same thing: a person who is trained to travel in a spacecraft. The Space Race introduced the separate words. Russians use the word 'cosmonaut' and Americans use the word 'astronaut'.

People and Science

Although he was not a scientist, US president **John F. Kennedy** (JFK) was very important in making the United States the first nation to put a human on the Moon.

On 12 September 1962, in a speech at Rice University in Texas, JFK said:

We choose to go to the Moon. We choose to go to the Moon in this decade and do the other things, not because they are easy, but because they are hard, because that goal will serve to organise and measure the best of our energies and skills, because that challenge is one that we are willing to accept, one we are unwilling to postpone, and one which we intend to win, and the others, too.

What do you think President Kennedy's words say about why humankind wants to travel into space?

🎧 **Fig. 26.1.1**
JFK speaking at Rice University in 1962

Space Race

Scientific discovery often involves scientists from all over the world working together. While the Space Race was a competition between scientists in different countries, it did lead to a number of important developments.

Research the pros and cons of this competition. Draw on your findings and any other relevant examples to write an evidence-based report about the place competition has in modern science.

Rockets

In response to President John F. Kennedy's desire to send a human to the Moon, the National Aeronautics and Space Administration (**NASA**) created three spaceflight programmes:

- Mercury
- Gemini
- Apollo.

In these early missions, giant rockets were used to launch astronauts into space. The astronauts were in a module on the rocket, which broke away in parts as it approached to the destination. These rockets could not be reused.

The **Apollo** mission landed Neil Armstrong on the Moon in 1969.

The Apollo mission was decommissioned in 1972. In 1981, the **Space Shuttle Program** began its first flights.

◑ Fig. 26.1.2
Apollo 11 being launched on 20 July 1969

Shuttles

A space shuttle is a spacecraft that can be used more than once and that carries people into outer space and back to Earth. It is attached to a fuel tank and solid rocket boosters (SRBs) ready to be launched into orbit.

When a space shuttle clears the Earth's atmosphere, the SRBs and fuel tank separate from the shuttle. These pieces then re-enter the Earth's atmosphere.

Fun Fact
Over 5,000 parts of SRBs were salvaged, refurbished and reused after every space shuttle flight.

The International Space Station (ISS)

◐ Fig. 26.1.3
The ISS over Earth

The **International Space Station** (ISS) is a spacecraft facility that orbits Earth with astronauts on board.

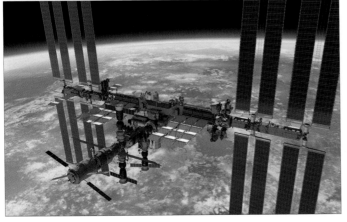

From the ISS, astronauts can investigate the effect of weightlessness on different living things, such as seeds, bacteria and the human body. This helps us understand the hazards of living in space. This knowledge may be useful in the future if we go on long space voyages to other planets.

The ISS is in low orbit. It makes one orbit of the Earth every 90 minutes. This makes the ISS ideal for observing global weather systems.

If the ISS orbits the Earth every 90 minutes, how many times will an ISS astronaut see the Sun rise in 24 hours?

How Does a Rocket Work?

When a spacecraft is launched:

1. The fuel in the tanks is ignited and explodes, colliding with the walls of the tank at high speed.

2. The tank exerts a force on the fuel, pushing it out through the exhaust pipes.

3. The fuel exerts an equal and opposite force on the rocket, driving it forward.

This is an interaction pair of forces.

GO Learn more about interaction forces in Physical World 17.3

Model rocket

A balloon attached to a straw can be used as a model to show how a rocket works. A student set up the model as follows:

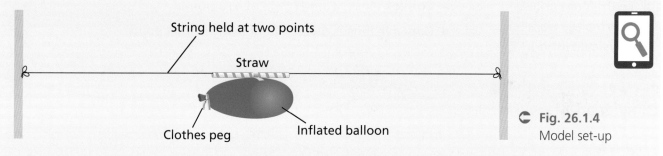

String held at two points

Straw

Clothes peg   Inflated balloon

↺ **Fig. 26.1.4**
Model set-up

1. Predict what happens when the clothes peg is removed. Explain your prediction.

2. Set up this model in the school laboratory. Remove the clothes peg and record your observations.

3. Explain why your predictions did or did not match your observations.

4. Sketch a diagram of this equipment and use arrows to show the forces involved.

Tweet an astronaut

Your class must send a tweet to an astronaut about life in space. Complete the task as follows:

1. Make contact with the astronaut you want to question. You could contact Chris Hadfield (@Cmdr_ Hadfield) or other astronauts such as @astro_reid, @astro_luca, @astro_ken or @astro_ron.

2. Come up with a hashtag that describes the task and your class. For example, #SpaceLife2BSci

3. Look for some tweets and replies that the astronauts have posted describing life in space.

4. Create a collage of the astronaut's quotes and include a summary of what life is like in space.

Looking at the Night Sky: Light Telescopes

Key Words

Light telescope

Convex

Concave

Learning Intentions

In this topic we are learning to:

- Distinguish between the types of light telescopes.
- Illustrate how light refracts through convex and concave lenses.

Astronomers study the night sky to better understand space. Light telescopes have allowed us to look at space for hundreds of years.

The Light Telescope

A **light telescope** uses visible light to produce magnified images of distant objects. Light telescopes use lenses and curved mirrors to focus on distant objects.

There are three types of light telescopes:

1. Refractor telescopes use lenses to refract light. This focuses an image of a distant object on the retina in the eye of the person looking through the telescope.
   - **Convex** lenses converge light to a point.
   - **Concave** lenses diverge light away from a point.

⬤ **Fig. 26.2.1**
A light telescope

GO Learn more about how the eye works in Physical World 19.2

⮕ **Fig. 26.2.2**
Convex and concave lenses

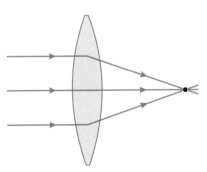

Convex lens

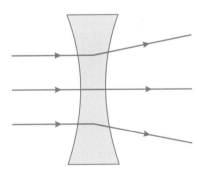

Concave lens

2. Reflector telescopes use plane and curved mirrors placed at different angles to reflect light. The type of curved mirror used is a concave mirror. This reflects light to a point in front of the mirror. Nearly all large modern astronomical telescopes are reflectors. This is because mirrors are lighter and easier to clean than lenses. They are also easier to make.

Back of mirror

Concave mirror

⬤ **Fig. 26.2.3**
A concave mirror reflecting light

3. Combination telescopes use a system of mirrors and lenses to reflect and refract light.

Changing views of the cosmos

Using the following information, construct a timeline about the development of light telescopes. Put the discoveries in order of when they took place and include pictures of the people and their inventions on the timeline.

- **1609:** Galileo develops a 0.0381 m lens telescope and sees the nearby planets Mercury and Venus.
- **1845:** Lord Rosse constructs a reflecting telescope in County Offaly with a 18.288 m diameter mirror and discovers the first spiral nebulae.
- **1948:** the 5.08 m Hale telescope is constructed in California. It continues to make new discoveries about galaxies and quasars.
- **1990:** the Hubble Space telescope is launched into orbit by the space shuttle *Discovery*. It continues to provide new revelations about deep space, the life and death of stars and the nature of our expanding universe.
- **1917:** the 2.54 m Hooker telescope is developed in California.
- **1924:** Edwin Hubble uses the Hooker telescope to discover the Andromeda nebula, proving that it lay beyond the boundaries of the Milky Way.
- **1781:** William Herschel discovers Uranus with a large reflecting telescope that he designed and built himself.
- **2005:** the twin-mirrored Large Binocular Telescope (LBT) opened in Arizona, produces sharper images than Hubble. The LBT allows us to see to the edge of the observable universe.

Fig. 26.2.4
The Hubble telescope takes pictures of space as it orbits Earth

People and Science

Galileo was an Italian astronomer. He made huge improvements to the light telescope. He is known as 'the father of modern astronomy'. His observations of the orbit of Venus and Mercury supported the heliocentric model of orbiting planets. Because he believed that the Earth revolved around the Sun, Galileo was accused of heresy by the Catholic Church. He had to deny his views and was sentenced to house arrest until the end of his life.

Fig. 26.2.5
Galileo

Fig. 26.2.6
Galileo's original telescope

Constellation

When you view the night sky with your eyes, you see constellations of stars. A constellation is a group of stars forming a specific pattern.

One of the most recognisable constellations in the night sky is Orion.

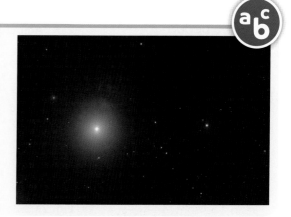

Fig. 26.2.7
Orion

Looking at the Night Sky: Radio Telescopes

Learning Intentions

In this topic we are learning to:

- Describe the properties of waves.
- Consider the uses of radio telescopes.

Modern astronomy uses telescopes that do not need to reflect or refract light.

A **radio telescope** uses radio waves to produce visual images of distant objects.

Radio telescopes detect radio waves coming from space. The waves are reflected by a concave dish on the telescope. The dish focuses the waves onto a receiver, where they are converted into a digital form to produce an image of the object being viewed.

Radio telescopes have two advantages over light telescopes:

- Radio telescopes work at any time of the day. Light telescopes can only be used at night.
- Radio waves can be transmitted and received in cloudy weather. You cannot use a light telescope in cloudy conditions.

🎧 **Fig. 26.3.1**
The 32 m radio telescope at the National Space Centre in Midleton, County Cork

Waves

A wave transfers energy from one point to another. It does this through vibrations.

Waves have many uses. For example, food can be heated using microwaves and cancerous tumours can be treated with gamma rays. We can hear people speak thanks to sound waves that travel through the air and we can surf on water waves.

GO Learn more about sound waves in the Physical World 19.4

Good vibrations 🅰🅱🅲

A person who is having a period of success is often described as 'riding on the crest of a wave'. Link this phrase to the features of waves.

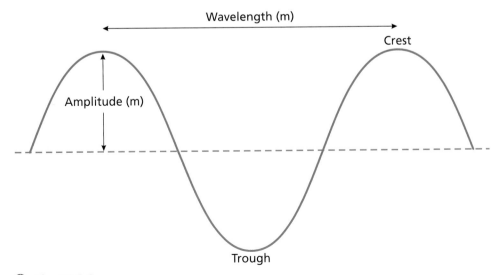

🎧 **Fig. 26.3.2**
Wave features

All waves share the following features:

- A **crest** is the top of the wave.
- A **trough** is the bottom of the wave.
- A **wavelength** is the distance from the crest of one wave to the crest of another, measured in metres (m).
- The frequency is the number of waves passing any point in one second. This is measured in hertz (Hz).
- An amplitude is the greatest displacement of a wave from its undisplaced position. This is measured in metres (m). (Note that amplitude is not the distance between the top and bottom of a wave.)

Wave motion

There are two types of wave motion: transverse and longitudinal. Research these types of waves and compare their characteristics. Use diagrams to support your answer.

Radio wave speed

The speed of a wave can be calculated by multiplying its frequency by its wavelength. If a radio wave has a wavelength of 0.75 m and a frequency of 400 MHz, calculate the speed of this radio wave. Compare your answer to the value for the speed of light in your *Formulae and Tables* booklet.

Other Waves in Space

Objects in space also give out other types of waves, such as X-rays, gamma rays and infrared radiation. These can be viewed using devices similar to radio telescopes.

These waves cannot get through the Earth's atmosphere, so the telescopes need to be launched into outer space to receive and understand them.

⊙ **Fig. 26.3.3**
An image of the Centaurus galaxy

People and Science

Jocelyn Bell Burnell is an astrophysicist from Northern Ireland. While studying at the University of Cambridge in 1967, she developed a radio telescope under the guidance of her supervisor Antony Hewish. Using this telescope, she discovered the first radio pulsars from outer space.

A pulsar is a fast rotating star that seems to flash brighter and dimmer. Her supervisor was awarded the Nobel Prize in Physics for this discovery. Bell Burnell was not included in the prize, much to the astonishment of the scientific community.

⊙ **Fig. 26.3.4**
Jocelyn Bell Burnell

Space and the Future

Key Words

Human missions
Flyby
Orbiter
Robotic lander
Commercial space
  travel
SETI

Learning Intentions

In this topic we are learning to:

- Distinguish between different types of space missions.

There are four types of space missions:

1. **Human missions** land on an object to study it carefully. These missions carry the greatest risk to human life. The Moon landings were the last human missions to land on another celestial body. To date, only 12 people have set foot on the Moon.

2. **Flyby** missions send a craft past a planet or other body, taking pictures on its way to another destination. These craft are known as probes. *Voyager 1* was a flyby space probe launched by NASA in 1977. In August 2012, it became the first human-made object to leave our solar system and enter interstellar space. In July 2015, the NASA *New Horizons* probe collected new data about the size of Pluto on a flyby mission.

○ **Fig. 26.4.1**
Neil Armstrong's footprint on the surface of the Moon. Why do you think it has not worn away?

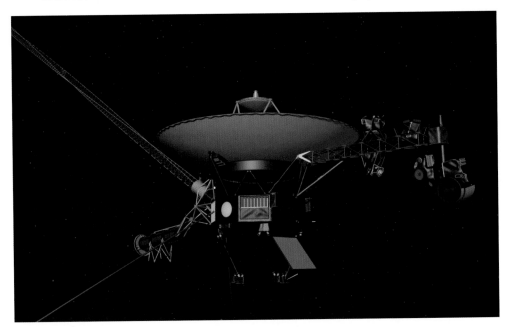

○ **Fig. 26.4.2**
Voyager 1

3. **Orbiter** missions circle around a planet or moon to take detailed measurements of the body. By collecting information about the atmosphere, surface terrain and potential landing spots, orbiters help inform future landing missions on these bodies.

4. **Robotic lander** missions land a spacecraft in a location that has been mapped out by an orbiter. NASA's Curiosity Mars rover, a wheeled robot, landed on Mars in August 2012. This rover is studying the climate and geology of the Red Planet to see if there was, or is, evidence of water underground, which would suggest that the planet may contain microscopic life.

○ **Fig. 26.4.3**
A 'selfie' taken by the Curiosity rover on the surface of Mars

Modelling mission observations

1. Decorate a ball with bright, different-shaped objects. This will be your planet.

2. Place the planet in the centre of your schoolyard. Split your class into three teams and carry out one of the following types of space missions:
   - Flyby: walk past the planet once.
   - Orbiter: walk in a circle around the planet for 30 seconds.
   - Robotic lander: choose one area of the planet to study in detail. Look at this area only, with one eye closed, for one minute.

3. Note your group's observations. This could take the form of a written report, a diagram, photographs or a short video, or a 'captain's log' audio file.

4. Is this a good model to represent types of space missions? How could it be improved?

Space Tourism

In the future, it is likely that **commercial space travel** will become a reality. Virgin Galactic have plans to launch members of the public into space on 'orbital spaceflights'. Passengers on the flights will experience a short period of 'weightlessness'.

Holiday time

With your lab partner, discuss if you would like to go on a space holiday to the ISS. Why or why not? Each astronaut on the ISS can bring one personal item. What would you bring?

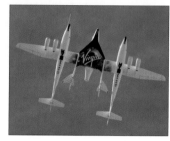

◯ **Fig. 26.4.4**
SpaceShipTwo, the planned craft for Virgin Galactic flights

Searching for Other Life

Scientists search for evidence of life in the universe in a number of ways:

- By analysing meteorites that fall to the Earth from space, looking for fossils or bacteria.

- By sending robots to explore other planets and moons in our solar system. For life as we know it to exist, liquid water must be present. In September 2015, NASA's Mars Reconnaissance Orbiter (MRO) found evidence of liquid water on Mars.

- By listening with radio telescopes for radio signals emitted by other civilisations. This is called the **SETI** (Search for Extra Terrestrial Intelligence) project.

◯ **Fig. 26.4.5**
SETI telescopes

The Golden Record

The Golden Record was carried by *Voyagers 1* and *2* as a greeting to any intelligent life that they might encounter. The records give information about Earth and its people, including greetings in 55 languages. These records will reach nearby stars in 40,000 years.

With your lab partner, discuss why you think the Voyager records are plated with gold.

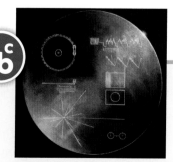

◯ **Fig. 26.4.6**
The Golden Record

Chapter Summary

- The Space Race is the competition between Russia (formerly the USSR) and the USA about the use of rockets for space flight. The NASA's Apollo mission landed Neil Armstrong on the Moon in 1969.

- A space shuttle is a spacecraft that can be used more than once and that carries people into outer space and back to Earth.

- The International Space Station (ISS) is a spacecraft facility that orbits Earth with astronauts on board.

- Rockets move forward because of an interaction pair of forces.

- Astronomical telescopes can be used to view the night sky and celestial bodies.

- Light telescopes use lenses and curved mirrors to focus on distant objects.

- Convex lenses converge light. Concave lenses diverge light.

- Radio telescopes use radio waves to produce visual images of distant objects. They have advantages over light telescopes.

- A wave transfers energy from one point to another. It does this through vibrations.

- The features of a wave are crest, trough, wavelength, frequency and amplitude.

- The Apollo mission landed a man on the Moon in 1969.

- The types of space mission are human, flyby, orbiter and robotic lander.

- Science continues to search for extraterrestrial life by analysing meteorites, searching for water on other planets and detecting radio wave signals from outer space.

The BIG Challenge

Make your own telescope

You can make a simple refractor telescope using the following equipment:

- Two tubes that can slide in and out of each other.

- Two convex lenses from the school laboratory. The larger lens, the objective lens, produces an image of the faraway object. The smaller lens, the eyepiece lens, magnifies the image even further.

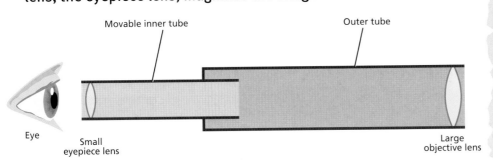

Movable inner tube | Outer tube
Eye
Small eyepiece lens | Large objective lens

🎧 Fig. 26.5.1
A simple telescope

Build a telescope like this and use it to look at the Moon. Investigate the factors that will give you the maximum magnification of an image of the Moon.

Go to your Portfolio to check what you have learned in this chapter.

Take the chapter 26 quiz on educateplus.ie.

Questions

1. Copy and fill in the blanks:

   a. Light telescopes use ▢▢▢ to ▢▢▢ light, focusing an ▢▢▢ in the eye of the observer.

   b. ▢▢▢ lenses converge light. ▢▢▢ lenses diverge light.

   c. A wave ▢▢▢ ▢▢▢ from one point to another through ▢▢▢.

   d. The features of a wave are a ▢▢▢, ▢▢▢, ▢▢▢, ▢▢▢, and ▢▢▢.

   e. The speed of a wave can be calculated by multiplying its ▢▢▢ by its ▢▢▢.

   f. Radio telescopes use ▢▢▢ ▢▢▢ to produce ▢▢▢ images of distant objects.

   g. NASA stands for ▢▢▢ ▢▢▢ ▢▢▢ ▢▢▢ ▢▢▢.

   h. The types of space mission are ▢▢▢, ▢▢▢, and ▢▢▢ ▢▢▢.

   i. Scientists analyse ▢▢▢ that fall to the Earth from space. They are looking for ▢▢▢ or ▢▢▢.

   j. The ▢▢▢ ▢▢▢ is listening for radio signals from outer space that might suggest signs of ▢▢▢.

2. Using information collected from online research, copy and complete the following table:

Spaceflight programme	Dates active from/to	Goals	Accomplishments
Mercury			
Gemini			
Apollo			

3. A group of students investigated the motion of a rocket. They built a model rocket and fired it into air for eight seconds, after which time it landed back on the Earth. They plotted the following graph of the distance it covered with time relative to the position of the Earth.

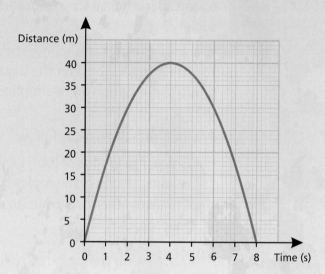

   a. What shape is this graph? What does this tell you about objects in freefall?

   b. Estimate the velocity of the object at 2 s.

4. Write a summary of the advantages and disadvantages of radio telescopes over light telescopes.

5. Write an evidence-based essay titled 'Humankind's greatest successes and failures in space exploration'.

6. Research why scientists are convinced that there has been water on Mars for billions of years. Write a maximum of five bullet points to support your answer.

7. Describe current strategies to search for extraterrestrial life in space.

Working as a Scientist

Responsible Science

What Does Space Travel Mean For Us?

In the future, space tourism could become a part of our lives. Have the public stopped to consider what space exploration, tourism or otherwise, means for them and society?

You will work in teams to investigate the evidence for and against space exploration. You are going to consider the hazards and benefits of exploring space to develop a group presentation on the implications of space exploration for society now and in the future.

Proceed with the task as follows:

- Break into groups of four. Each person in the group is to answer the questions relating to one of the topics below.
- Come together as a group to discuss your answers and thoughts relating to all four topics.

Topics:

1 **The ISS and the benefits of space travel**

a. Research the types of investigations carried out in the ISS laboratories. Why are these investigations helpful to humankind?

b. The ISS involves astronauts and space agencies from many countries across the world. What type of political and economic problems do you think they might have come up against?

2 **New knowledge and technologies**

a. GPS and satellite communications is just one way that space travel has changed our lives. How do you use satellite communications and GPS on a daily basis?

b. What other things do we have space travel to thank for? Consider healthcare, robotics and automation.

⊃ **Fig. 26.6.1**
A digital communications satellite

3 Cultural impact

a. How might space travel encourage us to think about our place in the universe?

b. Give some examples of space-travel-inspired films, television shows, songs, art and books.

⮑ **Fig. 26.6.2**
This iconic image of 'Earthrise' over the Moon, taken by the astronauts on *Apollo 8,* encouraged environmental awareness and global unity

4 Hazards

a. Research a disaster involving a spacecraft. For example, *Apollo 1, Challenger, Apollo 13* or *Columbia.* Where, when and why did these disasters take place?

b. Do you think that the potential loss of human lives is an acceptable cost of further space exploration?

Space Treaty

NASA has suggested that nations should unite to create a 'space treaty' aimed at solving some of the issues of space travel. This treaty would make sure that space exploration is meaningful, orderly and fair to all humans and nations.

Remember, it is important to remain objective and to give the public enough information to make their own decisions about how to live their lives. Your communication must be free from personal bias and based on the evidence you have researched.

5 **In your groups, draw up an Irish space treaty. Make sure to consider the benefits and hazards of space exploration and to address some of the ways you would deal with the issues of space travel in the future.**

6 **As a group, present the treaty to your class. As a class, come up with a way of assessing the quality of the presentations.**

Acknowledgements

While the names of the authors appear on the front of this book, its conception, development and realisation has been a massive team effort. As such, the authors wish to acknowledge the following:

Pat: Thanks to all my family and friends. Also, I would like to thank my former teachers in Patrickswell NS and Sexton St CBS.

Maria: Thank you to my family and friends, especially Colm. Many thanks, also, to my colleagues in the Chemistry Education Research Group at the University of Limerick led by Peter Childs and to the students and teachers of St Caimin's Community School, Shannon, County Clare.

David: I would like to extend my heartfelt gratitude to the students and teachers of Blackwater Community School, Lismore, County Waterford. I would also like to acknowledge my former teachers from Dungarvan CBS Primary and Secondary School. Finally, I thank my wife Fiona for the eternal patience, support and enthusiasm she has shown during the authoring process. To her and my wonderful children, Danny, Katie, Robert and Adam, I extend my deepest love and affection. Thanks for waiting, Mammy and kids, I can finally come and play!

As former UL education graduates, all three authors wish to warmly acknowledge the staff of the Departments of Life Sciences, Physics and Energy, Chemical and Environmental Science and the Department of Education and Professional Studies at the University of Limerick. The authors would like to thank Castletroy College for the use of their laboratory facilities.

Finally, we wish to sincerely thank the team at Educate.ie, especially Julie, Sinéad and Ian, for their guidance and tireless efforts. Thank you for navigating this journey with us.

The authors and publisher would like to thank the following for permission to reproduce extracts and data:

Barack Obama, 'Floor Statement of Support for Stem Cell Research' (17 July, 2006), US Government; Acid mine drainage data, Dundalk Institute of Technology (DkIT); Graphs showing increasing obesity rates among the adult population in OECD countries, 1990, 2000 and 2009 (or nearest years) and the prevalence estimates of diabetes, adults aged 20–79 years, 2010, reprinted courtesy of OECD (2011), *Health at a Glance 2011: OECD Indicators*, OECD Publishing, http://dx.doi.org/10.1787/health_glance-2011-en; 'Prenatal risk assessment and diagnosis graph' reprinted with permission from 'Down Syndrome: Prenatal Risk Assessment and Diagnosis', *American Family Physician,* 62.4 (15 August, 2000) © 2000 American Academy of Family Physicians. All rights reserved; Table showing percentage of Irish population of normal weight, overweight and obese in 1990, 2001 and 2011, National Adult Nutrition Survey Summary Report (March 2011), Table 4: Anthropometric measurements, www.iuna.net; Copper table data from the United States Geological Survey Mineral Commodity Summary, 2011; Bruce C. Trigger, A History of Archaeological Thought (Cambridge University Press, 1996); Robin Lloyd, 'Metric Mishap Caused by Loss of NASA Orbiter', CNN.com (30 September 1999), CNN.com, PARS International Corp.; Social networks used in Ireland infographic, reprinted courtesy of eightytwenty Digital Marketing; Sample electricity bill reprinted courtesy of Bord Gais; 'Climate change: How do we know?' NASA, http://climate.nasa.gov/evidence/; 'No Need to Panic About Global Warming', reprinted from *The Wall Street Journal* © 2012 Dow Jones & Company. All rights reserved; Graph showing Ireland's energy requirements 1990–2013, reprinted courtesy of the Sustainable Energy Authority of Ireland (SEAI).

The authors and publisher would like to thank the following for permission to reproduce photographs:

Adam Hart-Davis/Science Photo Library; AF Archive/Alamy; American Journal of Physiology; Andrew Lambert Photography/Science Photo Library; Anne Marie Coile/Wikimedia Commons; Barrington Brown/Science Photo Library; Bigstock; Biophoto Associates/Science Photo Library; Cavallini James/BSIP/Science Photo Library; CERN; CERN/Science Photo Library; Charles D. Winters/Science Photo Library; Charles W. Glynn/Creative Commons; CNN; Tyrone Turner/National Geographic Society/Corbis; Cordelia Molloy/Science Photo Library; David R. Frazier Photolibrary, Inc./Alamy; Dr Ken MacDonald/Science Photo Library; Dundalk Institute of Technology; E. R. Degginer/Science Photo Library; Eddie Mallin/Wikimedia Commons; Edelmann/Science Photo Library; Emilo Segre Visual Archives/American Institute of Physics/Science Photo Library; Erich Schrempp/Science Photo Library; Erik van Leeuwen/Wikimedia Commons; ESA/Rosetta/Philae/DLR; Foodcollection.com/Alamy; Frances Roberts/Alamy; freeimages.com; Friedrich Stark/Alamy; geardiary.com; Geni/Wikimedia Commons; Ger MacCarthy/National Space Centre; Gerd Guenther/Science Photo Library; Getty/AFP; Getty/David Taylor; Getty/Michael Blann; Giani Tortoli/Science Photo Library; GIPhotostock/Science Photo Library; Hawk-Eye; Herve Conge, ISM/Science Photo Library; Isifa Image Service s.r.o./Alamy; Jack Bostrack, Visuals Unlimited/Science Photo Library; Jason E Bond/Wikimedia Commons; Jeff Foust/Wikimedia Commons; Jim Varney/Science Photo Library; J. Martin Harris Travel and Leisure Photography/PSDC; Joerg Boethling/Alamy; Jose Antonio Peñas/Science Photo Library; Kevin Wheal/Alamy; Leslie Garland Picture Library/Alamy; Louise Howard, Darmouth Electron Microscope Faculty/Wikimedia Commons; Maggie Bartlett, NHGRI; Mark Leach/Alamy; Martyn F. Chillmaid/Science Photo Library; Mauro Fermariello/Science Photo Library; Maximilien Brice, CERN/Science Photo Library; Mediablitzimages/Alamy; NASA; Met Éireann; NASA/Caltech; NASA/Capella Observatory; NASA/Chris Hadfield; NASA/ESA/S; NASA/JPL/Space Science Institute; NASA/JPL/University of Arizona; NASA/Jet Propulsion Laboratory, University of Texas Center for Space Research/GeoForschungsZentrum Potsdam; NASA/JPL-Caltech; NASA/MSFC/MEO/BillCooke; NASA/NOAA; NASA/SDO; NASA/SDO/AIA; NASA/SOHO/Tony Phillips; NASA/Space Telescope Science Institute; National Institutes of Health/NIAID/Science Photo Library; National Portrait Gallery, London/Wikimedia Commons; Nigel Cattlin/Alamy; Nobel Media/Yana Audas/University of Manchester; OECD; Omikron/Science Photo Library; Paul D. Stuart/Science Photo Library; Peter Gardiner/Science Photo Library; PR. G. Gimenez-Martin/Science Photo Library; Princeton University/American Institute of Physics/ Science Photo Library; RGB Ventures/SuperStock/Alamy; Richard Giles/Wikimedia Commons; Rijksmuseum/Wikimedia Commons; Robin Scagell/Science Photo Library; RSA; Russell Kightley/Science Photo Library; Science Photo Library; Science Photo Library/Alamy; Science Source/Science Photo Library; sciencephotos/Alamy; SEAI; Shutterstock; Sinclair Stammers/Science Photo Library; Sportsfile; Stefan Servos/Wikimedia Commons; Stephen & Donna O'Meara/Science Photo Library; Sularko (Museum Victoria)/Wikimedia Commons; Tek Image/Science Photo Library; The Science Picture Company/Alamy; Tom Fleming/Science Photo Library; Tony Lilley/Alamy; T-Service/Science Photo Library; Universal Images Group Limited/Alamy; US Department of Defense; US Department of Energy/Science Photo Library; Vincent Moncorge/Look at Sciences/Science Photo Library; war posters/Alamy; Wikimedia Commons; Wildscreen/Wikimedia Commons; Yohan euan o4/Wikimedia Commons

The author and publisher have made every effort to trace all copyright holders. If any have been overlooked, we would be happy to make the necessary arrangements at the first opportunity.

Index

Periodic Table of the Elements

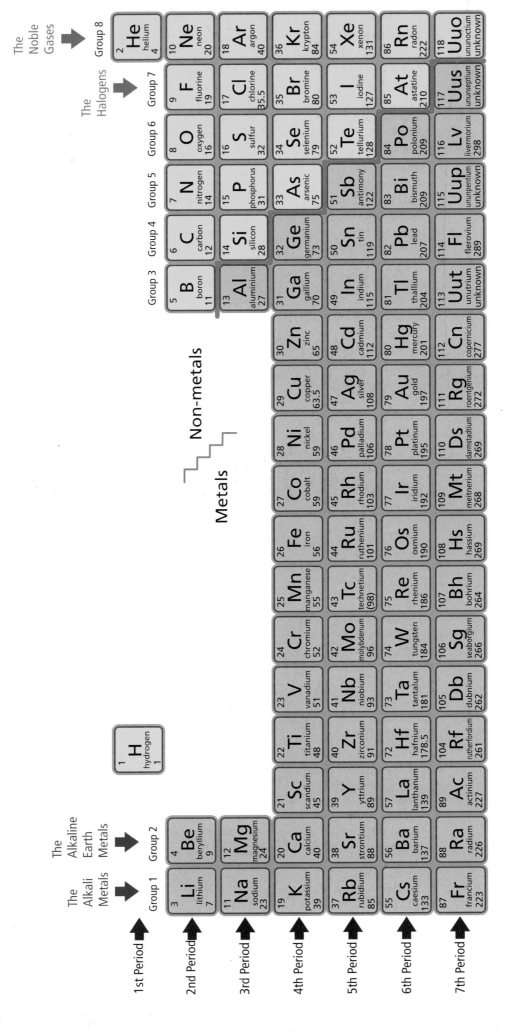